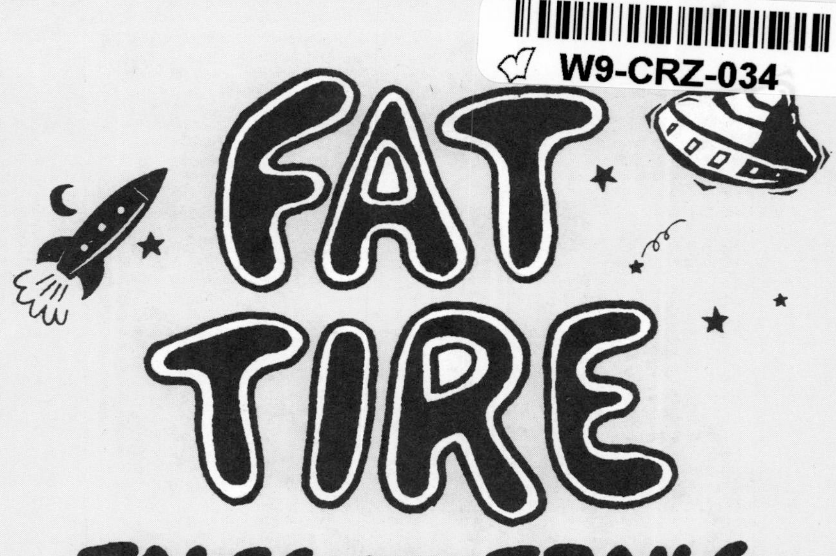

TALES AND TRAILS

MUTANT approved!

"In the beginning, there was FAT!"
- *Genisis: The Fat Tire Bible*

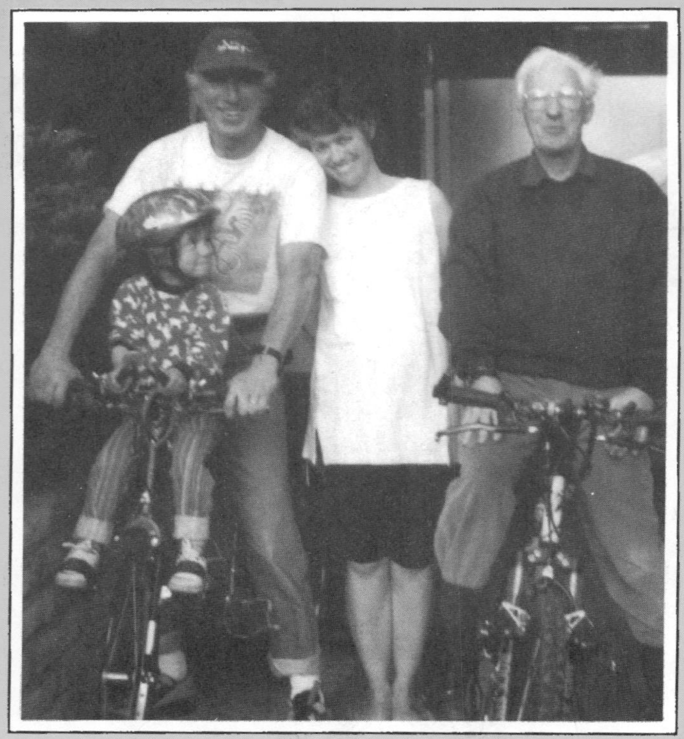

ALWAYS BE KIND. KEEP THE GOOD ATTITUDE.
NEVER GIVE UP.

FAT TIRE TALES & TRAILS

ARIZONA MOUNTAIN BIKE TRAIL GUIDE

PUBLISHED BY COSMIC RAY tm
FLAGSTAFF, ARIZONA

NEW MIGHTY MOTO *LOCALS ONLY* 22ND EDITION

(*WAY OVER* 100,000 SERVED)

Printed on recycled paper with blood, sweat and vegetable ink.

"You are here on earth to fart around.
Don't let anyone tell you any different."
Kurt Vonnegut

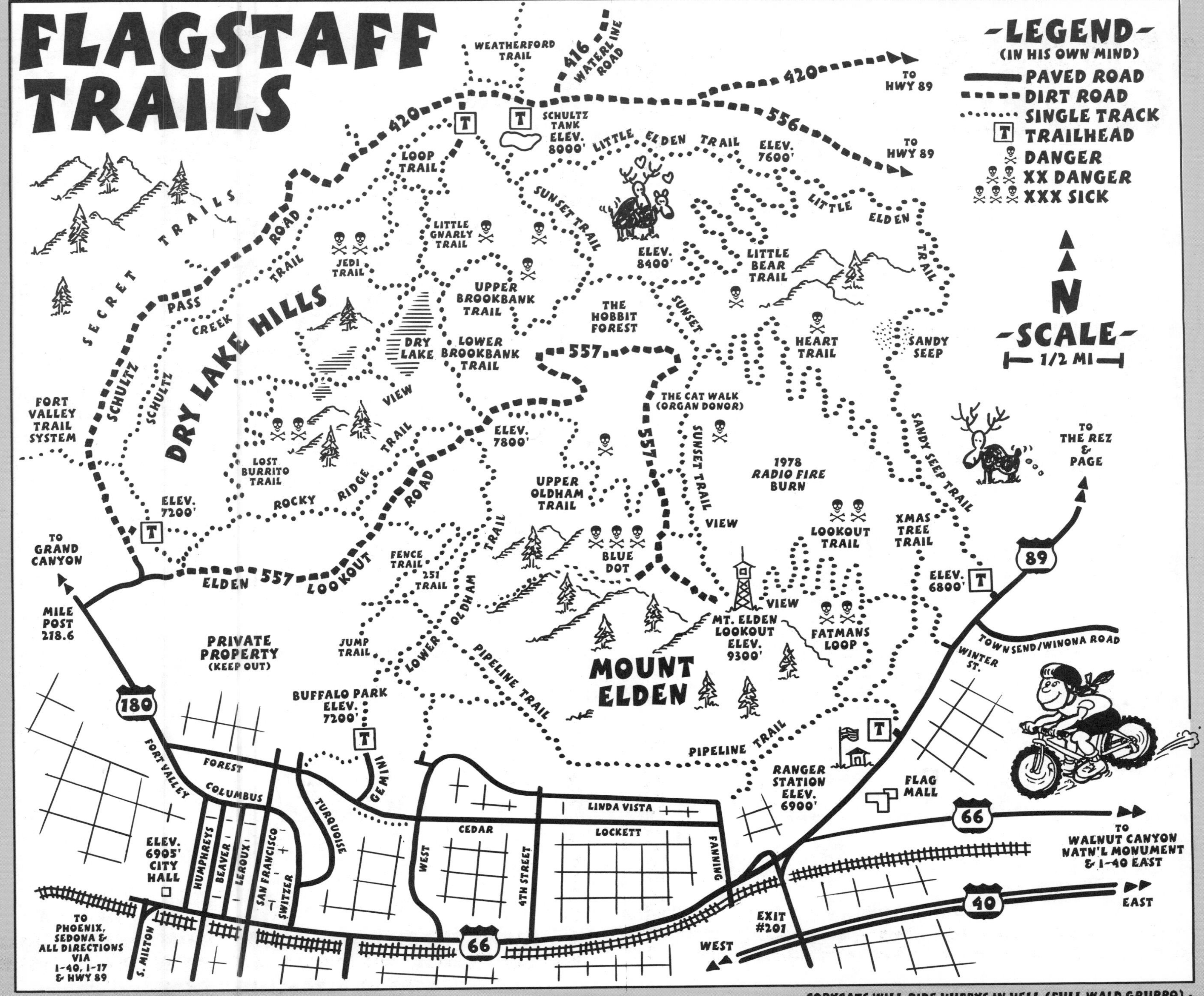
FLAGSTAFF TRAILS
-LEGEND-
(IN HIS OWN MIND)
PAVED ROAD
DIRT ROAD
SINGLE TRACK
TRAILHEAD
DANGER
XX DANGER
XXX SICK
N
-SCALE-
1/2 MI
WEATHERFORD TRAIL
416 WATERLINE ROAD
420
TO HWY 89
556
TO HWY 89
SCHULTZ TANK ELEV. 8000'
LITTLE ELDEN TRAIL
ELEV. 7600'
LITTLE ELDEN TRAIL
LOOP TRAIL
SUNSET TRAIL
SECRET TRAILS
ROAD
LITTLE GNARLY TRAIL
JEDI TRAIL
ELEV. 8400'
LITTLE BEAR TRAIL
SECRET PASS TRAIL
UPPER BROOKBANK TRAIL
THE HOBBIT FOREST
SUNSET
DRY LAKE HILLS
CREEK
DRY LAKE
LOWER BROOKBANK TRAIL
557
HEART TRAIL
SANDY SEEP
FORT VALLEY TRAIL SYSTEM
SCHULTZ
SCHULTZ
VIEW
THE CAT WALK (ORGAN DONOR)
SUNSET TRAIL
SANDY SEEP TRAIL
TO THE REZ & PAGE
ELEV. 7800'
557
LOST BURRITO TRAIL
TRAIL
1978 RADIO FIRE BURN
ROCKY RIDGE
ROAD
UPPER OLDHAM TRAIL
ELEV. 7200'
VIEW
LOOKOUT TRAIL
XMAS TREE TRAIL
TO GRAND CANYON
FENCE TRAIL
TRAIL
BLUE DOT
89
251 TRAIL
ELEV. 6800'
ELDEN 557 LOOKOUT
OLDHAM
VIEW
MILE POST 218.6
MT. ELDEN LOOKOUT ELEV. 9300'
FATMANS LOOP
PRIVATE PROPERTY (KEEP OUT)
JUMP TRAIL
LOWER
PIPELINE TRAIL
MOUNT ELDEN
TOWNSEND/WINONA ROAD
WINTER ST.
180
BUFFALO PARK ELEV. 7200'
FORT VALLEY
FOREST
GEMINI
PIPELINE TRAIL
RANGER STATION ELEV. 6900'
FLAG MALL
COLUMBUS
TURQUOISE
LINDA VISTA
66
TO WALNUT CANYON NATN'L MONUMENT & I-40 EAST
CEDAR
LOCKETT
ELEV. 6905' CITY HALL
HUMPHREYS
BEAVER
LEROUX
SAN FRANCISCO
SWITZER
WEST
4TH STREET
FANNING
40
EAST
TO PHOENIX, SEDONA & ALL DIRECTIONS VIA I-40, I-17 & HWY 89
S. MILTON
66
EXIT #201
WEST
© 2003 COSMIC RAY COZRAY@JUNO.COM
COPYCATS WILL RIDE HUFFYS IN HELL (FULL WALD GRUPPO).

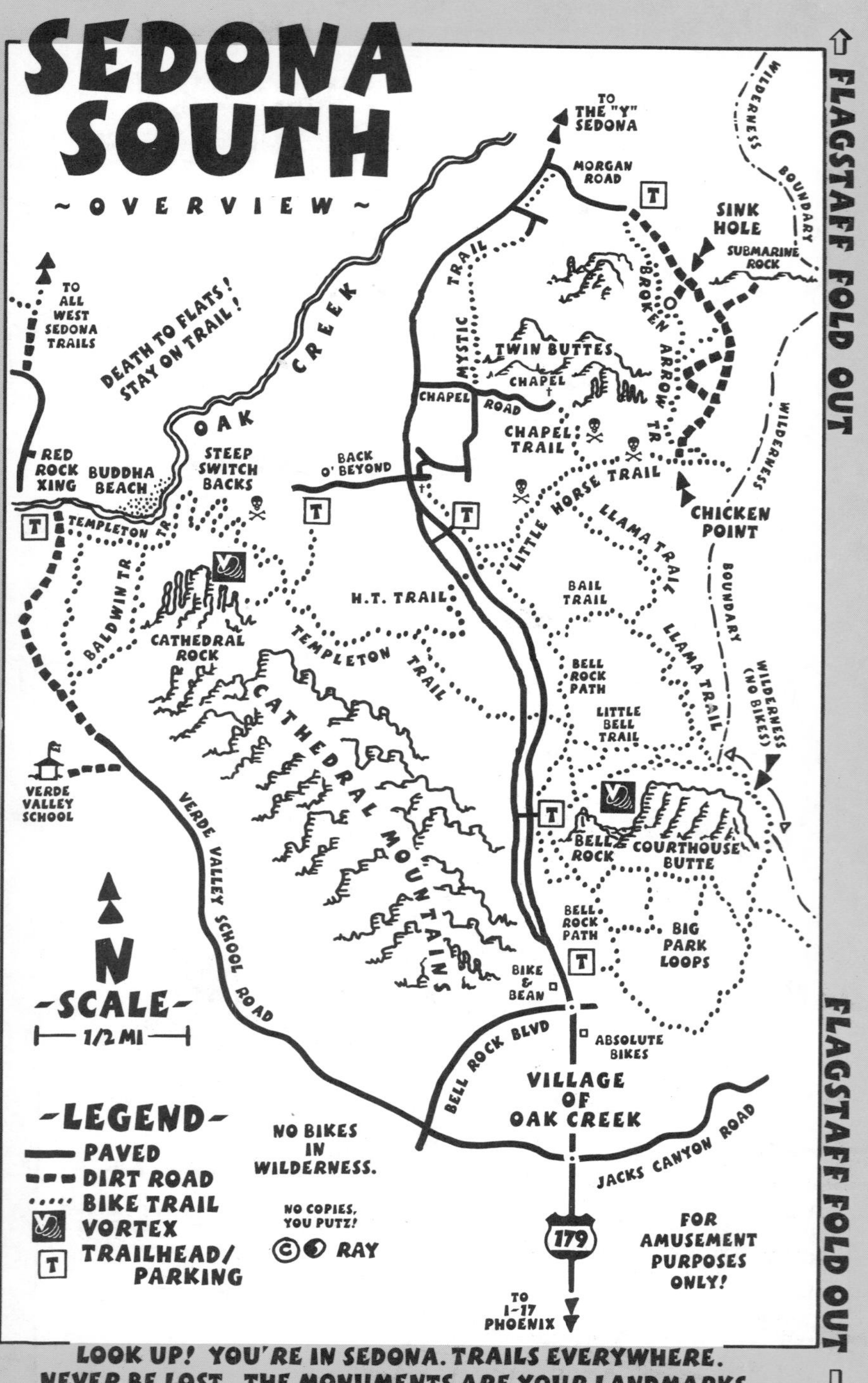

FLAGSTAFF FOLD OUT

LOOK UP! YOU'RE IN SEDONA. TRAILS EVERYWHERE.
NEVER BE LOST. THE MONUMENTS ARE YOUR LANDMARKS.

FLAGSTAFF FOLD OUT

SEDONA WEST
~ OVERVIEW ~

LEGEND
PAVED
DIRT ROAD
SINGLE TRACK
TRAILHEAD/ PARKING
VORTEX

NO COPIES PLEASE!

OAK CREEK · TO FLAGSTAFF · 89A · TO I-17 EXIT #320 6 MILES · WILDERNESS (NO BIKES) · SCHNEBLY HILL ROAD · MUNDS WAGON TRAIL · COW PIES · SLICK ROCK · HUCKABY TR · MIDGLEY BRIDGE · JIM THOMPSON TRAIL · JORDAN · SINK HOLE · JORDAN TR · SECRET TRAILS · THE "Y" · SOLDIER PASS RD · MTN SHADOWS · COFFEE POT · TEA CUP · SUNSET · MTN BIKE HEAVEN · CAPITOL BUTTE · THUNDER MTN TR · SANBORN · ANDANTE · SHELBY · CHIMNEY ROCK · THUNDER MTN RD · LOST WATCH TRAIL · DRY CREEK RD · PLUMBER'S CRACK TRAIL · AIRPORT · AIRPORT LOOP · BANDIT · AIRPORT MESA TRAILS · HIGH SCHOOL POST · OLD RIDGE · HERKENHAM · MORGAN ROAD · BROKEN ARROW TRAILS · TWIN BUTTES · CHICKEN POINT · CHAPEL TRAIL · LITTLE HORSE · 179 · TO VILLAGE OF OAK CREEK · BUDDHA BEACH · CATHEDRAL ROCK · SECRET SLICK ROCK · RED ROCK XING · VERDE VALLEY SCHOOL ROAD TO V.O.C. · UPPER LOOP · PYRAMID TRAILS · SCHEURMAN MOUNTAIN · NOD A TRAIL · LOWER RED ROCK LOOP ROAD · TO RESORT · DEADMANS PASS · MESCAL MTN · SNAKE TR · TWO FENCE TR · CYPRESS TRAIL · GIRDNER TRAIL · COLOR COVE · SEDONA CULTERAL PARK · DRY CREEK TRAILS · DAWA TRAIL · POWERLINE · COCKS COMB TRAIL · RUPP TRAIL · DOE MOUNTAIN · COCKS COMB · BOYNTON PASS RD · AERIE ROAD · TO RUINS · TO COTTONWOOD

© RAY

NO COPIES PLEASE!

DEATH TO FLATS!
STAY ON TRAIL AND SLICKROCK.
SLIME YOUR TUBES.
CARRY 2 SPARES.

LOOK UP!
YOU WILL NOT GET LOST IF YOU LOOK UP AND ORIENT YOUR POSITION TO ONE OF SEDONA'S BEAUTIFUL MONUMENTS.

LOOK UP! YOU'RE IN SEDONA. TRAILS EVERYWHERE.
NEVER BE LOST. THE MONUMENTS ARE YOUR LANDMARKS.
STAY ON ESTABLISHED TRAILS.

LOST ON THE REZ, 1981

"We test our shred."

RATING THE RIDES

For comparison's sake, all rides were rated by me, a seedy but sincere middle age male in reasonably good physical condition if otherwise unencumbered by the though process.

EASY: Some hills with nothing too steep or too long. A weenie ride. If you can't handle this you are one hopeless sofa-tater. I suggest more soda pop, Doritos and TV including shopping and game shows, golf, surgery, info-mercials, Survivor re-runs, soaps and channel surfing. Get plenty of quality couch time, high dollar gin, sex toys and video games. See a doctor .

MODERATE: Guaranteed to get the dead laughing and singing again. Interesting terrain with some healthy exposure to risk. Good sweaty, stinky, hard work, but still not killer.

DIFFICULT: Rough, tough, painful, hardass and muy dangeroso with occasional warp speed, climbing and distance. Not for the respiratorily challenged. Sort of like straight espresso. If you don't know what it is, you don't want it.

EXTREME: Caution! May set off low self esteem panic attack. Possible bloodbath. Parents would not approve. Nor your insurance agent, doctor, spouse or bike if it could talk. Also known as puck-10, no-brainer, e-ticket, hairball, burly, barny or barndog, abusive, gonzo, mongo, mondo, psycho, way super gnarly, hideous, hateful and gruesome. Do you lack common sense? Is your brain adrift in a sea of cheap beer or what.

"Saddle up effendi, we ride!"
-Aladdin

BE THOUGHT NEITHER CHURLISH LOUT, NOODGE NOR TRAIL TURD! KNOW HOW TO FIX A FLAT AND CARRY THY OWN KIT!

SPARE PARTS: Tube, patch kit, tire booting material, length of wire, chain link, spoke, duct tape and imagination.

TOOLS: combo tool (fix anything but a broken heart!)
chain tool (know how to use it)
tiny combo wrenches (8-9-10 mm)
petite hex (allen) wrenches (sizes to fit)
good mini-pump (check periodically)
tire irons (lose the screwdriver)
swiss army knife with corkscrew (you never know!)
sticks and stones (various sizes found on site)

AND: cell phone, small compass, T.P. and trowel (bury it deep!), fresh condom, matches, sunblock, a few crisp apples, one smoked salmon, a good hard cheese and a 1978 *SILVER OAK Alexander Valley* Cabernet to whittle away at the time.

MOUNTAIN BIKING IS HAZARDOUS!

Despite what some slicker-than-a-cheap-chicken lawyer might whisper in your ear, it ain't my fault!

THEREFORE, Cosmic Ray must advise that mountain biking is risky as heck. I have scars to prove it! This book is no substitute for topo maps, route finding skill, compass, good judgement, sense of humor, manners or cognitive thought. Oh yeah, wear a helmet.

FURTHER, I've done my best. I'm not responsible for wind, weather, beasts, boners, big rocks, sign changes, puddles, detours or ANY misfortune that pegs the puck-o-meter or gets your butt fur in a knot.

MOREOVER upon buying or snaking this book and reading this disclaimer you release and discharge me, my heirs and representatives from mistakes, getting lost or wrecking. Hey, poop happens. Lighten up.

REALIZE that it ain't Ray's quackin' fault. It's YOUR responsibility to be familiar with route, road, trail, grief factor, weather, water supply, mechanical condition, mind set, companions, lions, tigers, bears, undies, acts of God, pump, patch kit, camel sack and every other dang thing.

FINALLY, it's OK to be weak of physique or lame of brain, but if you be thin of grin PLEASE STAY SAFE AT HOME! Thank You.

ARIZONA TRAIL/ WALNUT CANYON

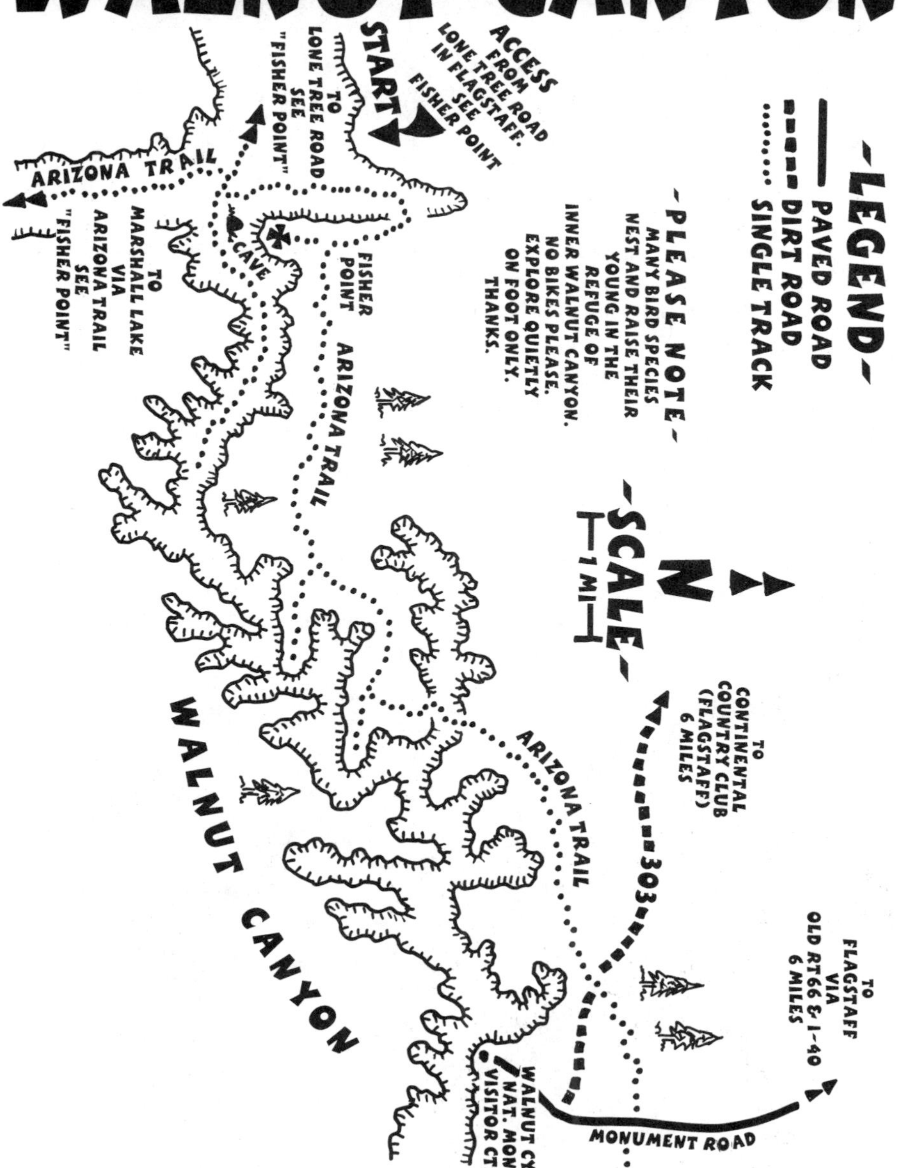

ACCESS FROM LONE TREE ROAD IN FLAGSTAFF. SEE FISHER POINT
START
TO LONE TREE ROAD SEE "FISHER POINT"
ARIZONA TRAIL
TO MARSHALL LAKE VIA ARIZONA TRAIL SEE "FISHER POINT"
CAVE
FISHER POINT
ARIZONA TRAIL
-LEGEND-
PAVED ROAD
DIRT ROAD
SINGLE TRACK
-PLEASE NOTE-
MANY BIRD SPECIES NEST AND RAISE THEIR YOUNG IN THE REFUGE OF INNER WALNUT CANYON. NO BIKES PLEASE. EXPLORE QUIETLY ON FOOT ONLY. THANKS.
-SCALE-
1 MI
N
TO CONTINENTAL COUNTRY CLUB (FLAGSTAFF) 6 MILES
303
ARIZONA TRAIL
WALNUT CANYON
TO FLAGSTAFF VIA OLD RT66 & I-40 6 MILES
WALNUT CYN. NAT. MON. VISITOR CTR.
MONUMENT ROAD

FLAGSTAFF

Flagstaff ARIZONA TRAIL
SINGLE TRACK TO WALNUT CANYON

DISTANCE: 15 MILES 1-WAY
(CAR SHUTTLE RETURN OR 30 MILES TOTAL)
TIME: 3 TO 4 HOURS
EFFORT: HARD CORE
SKILL: MEDIUM TO EXPERT
PUCK-O-METER: PUCK 5
SOME TECHNICAL STUFF
FIND ROUTE: MODERATE
SEASON: APR to NOV

DESCRIPTION: Legendary Flagstaff mountain biker Carl Tobin likened this ride to a 3-ring circus . . . a bit of everything in big doses. There is scenery, single track carving, short tough climbs and hairy descents as well as enough speed and technical daring-do to keep you well awake. Best of all, you ride 12 miles right near the rim of Walnut Canyon. Be sure to do the little jog out to the Fisher Point view. Stunning.

I seldom see other riders on this trail. On my first time I ran out of food by the time I got to the National Monument. I was not too proud to elbow squirrels out of the way and beg their cookies from picnicing tourists. Bring water *and* food!

DIRECTIONS: Find your way to Fisher Point. See the FISHER POINT map on page 10 and connect the dots. You will find yourself staring at a huge gorgeous sandstone cliff with a big cave hollowed out at the base. About 100 feet before the cave there is a trail to the left (north) that takes you ziggity zagging steeply up to the top of the cliff and Fisher Point. After the view, get back on the main trail and continue all the way out to Walnut Canyon National Monument Visitor Center. Take every opportunity along the way to ride out to the rim for more views. Spot ruins on the opposite wall. The visitor center offers a great interpretive walk to some well preserved cliff dwellings inside Walnut Canyon.

OPTIONS: Return the way you came or head home loop style via Monument Road (see map) and Old Route 66. A shorter easier option is to take FS 303 back to town.. See map. A lazy weenie way is to leave a car parked at the visitor center packed with Doritos, tunes and cold drinks. Yes!

"24 hours in a day. 24 beers in a case. Coincidence?"
-ancient mystery

FLAGSTAFF

DRY LAKE HILLS

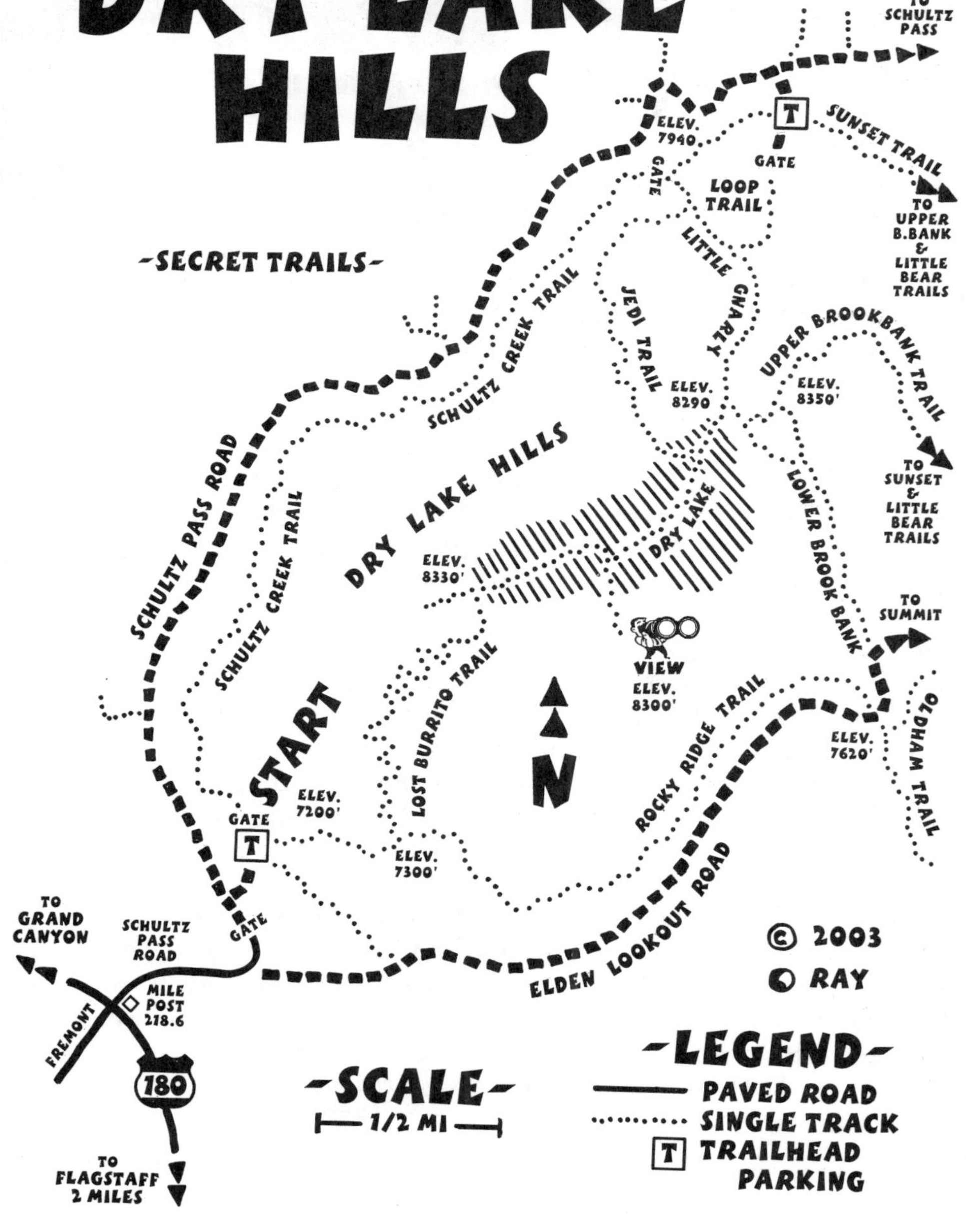

-SCALE-

1/2 MI

-LEGEND-

PAVED ROAD

SINGLE TRACK

T TRAILHEAD PARKING

Flagstaff DRY LAKE HILLS & SCHULTZ CREEK TRAIL

DISTANCE: 8.5 MILES
TIME: 2 HOURS
EFFORT: MEDIUM TO HARD
SKILL: INTERMEDIATE
PUCK-O-METER: PUCK 6
SOME FAST & SOME TECHNICAL SECTIONS
FIND ROUTE: MODERATE
SOME TURNS SIGNED, SOME NOT
SEASON: APR to NOV

0 **LOOP MILES** 8.5

PRIMO TRAIL
WORTH A JOURNEY

SCHULTZ CREEK TRAIL is the best bit of single track in Flag. 4 miles zen up and 4.5 down along a normally dry creek with a loop at the top plus more possibilities. See 'da map.

THE UP & OVER 9 mile option leads UP Schultz, UP Little Gnarly, DOWN Lower Brookbank, DOWN Rocky Ridge and back to GO. The 3.5 mile roll up Schultz is fairly easy. Climbing Little Gnarly for a mile will challenge your wind and tech skills. No dabs allowed. The Dry Lake 420° view detour is worthy. Down the speedy Brookbank mile will challenge your nerve. Same goes for the final 3.0 fast tech miles over Rocky Ridge. No dabs and you're a champ. Now do it in reverse, smarty.

JEDI LOOP is more technical. UP Schultz 3.5 miles to the gate. RIGHT up Little Gnarly to the top then RIGHT at the split just before the pond. JEDI TRAIL is the first right after that. Ramp up over a monster log followed by steep narrow switchbacks back down to Little Gnarly and finally down Schultz. The puck-o-meter spins off the dial on the tight and narrow Jedi Master descent.

LOST BURRITO has caused more grief than any trail I know. It's famous. It's scary. It's barely a trail. No skidding allowed. Control erosion. If you have to skid, you should walk. Named for my mutant pal Rex Phester riding UP the stupid thing. He lost a partial Martan's breakfast burrito in one, hunky, undigested, golf ball size urp. SICK*!*

SECRET TRAILS is terra incognita. Locals say it's my ass if I draw a map, so I'm showing you about where they *are*. That's it. The rest is up to you. Have fun, my friend.

"A rolling wheel is a fast wheel."
- Ken Lane

ELDEN LOOP

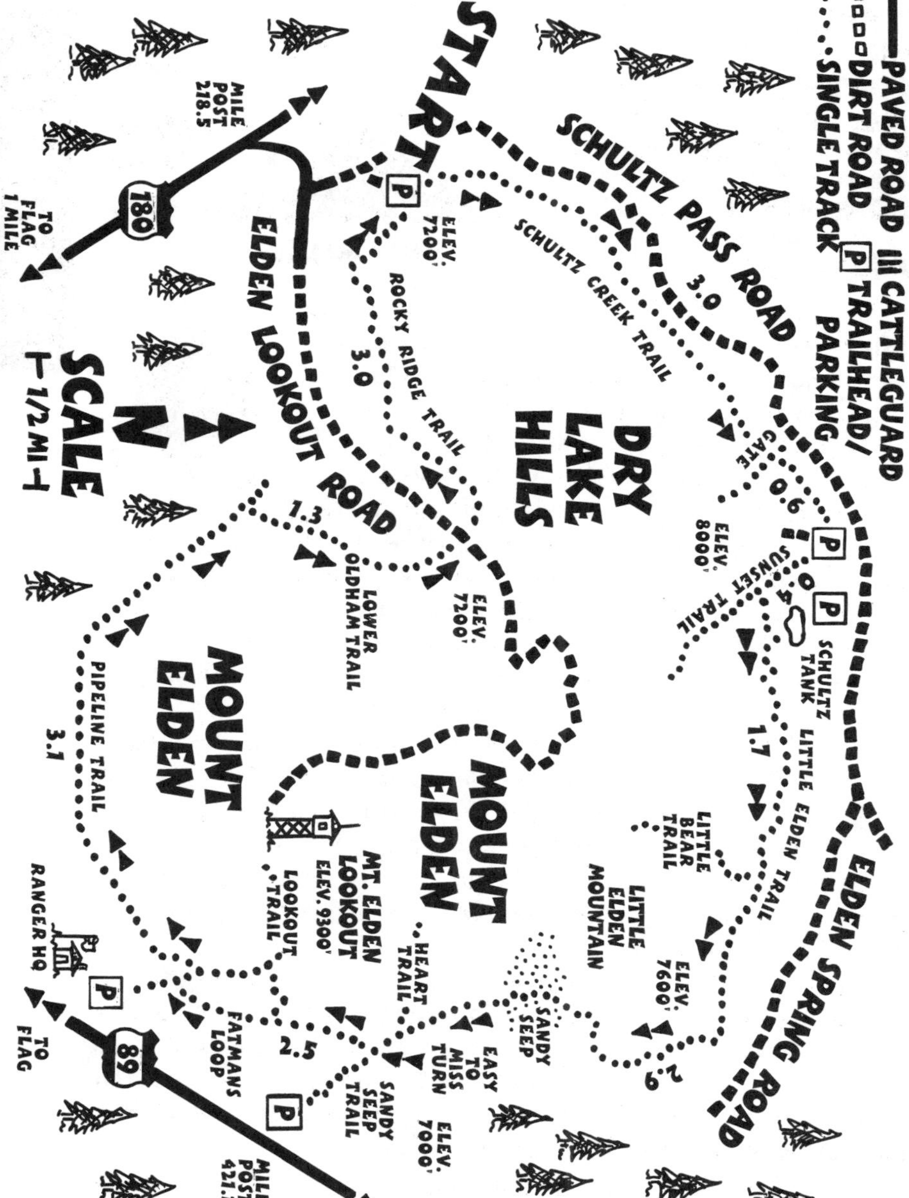

FLAGSTAFF

Flagstaff MOUNT ELDEN LOOP
EPIC SINGLE TRACK LOOP

DISTANCE: 18.5 MILES
TIME: 3 TO 5 HOURS
EFFORT: BIBLICAL
SKILL: EXPERT
PUCK-O-METER: PUCK 6.5
SOME FAST & TECHNICAL SECTIONS
FIND ROUTE: SIGNED
SEASON: APR to NOV

AT A GLANCE

9000
ELEV. (FT.)
6500
0 LOOP MILES 18.5

FLAGSTAFF

DESCRIPTION: Mount Elden single track is legend. This loop connects the dots around Elden Mountain. You'll call this siege epic . . . yup, *really* epic, as in take no prisoners, shoot the wounded, eat the weak! This be the real thing. The route is *mostly* signed. Go clockwise. Keep Elden on your right. Follow the contour of the mountain. Take no false trail leading steep up nor down to town. Follow the signs. I've done this route a dozen times. Map is to scale and pretty darn spot on.

MILEAGE LOG

0.0 START at Schultz Creek Trailhead and head up Schultz Creek Trail. See the map.
3.0 Gate. CONTINUE straight and up.
3.6 Sunset Trail Trailhead. Hop on Sunset.
4.0 LEFT onto Little Elden Trail around Schultz Tank and head down killer single track.
5.7 Little Bear flashes by on your right. IGNORE.
8.6 HEADS UP! After Sandy Seep, easy to miss turn is coming up. See the map. Take a RIGHT. More great single track to Fatman's Loop.
11.1 Across the bottom of Fatman's then the trail takes a tricky jog. Hop on Pipeline Trail. Signed.
14.2 Lower Oldham Trail. Take a RIGHT up and steep over to Elden Lookout Road.
15.5 Legs like jello? Get ready for Rocky Ridge! Rough, tough and technical. Caution, you're getting tired.
18.5 Back to go. May I suggest a cold one or two.

"When the chips are down, the buffalo is empty."
-Anon

FLAGSTAFF

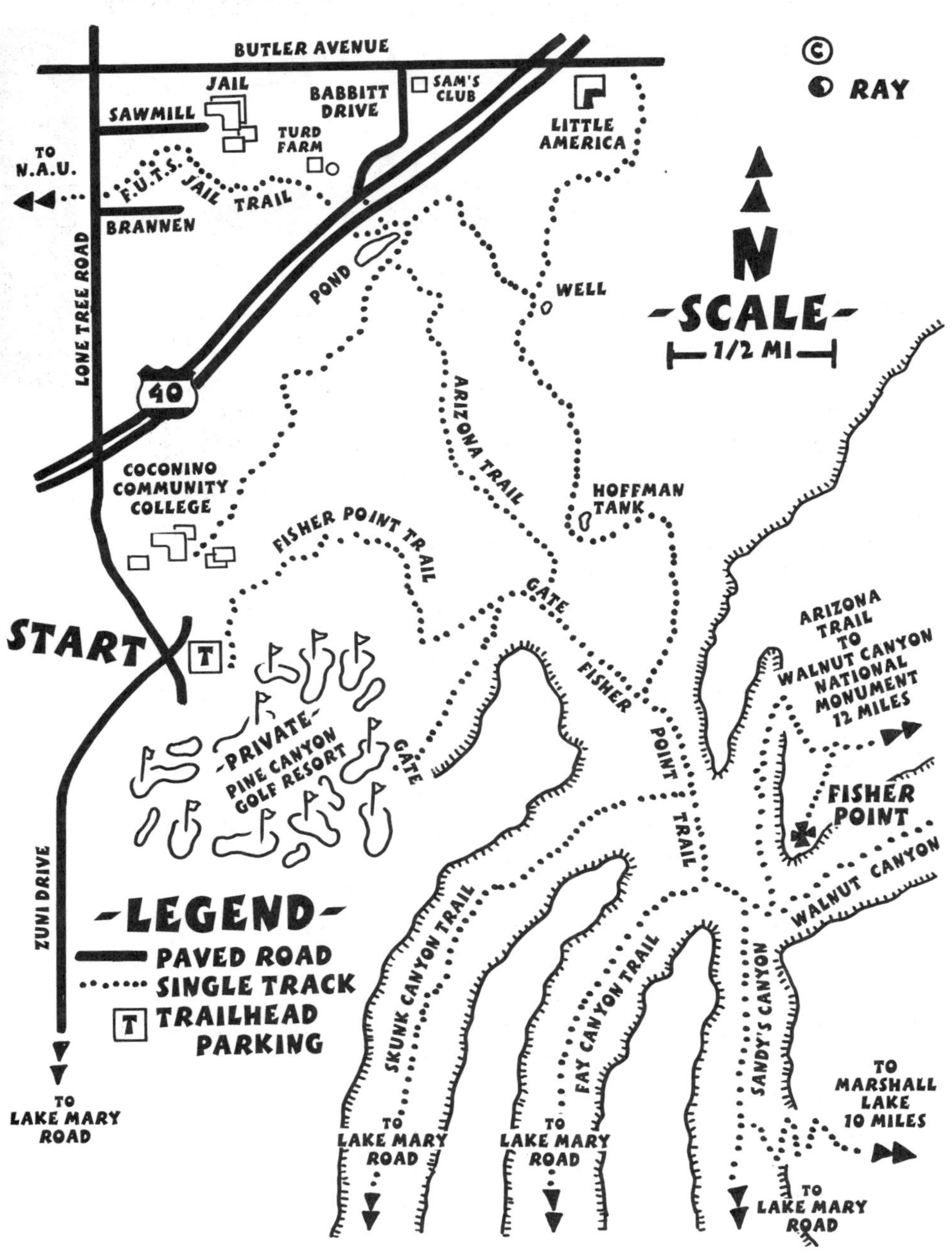

BUTLER AVENUE
© RAY
JAIL
SAWMILL
BABBITT DRIVE
SAM'S CLUB
LITTLE AMERICA
TURD FARM
TO N.A.U.
F.U.T.S. JAIL TRAIL
BRANNEN
LONE TREE ROAD
POND
WELL
N
-SCALE-
1/2 MI
40
ARIZONA TRAIL
COCONINO COMMUNITY COLLEGE
HOFFMAN TANK
FISHER POINT TRAIL
GATE
START
T
FISHER POINT TRAIL
ARIZONA TRAIL TO WALNUT CANYON NATIONAL MONUMENT 12 MILES
-PRIVATE- PINE CANYON GOLF RESORT
GATE
FISHER POINT
WALNUT CANYON
ZUNI DRIVE
-LEGEND-
PAVED ROAD
SINGLE TRACK
T TRAILHEAD PARKING
SKUNK CANYON TRAIL
FAY CANYON TRAIL
SANDY'S CANYON
TO MARSHALL LAKE 10 MILES
TO LAKE MARY ROAD
TO LAKE MARY ROAD
TO LAKE MARY ROAD
TO LAKE MARY ROAD

FISHER POINT

Flagstaff FISHER POINT
EASY TRAILS TO VIEW & CAVES

DISTANCE: 8.2 MILES
TIME: 2.5 to 3 HOURS
EFFORT: INTERMEDIATE
SKILL: ROOKIE
PUCK-O-METER: PUCK 2
NO FEAR WHATSOEVER
FIND ROUTE: MODERATE
SEASON: APR to NOV

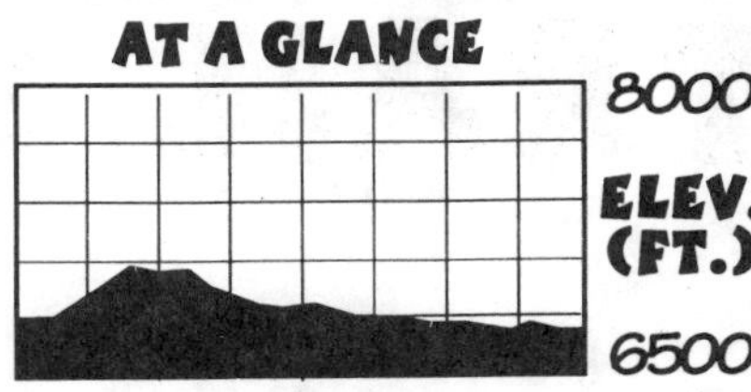

FLAGSTAFF

DESCRIPTION: Except for a good short climb from the get go, this easy trail is perfect for the novice. Secluded Fisher Point is primo for picnic, sunbath or grooving on the humongo buff Coconino sandstone rock face and its cave at the entrance to Walnut Canyon. Stash the bike here and explore the canyon floor on foot. Tangled Walnut Canyon is cool and quiet with birds, brush and a cave a half mile in on your right.

DIRECTIONS: Begin not too far from the N.A.U. Skydome. Park at the dome. Start at Lone Tree and Zuni. A new pain-in-butt golf course has made access a little more difficult, but in a few minutes you can work your way through to the trails and on to Fisher Point. There are many side trails to amuse you. However, if you follow bike tracks, my map and stay on the main trail, you'll get there no problemo. Otherwise, explore. You can't get very lost. You are surrounded by Flagstaff streets, the new golfing community and other paved roads. You will always come out somewhere near town.

OPTIONS: Check out the map. If you feel energetic, do the longer 25 mile round trip ride out to Marshal Lake on well marked AZ Trail and return via paved Lake Mary Road. You have a short, wicked steep climb out of Sandy Canyon, but the rest is easy smooth all the way. The AZ Trail is marked. The paved road has good shoulder until just before town.

Also, from up on Fisher Point you can enjoy an epic tour on the Arizona Trail along Walnut Canyon rim all the way to Walnut Canyon National Monument. See "Arizona Trail to Walnut Canyon" on page 5. If you choose either of these options, plan to be out all day. Don't forget food and water.

"The stone age didn't end due to any lack of stones."
-National Geographic

FORT VALLEY TRAIL SYSTEM

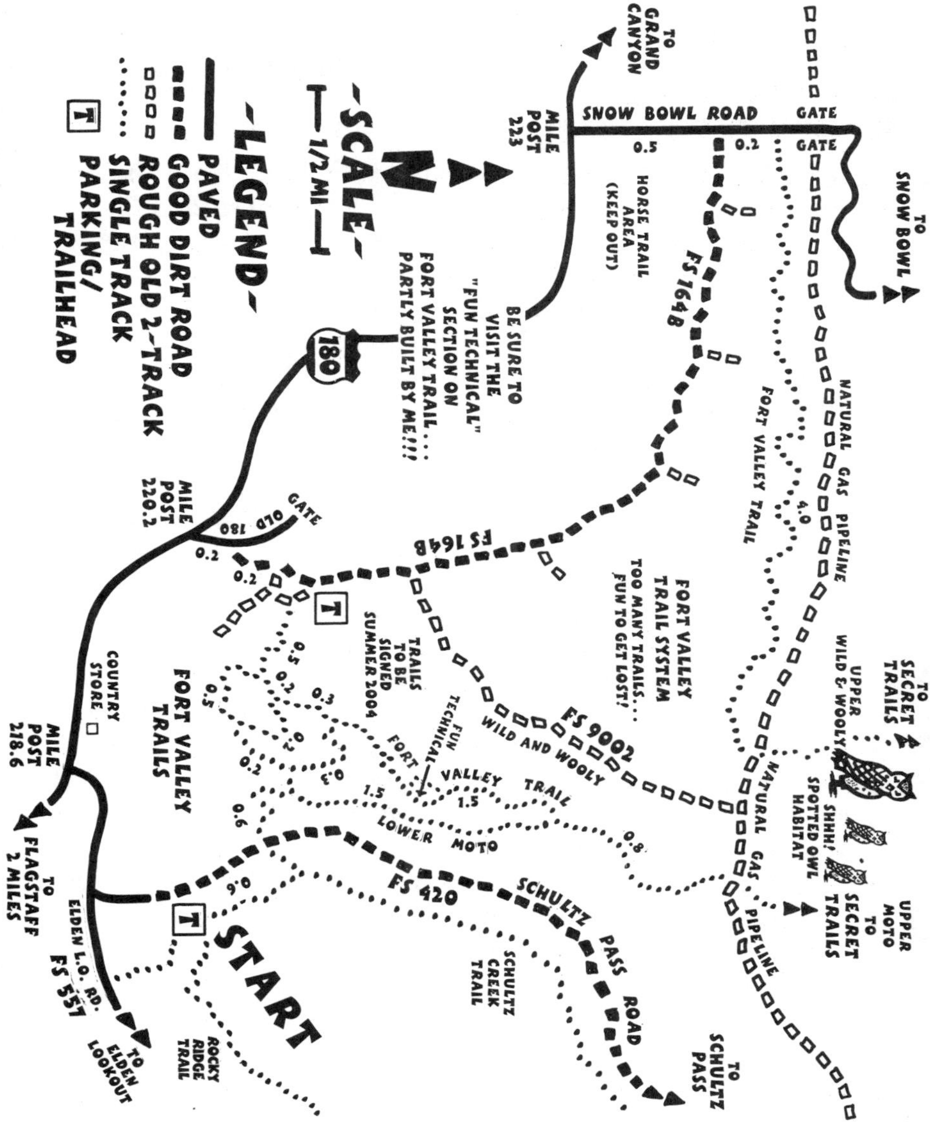

TO GRAND CANYON
MILE POST 223
SNOW BOWL ROAD
GATE
GATE
0.5
0.2
TO SNOW BOWL
HORSE TRAIL AREA (KEEP OUT)
FS 164B
N
-SCALE-
1/2 MI
-LEGEND-
PAVED
GOOD DIRT ROAD
ROUGH OLD 2-TRACK
SINGLE TRACK
T PARKING/ TRAILHEAD
BE SURE TO VISIT THE "FUN TECHNICAL" SECTION ON FORT VALLEY TRAIL.... PARTLY BUILT BY ME!!!
180
NATURAL GAS PIPELINE
FORT VALLEY TRAIL
4.0
MILE POST 220.2
OLD 180
GATE
0.2
0.2
FS 164B
FORT VALLEY TRAIL SYSTEM
TOO MANY TRAILS... FUN TO GET LOST!
TRAILS TO BE SIGNED SUMMER 2004
T
COUNTRY STORE
FORT VALLEY TRAILS
0.5
0.5
0.2
0.3
0.2
0.2
0.3
FUN TECHNICAL
FORT VALLEY TRAIL
1.5
1.5
FS 9002
WILD AND WOOLY
UPPER WILD & WOOLY
TO SECRET TRAILS
SPOTTED OWL HABITAT
SHHH!
MILE POST 218.6
TO FLAGSTAFF 2 MILES
0.6
LOWER MOTO
0.8
NATURAL GAS PIPELINE
UPPER MOTO
TO SECRET TRAILS
0.6
FS 420
SCHULTZ PASS ROAD
T
START
SCHULTZ CREEK TRAIL
ELDEN L.O. RD. FS 557
TO ELDEN LOOKOUT
ROCKY RIDGE TRAIL
TO SCHULTZ PASS

FLAGSTAFF

Flagstaff **FORT VALLEY TRAILS**
OODLES OF SINGLE TRACK NOODLES

DISTANCE: 2 TO 10 MILES
TIME: 1 TO ??? HOURS
EFFORT: EASY TO HARD
SKILL: ALL LEVELS
PUCK-O-METER: PUCK 1 TO 7
SOME EASY, SOME FAST & TECHNICAL
FIND ROUTE: FEW SIGNS
SEASON: APR to NOV

DESCRIPTION: Noodles and oodles of 1-track trails. Few signs. No real guarantee you won't get lost. If you want a guarantee, buy a toaster. Not to worry though. You're surrounded by busy roads. You'll come out somewhere.

These trails were built by volunteer labor . . . mountain biker *hand* labor . . . shovel by evil shovel, stone by stubborn stone. The area has been a secret maze of game trails, social trails, motorcycle and horse trails since the long ago, but times change. Flag grew. Now comes the time to organize this mess, deal with the traffic, protect the woods and allow for some quiet so those cute spotted owls can do the wild thing and then raise the young'uns in peace. Hey, we all gotta share. Stay on established trails and no yelling, thank you very much.

These Fort Valley trails are soon to be signed with some old social trails erased and other new trails created. Go explore. Make your own loops. The trails traverse the lower slope of the mountain. If you are lost, go down hill. If you want to get more lost, go uphill. Fort Valley Trails hook up with the Elden Trail System and the network of Secret Trails . . . Moto, Secret, Orion, Hot Shot and others too secret to say. I've said too much already. One more word out of me and I'll be tied to a tree and left for squirrel bait !

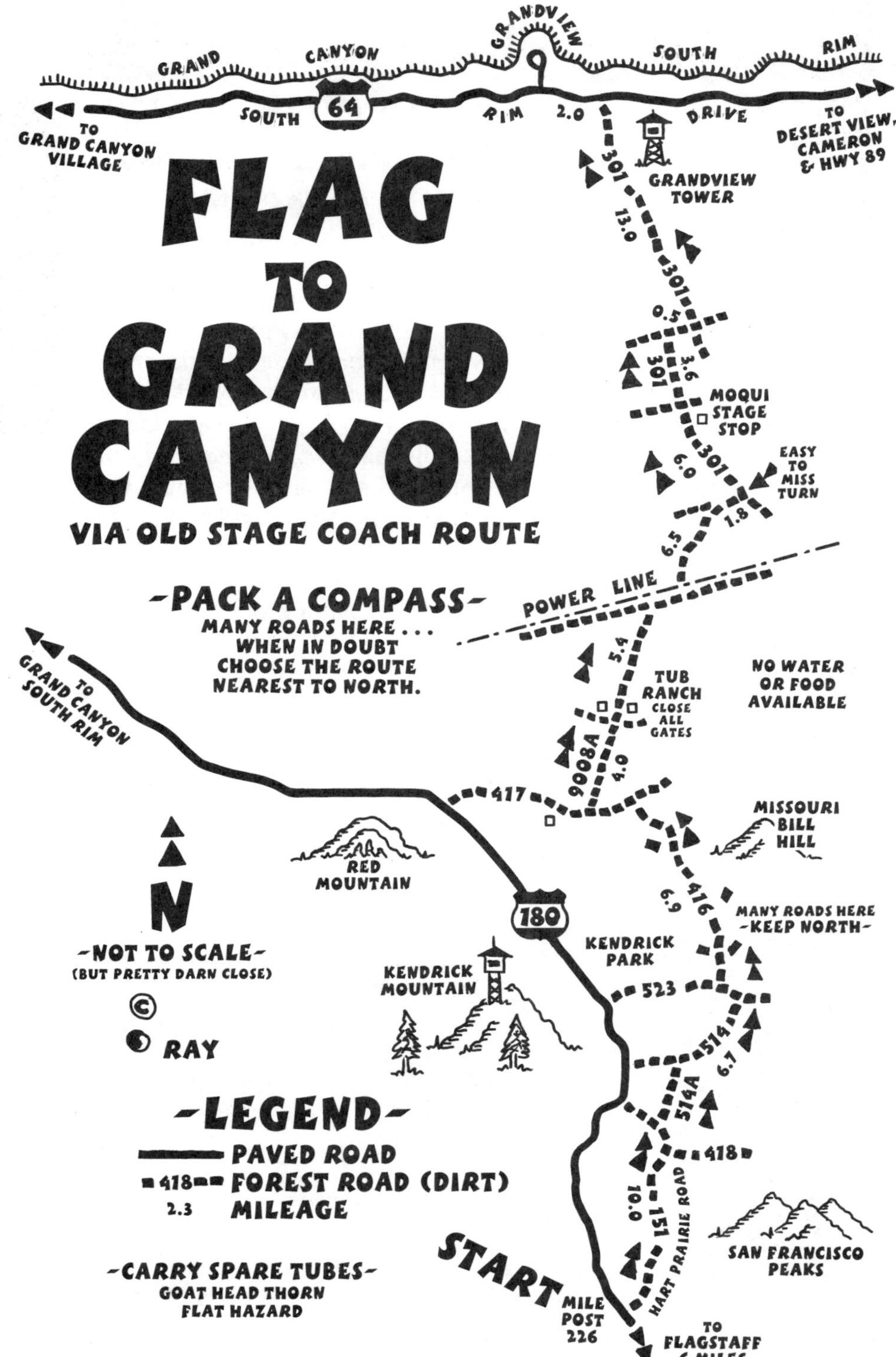

FLAG TO GRAND CANYON
VIA OLD STAGE COACH ROUTE
GRAND CANYON SOUTH RIM
GRANDVIEW
64
SOUTH RIM DRIVE
2.0
TO GRAND CANYON VILLAGE
TO DESERT VIEW, CAMERON & HWY 89
GRANDVIEW TOWER
301
13.0
301
0.5
301
3.6
MOQUI STAGE STOP
6.0
301
EASY TO MISS TURN
1.8
6.5
POWER LINE
-PACK A COMPASS-
MANY ROADS HERE . . .
WHEN IN DOUBT
CHOOSE THE ROUTE
NEAREST TO NORTH.
5.4
TUB RANCH
CLOSE ALL GATES
NO WATER OR FOOD AVAILABLE
TO GRAND CANYON SOUTH RIM
9008A
4.0
417
MISSOURI BILL HILL
RED MOUNTAIN
180
6.9
416
MANY ROADS HERE
-KEEP NORTH-
N
-NOT TO SCALE-
(BUT PRETTY DARN CLOSE)
© RAY
KENDRICK PARK
KENDRICK MOUNTAIN
523
514
6.7
514A
-LEGEND-
PAVED ROAD
418 FOREST ROAD (DIRT)
2.3 MILEAGE
418
10.0
151
HART PRAIRIE ROAD
SAN FRANCISCO PEAKS
START
MILE POST 226
TO FLAGSTAFF 6 MILES
-CARRY SPARE TUBES-
GOAT HEAD THORN
FLAT HAZARD

Flagstaff TO GRAND CANYON
HISTORIC STAGE COACH ROUTE

FLAGSTAFF

DISTANCE: 70 MILES
TIME: 2 DAYS
EFFORT: LONG EASY RIDE
SKILL: EASY DIRT ROADS
PUCK-O-METER: PUCK 2
DON'T GET LOST. BRING A COMPASS
FIND ROUTE: EASY
SEASON: APR to NOV

AT A GLANCE

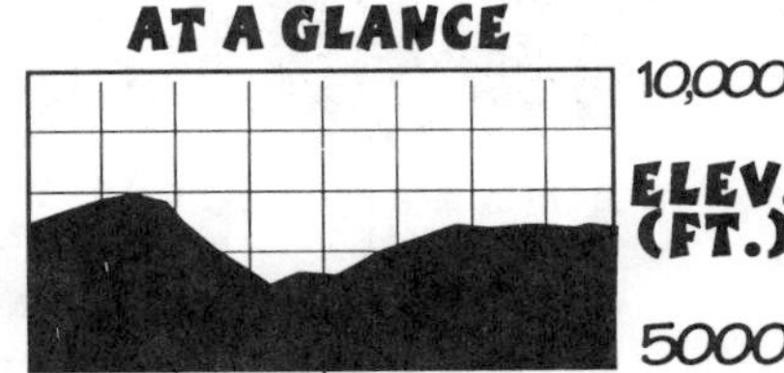

DESCRIPTION: Moqui Station was one of three stops enroute Flag to The Canyon, 1892 to 1899. A 12 hour trip cost $20 (1890s dollars!) and ran three times a week with six-horse coaches and a trailer. On September 7, 1897 Coconino Cycling Club team captain C. H. Coble and his studly crew mounted up and beat the stage coach to The South Rim on their trusty single speeds!

An 1890s writer said, "The road is good and level with some heavy grades. It winds among the slopes of the San Francisco Mountains for the first 25 miles through a fine forest of pine. The next 25 miles lead across a rolling prairie and the rest through the forest which skirts the rim of The Grand Canyon. Riders will find advantage to fit wheels with a gear not exceeding 66 inches. To The Grand Canyon is 70 miles. Any rider can do it in 8 to 12 hours." On 1-speed clunkers yet!

This is an ideal 2-day tour. Keep your compass pointed north. The gate where FS 417 meets 9008A is a good spot to meet support with camping gear. Bring lots of water, food and tubes for goathead thorns. SLIME tube sealant is highly recommended. Inquire locally before you go or e-mail me.

COCONINO CYCLING CLUB AT THE GRAND CANYON, SEPTEMBER 7, 1897

LAVA CAVE & WING MTN.

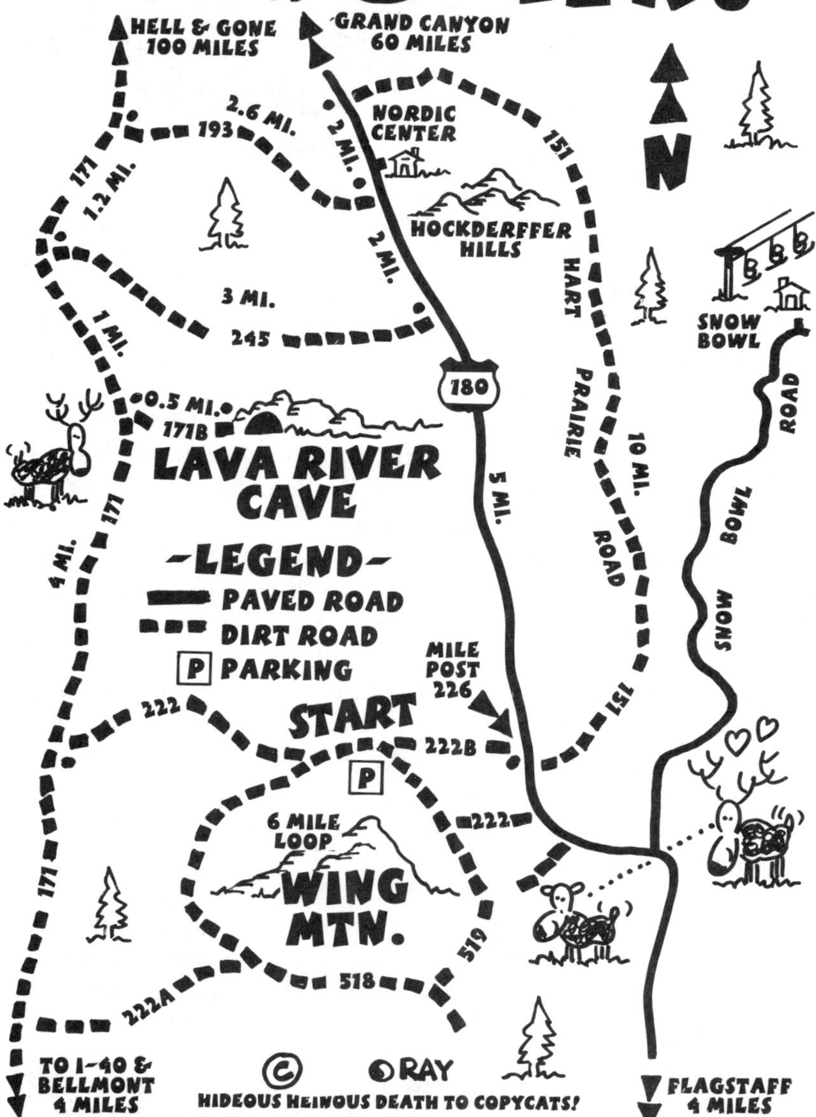

FLAGSTAFF

Flagstaff LAVA RIVER CAVE
EASY FOREST ROADS TO COOL CAVE

FLAGSTAFF

DISTANCE: 30 MILE LOOP
TIME: 5 TO 6 HOURS
EFFORT: MODERATE
SKILL: EASY
PUCK-O-METER: PUCK 0
UNLESS YOU'RE AFRAID OF THE DARK
FIND ROUTE: EASY
SEASON: APR to NOV

DESCRIPTION: Extending nearly a mile under the forest floor, Lava River Cave gets tight in one spot, but the ceiling is 30 feet high in another. Bring a snack, plenty of water, 3 flashlights and warm clothing. The cave is quite cool and dark and this is no place for a panic attack! Discovered by loggers in 1915, this is the longest lava tube in Arizona. Formed 700,000 years ago, lava ran from a nearby volcano then cooled on the top and bottom while continuing to flow and then emptied creating a tube.

The long smooth dirt road out to Lava Cave sports views of The Peaks through a fine open forest of pine and aspen along a gentle climb. No food or water along the way.

DIRECTIONS: Start at the parking area near Wing Mountain and follow the map to the cave. Return via HWY 180 or Hart Prairie Road for a nice long easy loop.

OPTION: The smooth and easy 6-mile Aspen Loop around Wing Mountain makes for an ideal family trek, especially in the fall when the aspen leaves are blazing.

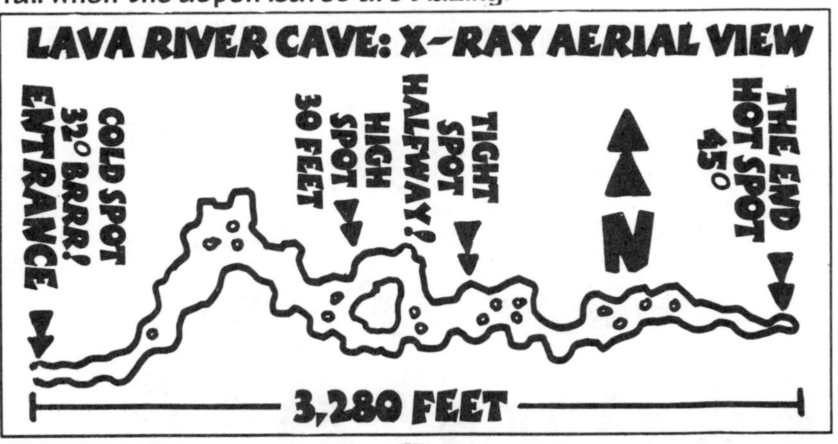

LITTLE BEAR LOOP

FLAGSTAFF

Flagstaff LITTLE BEAR LOOP
RAY'S FAVORITE SINGLE TRACK LOOP

DISTANCE: 17.3 MILES
TIME: 3 to 4 HOURS
EFFORT: SERIOUS CLIMB
SKILL: ADVANCED
PUCK-O-METER: PUCK 8
TWO FAST SINGLE TRACK DESCENTS
FIND ROUTE: FAIR EASY
SEASON: APR to NOV

AT A GLANCE

DESCRIPTION: You'll yell *"YEAH BABY!"* so loud that local squirrels will think somebody musta got lucky. Single track climbs, descents, switchbacks and views high along Flag's best trails link up to make this ride epic-didlyicious. Crank up Schultz Creek Trail, grind up Little Gnarly and up Upper Brookbank, fly down Little Bear, up Little Elden and finally, blast down twisty-turny Schultz Creek Trail to the blazing finish. Just holler *"YEAH BABY!"*

PRIMO TRAIL
WORTH A JOURNEY

MILEAGE LOG

0.0 START at Schultz Creek trailhead (see map) and enjoy a very fine, all zen do-able climb up Schultz Creek.
3.6 Gate. Go RIGHT up Little Gnarly. Stay RIGHT and climb all the way up to a little pond.
4.7 Lovely small pond. Go LEFT on single track.
4.8 LEFT up for a short, steep single track short cut.
4.9 LEFT onto Upper Brookbank. More tough climbing.
6.9 *AHHH!* The top. Now bear right down Sunset Trail.
7.2 LEFT at top of Little Bear. Down and fast. Be ready for hikers and horses. Mind your manners.
10.9 LEFT onto Little Elden and a short climb back up.
12.8 RIGHT onto Sunset Trail.
13.1 Sunset Trailhead parking lot. Go across the lot and head down Schultz Creek Trail.
13.7 Gate. You were here on the way up. Go back through gate and enjoy wicked fun descent. You earned this twisting, turning, jumping descent.
17.3 Finish. Whaddaya think? Best ride ever? Heck *YES!*

"I thought of that while riding my bicycle."
- *Albert Einstein*

OBSERVATORY MESA

A-1 MOUNTAIN
RADIO TOWER
A-1 MOUNTAIN ROAD
TO I-40 AT A-1 MTN RD EXIT
GATE
515
518 B
CATTLE GUARD
LANGE TANK
A-1 TANK
506
TO HWY 180
GATE
GATE
515 D
9113 C
506
9012 L
515
515 B
GATE
GATE
TUNNEL SPRING
515
CATTLE GUARD
URBAN TRAIL
W. RIDGE
LOWELL OBSERVATORY
CURLING SMOKE
B.I.A. DORMS
STEEP UP
THORPE PARK
TOLTEC
SANTA FE
START
BALL FIELDS
MILTON
LIBRARY
CITY HALL
URBAN TRAIL
ROUTE 66

-SCALE-
1 MI

-LEGEND-
PAVED ROAD
DIRT ROAD
URBAN TRAIL
ROUGH & ROCKY

FLAGSTAFF

Flagstaff OBSERVATORY MESA
CLOSE-TO-TOWN FOREST TRAILS

FLAGSTAFF

DISTANCE: 2 to 20 MILES
TIME: 1 TO 3 HOURS
EFFORT: NOVICE RIDE
SKILL: BEGINNER
PUCK-O-METER: PUCK 4
CAUTION ON URBAN TRAIL DESCENT
FIND ROUTE: MODERATE
SEASON: APR to NOV

AT A GLANCE

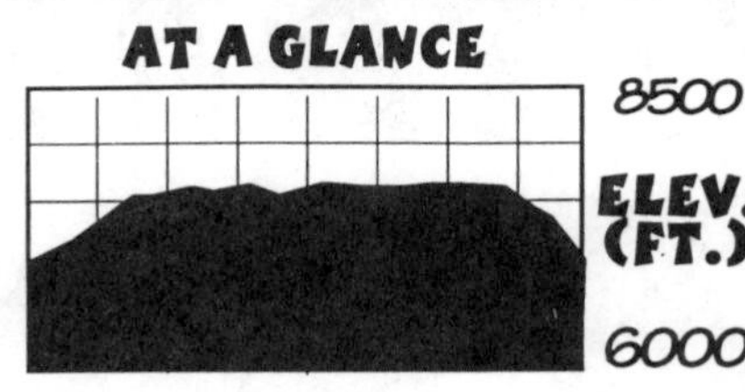

DESCRIPTION: So many roads that even the elk get lost! Percival Lowell got lost and built his observatory 100 years ago with the family fortune to look for Pluto and life on Mars. Bet his parents loved that. No life found on Mars . . . so far.

Golden barked old Ponderosa pine giants shade the forest below. Massive elk with majestic racks migrate here in fall. I got wet and nearly froze my toes one very late fall. Ow! Access is via a steep 500 ft. climb onto the mesa up an Urban Trail (see map). Orientation is easy. The San Francisco Peaks are in sight northeast. The main road is FS 515. Close all gates and respect private property. Loops are possible under the forest canopy then down Tunnel Springs and follow the RR tracks to town. A rocky hellacious descent to Tunnel Springs is quite the hairball buttruff (i.e. Too easy to ride standing up, but too rough to ride comfortably seated!). E-ticket fun, but crazy not to wear a helmet.

"For every problem there is a solution that is neat, simple and wrong."
-H.L. Mencken

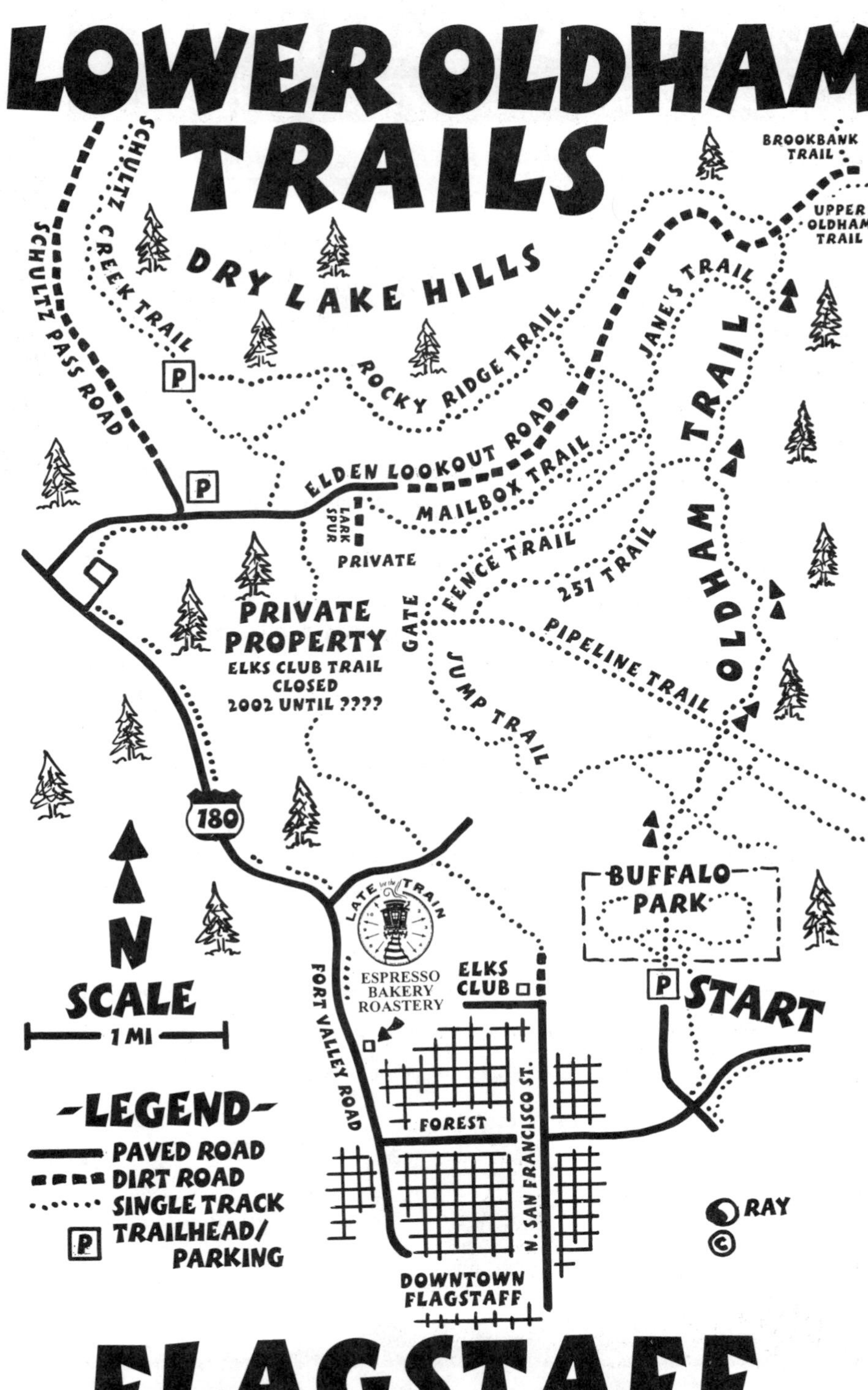
LOWER OLDHAM TRAILS
DRY LAKE HILLS
BROOKBANK TRAIL
UPPER OLDHAM TRAIL
SCHULTZ CREEK TRAIL
SCHULTZ PASS ROAD
ROCKY RIDGE TRAIL
JANE'S TRAIL
OLDHAM TRAIL
ELDEN LOOKOUT ROAD
MAILBOX TRAIL
LARK SPUR
PRIVATE
FENCE TRAIL
251 TRAIL
GATE
PRIVATE PROPERTY
ELKS CLUB TRAIL CLOSED 2002 UNTIL ????
PIPELINE TRAIL
JUMP TRAIL
180
BUFFALO PARK
LATE for the TRAIN
ESPRESSO BAKERY ROASTERY
ELKS CLUB
START
N
SCALE
1 MI
FORT VALLEY ROAD
FOREST
N. SAN FRANCISCO ST.
-LEGEND-
PAVED ROAD
DIRT ROAD
SINGLE TRACK
TRAILHEAD/ PARKING
RAY ©
DOWNTOWN FLAGSTAFF
FLAGSTAFF

Flagstaff OLDHAM TRAIL (LOWER)
BIG FUN SINGLE TRACK PLAY AREA

DISTANCE: 3 to 5 MILES
TIME: AN HOUR OR TWO
EFFORT: INTERMEDIATE
SOME BOULDERS TO GET THROUGH
SKILL: INTERMEDIATE
PUCK-O-METER: PUCK 5
SOME PUCK 7 BOULDERS TO WORK THROUGH
FIND ROUTE: MODERATE
SEASON: APR to NOV

DESCRIPTION: Lower Oldham Trail cuts through a maze of some of the coolest single track around. If you love to carve some fairly level groove with only a rare occasional short technical bit, this is for you. The descent from Elden Lookout Road is railing fast with a couple of good drops and jumps. Riding UP this section is good, challenging, hard breathing fun. Beginners or kids may find it real tough. Lower Oldham Trail is a favorite route connecting Buffalo Park in town with the Mount Elden/Dry Lake Hills Trail System. Connections exist to Upper Oldham, Dry Lake Hills, Schultz Creek, Little Bear, Sunset, Pipeline and Brookbank Trails, but first I suggest a thorough exploration of the single track playground weaving in and around Lower Oldham. It's close to town, gently rolling and just challenging enough to get your butt fur dialed for the rest of the day. It is usually clear of snow by April 1 even as the upper trails may be still locked in deep snow. Lower Oldham hooks up from town very nicely with fun, famous and slightly more technical Rocky Ridge Trail, just across Elden Lookout Road. See the map.

My map is pretty complete, but there is a maze of trail here. The area covers only about 4 square miles and is surrounded on all sides by roads or steep boulder walls. You can't get too lost. Stay out of anything that looks like private property. Watch for hikers and horses, especially weekends.

DIRECTIONS: Easy as pie to find. Begin Lower Oldham Trail from either end at Buffalo Park or Elden Lookout Road. Buffalo Park has good parking and also provides a safe and car-less access. Best not to ride on danger HWY 180.

"I'm not afraid of dying, I just don't want to be there when it happens."
-Woody Allen

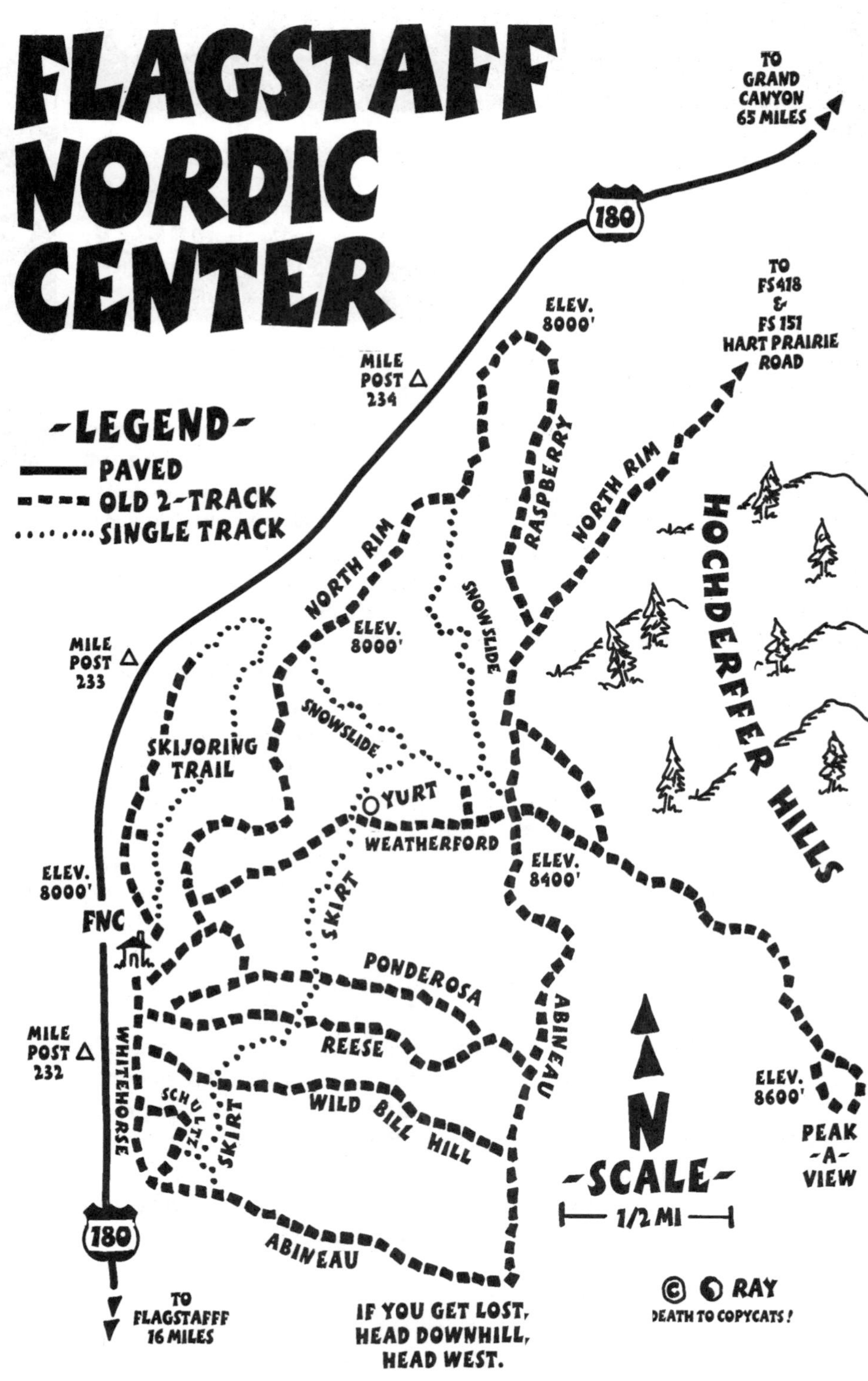
FLAGSTAFF NORDIC CENTER
TO GRAND CANYON 65 MILES
180
TO FS418 & FS 151 HART PRAIRIE ROAD
ELEV. 8000'
MILE POST 234
-LEGEND-
PAVED
OLD 2-TRACK
SINGLE TRACK
RASPBERRY
NORTH RIM
NORTH RIM
HOCHDERFFER HILLS
SNOW SLIDE
ELEV. 8000'
MILE POST 233
SNOWSLIDE
SKIJORING TRAIL
YURT
WEATHERFORD
ELEV. 8400'
ELEV. 8000'
FNC
SKIRT
PONDEROSA
ABINEAU
MILE POST 232
WHITEHORSE
REESE
SCHULTZ
SKIRT
WILD BILL HILL
N
ELEV. 8600'
PEAK -A- VIEW
-SCALE-
1/2 MI
180
ABINEAU
© RAY
DEATH TO COPYCATS!
TO FLAGSTAFF 16 MILES
IF YOU GET LOST, HEAD DOWNHILL, HEAD WEST.

Flagstaff NORDIC SKI CENTER
EASY 2-TRACK TO SCENIC SPOT

DISTANCE: 2 to 25 MILES
TIME: 1 to 3 HOURS
EFFORT: EASY to MEDIUM
SKILL: BEGINNER

PUCK-O-METER: PUCK 2
NO FEAR ON EASY DESCENTS
FIND ROUTE: MODERATE
SEASON: MAY to OCT
GREAT FALL COLORS!

DESCRIPTION: High in the aspen above Flagstaff, the XC ski trails of Flagstaff Nordic Center are deep in snow all winter. A ski track guides your way through the cold crisp air. When spring rolls around they hang up the skinny skis, trails dry and it's time to roll.

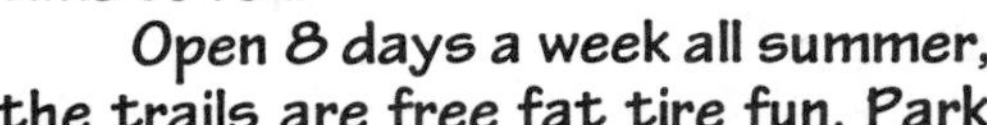

Open 8 days a week all summer, the trails are free fat tire fun. Park at the lodge and go through the pedestrian gate. Huge aspen groves punctuate the towering pines. The golden aspen leaf display peaks around October 1. I've jumped an early morning fall herd of 50 gigantic elk. Views extend to a telephoto shot of The Peaks. Beginners love the easy 2-track trails with no steep climbs. Not much danger of getting lost either. The summer trails may be unmarked, but the place is surrounded by a fence. Just head downhill and you're home.

Serious hammerheads who feel that need for speed find the trails interesting and uncrowded. When it's 113° in Phoenix, it's in the early to mid-seventies up here. Wear your helmet, carry food, water and emergency rain gear. The summer monsoon can be wicked wet, but over quick.

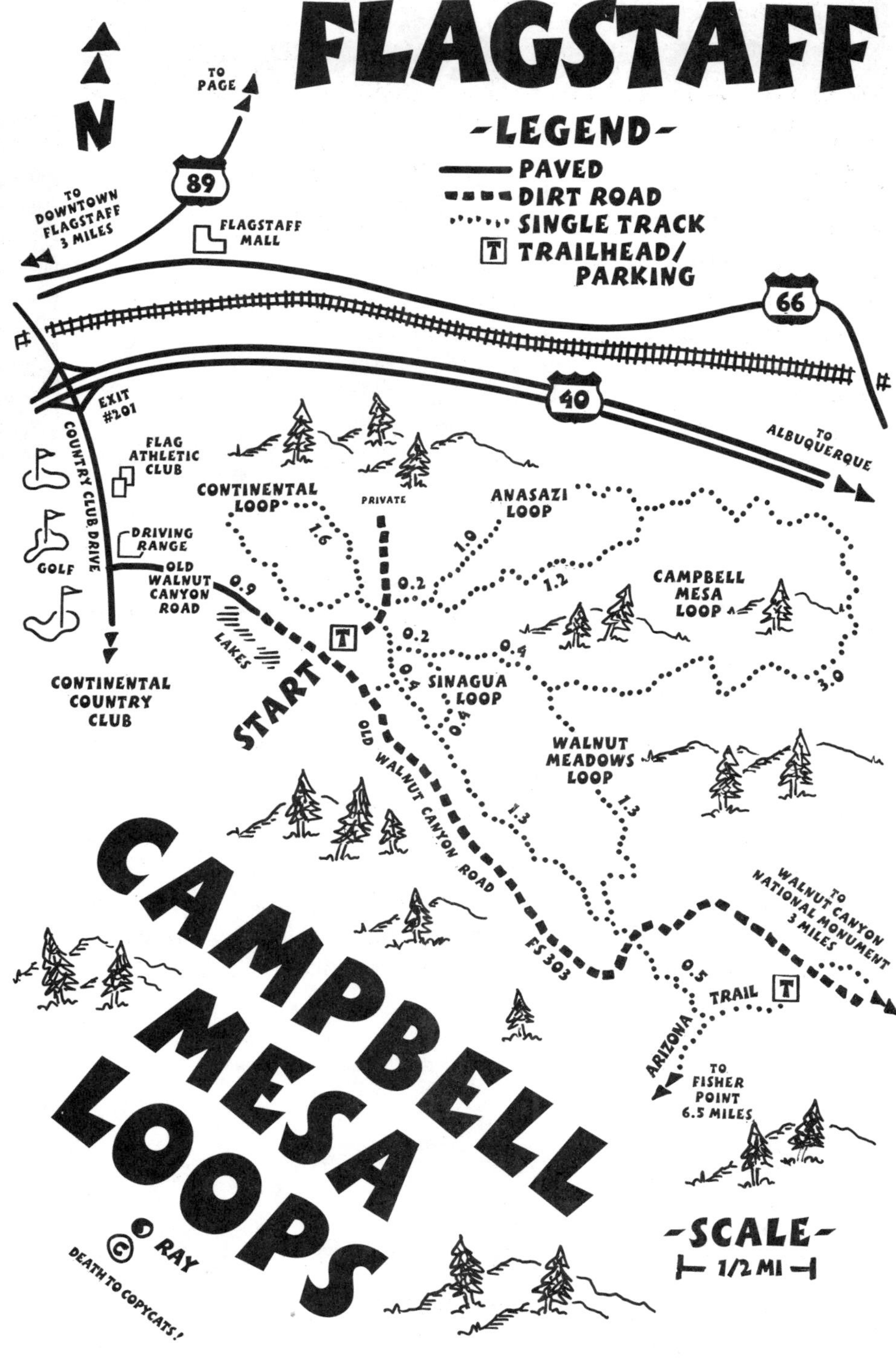
FLAGSTAFF
N
TO PAGE
89
TO DOWNTOWN FLAGSTAFF 3 MILES
FLAGSTAFF MALL
-LEGEND-
PAVED
DIRT ROAD
SINGLE TRACK
T TRAILHEAD/ PARKING
66
40
EXIT #201
TO ALBUQUERQUE
COUNTRY CLUB DRIVE
FLAG ATHLETIC CLUB
CONTINENTAL LOOP
PRIVATE
ANASAZI LOOP
DRIVING RANGE
GOLF
OLD WALNUT CANYON ROAD
CAMPBELL MESA LOOP
LAKES
START
SINAGUA LOOP
CONTINENTAL COUNTRY CLUB
WALNUT MEADOWS LOOP
OLD WALNUT CANYON ROAD
FS 303
TO WALNUT CANYON NATIONAL MONUMENT 3 MILES
ARIZONA TRAIL
TO FISHER POINT 6.5 MILES
CAMPBELL MESA LOOPS
© RAY
DEATH TO COPYCATS!
-SCALE-
1/2 MI

Flagstaff CAMPBELL MESA
FUN, FAST, EASY SINGLE TRACK LOOPS

FLAGSTAFF

DISTANCE: 9.5 MILES
TIME: 1 to 2 HOURS
EFFORT: FAIRLY EASY
SKILL: NOT AT ALL TRICKY
PUCK-O-METER: PUCK 2.0
THE FASTER YOU GO, THE SMOOTHER IT GETS
FIND ROUTE: SIGNED
SEASON: APR to NOV

AT A GLANCE

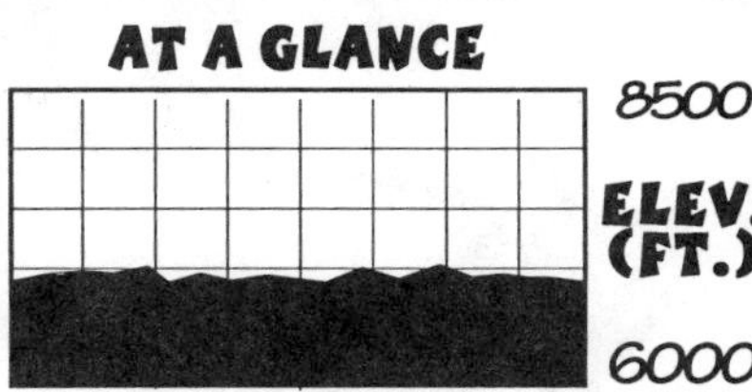

DESCRIPTION: Smooth, ripping fast, easy singletrack loops like spokes on a wheel. Beautiful, open forested scenery. No big climbs. No rocks. No crowds. Great wildflowers in season. So smooth you can time-trial every loop in the place in under an hour. Climbs are short and easy with only 500' of climbing over the whole 9.5 mile trail system. Perfect for beginners and kids looking to hone singletrack skills before tackling tougher trails or experts looking for speed work.

You can't get lost. All trails are signed and all lead back to the trailhead except for one well marked, signed turnoff to the Arizona Trail. Look out for the occasional hiker or other mountain biker going fast in the opposite direction.

DIRECTIONS: Easy to find near Continental Country Club in East Flag. From I-40, take CCC/Page Exit #201 and head south 0.9 miles to Old Walnut Canyon Road. Take a LEFT and go another 0.9 miles to the parking lot on the LEFT. OR from downtown Flag, take Route 66 EAST until you see the sign for CCC. Bear RIGHT over the overpass and follow the map.

ROCKY RIDGE TRAIL

© RAY

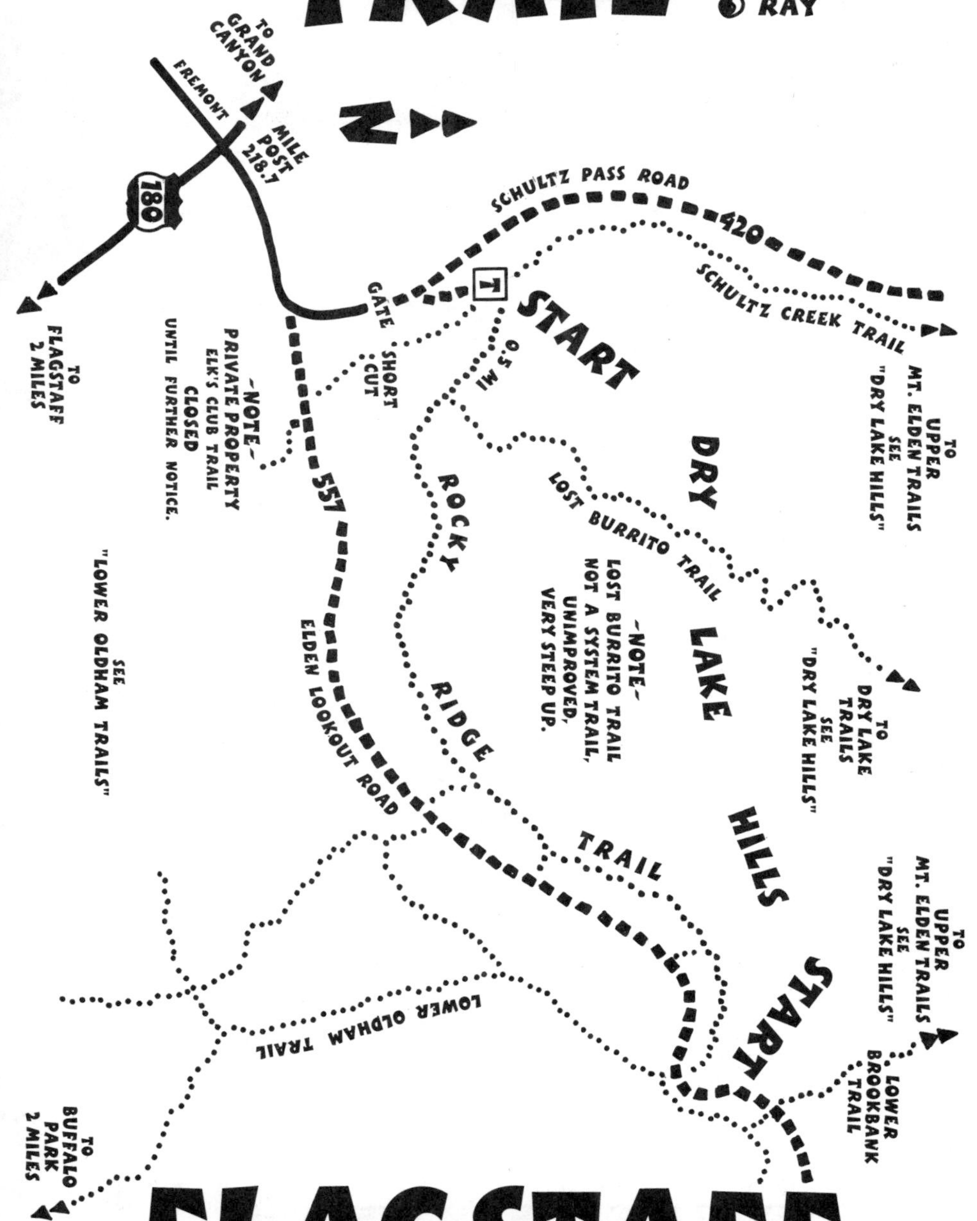

Flagstaff ROCKY RIDGE TRAIL
GROOMED, INTERMEDIATE SINGLE TRACK

DISTANCE: 3.0 MILES
EFFORT: HARD FAST WORK
SKILL: INTERMEDIATE
PUCK-O-METER: PUCK 4
BUT STILL EASY TO WRECK AT SPEED.
FIND ROUTE: EASY
SEASON: MAR to NOV

DESCRIPTION: Gravity school is in session. Be wary lest the earth rise up and smite thee. Close-to-town intermediate single track through ponderosa pine, Gambel oak and twisty, gnarly alligator bark juniper. "Rockless Ridge" or "Rocket Ridge" as locals now call it, is manicured by "improvements" to where adrennelin freaks have to haul ass twice as fast to peg their PUCK-O-METER. Call an ambulance! However, 90% of nearly-normal, nearly-human bikers tell me they love it. The top half from Elden Road down, drops about 200 feet making for great momentum and speed and thereafter rolls up and down across Rocky Ridge and hooks up with all other Mt. Elden trails . . . Schultz, Little Bear, Secret, Moto, Brookbank, Oldham, Blue Dot, Jedi, Ft. Valley and so on and on. See map.

DIRECTIONS: North out of Flag on HWY 180 for 2 miles to milepost 218.6. Turn right at Schultz Pass sign and follow the map up Elden Lookout Road. Sign on left says Rocky Ridge.

FLAG TO SEDONA

VIA OLD MUNDS HIGHWAY

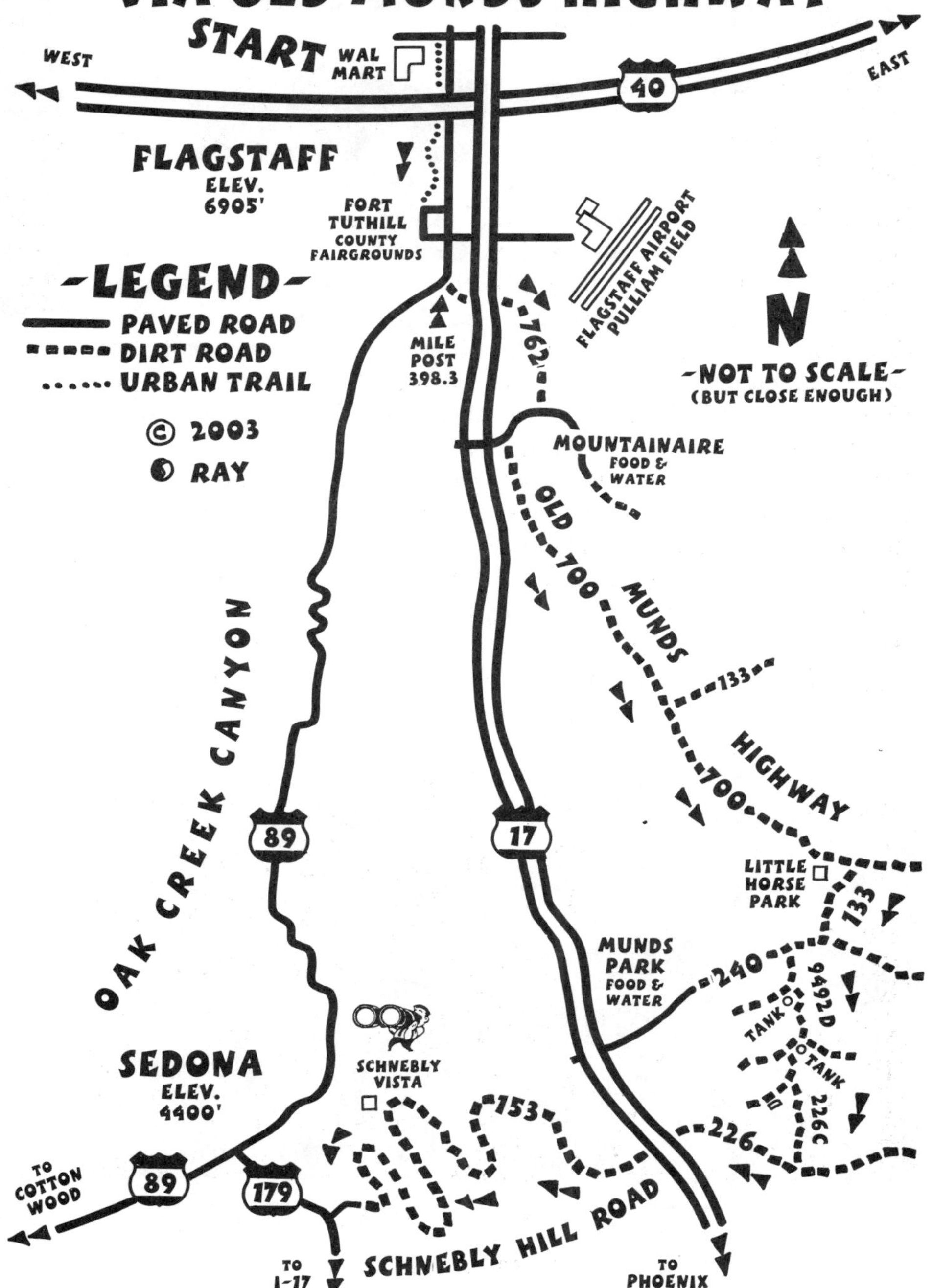

START
WEST
EAST
WAL MART
40
FLAGSTAFF
ELEV. 6905'
FORT TUTHILL COUNTY FAIRGROUNDS
FLAGSTAFF AIRPORT PULLIAM FIELD
N
-LEGEND-
PAVED ROAD
DIRT ROAD
URBAN TRAIL
© 2003
RAY
MILE POST 398.3
762
-NOT TO SCALE-
(BUT CLOSE ENOUGH)
MOUNTAINAIRE
FOOD & WATER
OLD
700
MUNDS
133
HIGHWAY
700
OAK CREEK CANYON
89
17
LITTLE HORSE PARK
133
MUNDS PARK
FOOD & WATER
240
9492D
TANK
TANK
226C
SEDONA
ELEV. 4400'
SCHNEBLY VISTA
153
226
TO COTTON WOOD
89
179
SCHNEBLY HILL ROAD
TO I-17
TO PHOENIX

Flagstaff FLAG TO SEDONA
VIA OLD MUNDS HIWAY & SCHNEBLY HILL

DISTANCE: 43.8 MILES
TIME: ALL DAY
EFFORT: LOOOOONG RIDE
SKILL: MOSTLY EASY
PUCK-O-METER: PUCK 4
(You'll be tired on the long descent.)
ROUTE: ONE TRICKY SPOT
SEASON: MAY to NOV

AT A GLANCE

DESCRIPTION: Old wagon roads from Flag pines to Sedona redrocks. Pass thru stands of ponderosa pines and aspen before dropping into juniper and pinyon. Descend 3000 ft. in 6 miles. Check out one of the best views on the planet. Have a shuttle waiting in Sedona!

MILEAGE LOG

0.0 START south on urban trail next to Wal-Mart, across from Red Lobster, corner of McConnell and Beulah.
3.0 Fort Tuthill Fairgrounds. Head out to HWY 89A.
3.5 RIGHT turn on paved 89A. Watch for cars.
4.2 LEFT onto dirt road Old Munds Highway at milepost 398.3 directly across from *Jackson's Grill.*
7.3 Jog RIGHT on paved Mountainaire Road.
7.6 LEFT on FS 700, Old Munds Highway, then a long roll past Newman Park & Coyote Park to Little Horse Park.
20.6 RIGHT turn on FS 133 at sign "Little Horse Park".
22.4 RIGHT again on FS 240. Next comes the easy-to-miss, tricky turn in EXACTLY 1.25 miles.
23.7 Old 2-track on left is FS9492D. Now keep due SOUTH. FOLLOW THE MAP DETAIL! OR do The Cheat short cut into Munds Park, have a snack and ride the wide I-17 shoulder to Schnebly Hill Rd. It's 2 smooth legal miles.
28.8 "T" into FS 226. Go RIGHT onto Schnebly Hill Road and down Schnebly all the way to Sedona OR Munds Wagon Trail single track starts just after Schnebly Overlook. See the Schnebly Hill map on page 90.
43.8 SEDONA! Tired? Hungry? You are somewhat dazed and confused, but you are also one AWESOME POSSUM!

"To be old and wise, you must first be young and stupid."
-Cosmic Ray's College of Knowledge

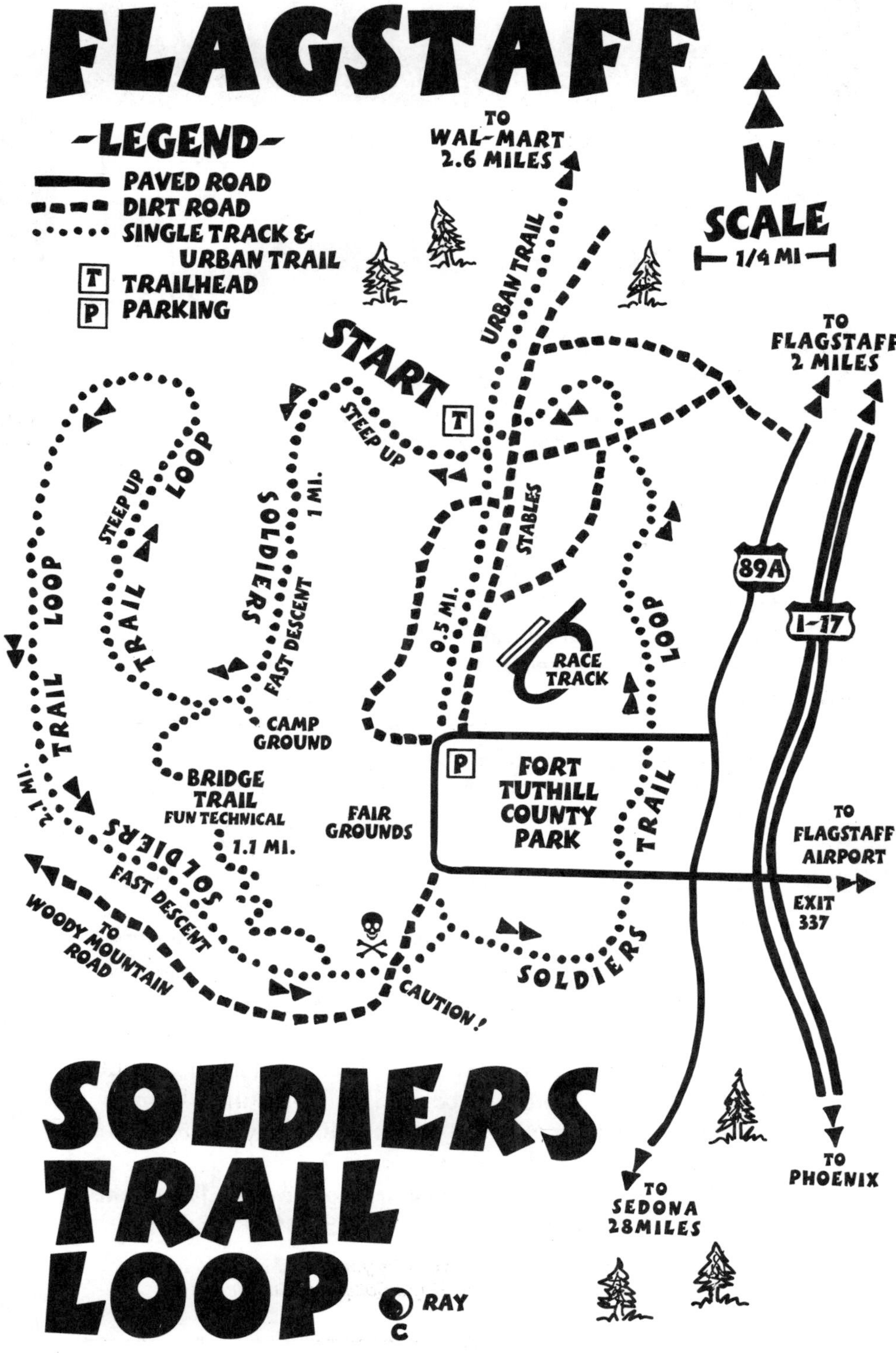
FLAGSTAFF
-LEGEND-
PAVED ROAD
DIRT ROAD
SINGLE TRACK &
URBAN TRAIL
T TRAILHEAD
P PARKING
N
SCALE
1/4 MI
TO
WAL-MART
2.6 MILES
URBAN TRAIL
START
STEEP UP
LOOP
STEEP UP
TRAIL
SOLDIERS
1 MI.
FAST DESCENT
STABLES
0.5 MI.
LOOP
TRAIL
CAMP
GROUND
BRIDGE
TRAIL
FUN TECHNICAL
1.1 MI.
FAIR
GROUNDS
RACE
TRACK
FORT
TUTHILL
COUNTY
PARK
LOOP
TRAIL
2.1 MI.
SOLDIERS
FAST DESCENT
TO
WOODY MOUNTAIN
ROAD
CAUTION!
SOLDIERS
TO
FLAGSTAFF
2 MILES
89A
I-17
TO
FLAGSTAFF
AIRPORT
EXIT
337
TO
SEDONA
28MILES
TO
PHOENIX
SOLDIERS
TRAIL
LOOP
RAY

Flagstaff SOLDIERS TRAIL
QUICK LOOP AT TUTHILL

DISTANCE: 5 MILESPLUS
TIME: 1 HOUR PLUS
EFFORT: GO FAST
BREATHE HARD
SKILL: EASY
PUCK-O-METER: PUCK 3
ONE FAST DESCENT WITH GOOD TURNS
FIND ROUTE: SIGNED
SEASON: ALL YEAR

DESCRIPTION: Close to town. Easy to moderate. Some wide trail. Some interesting single track options. East and south facing makes for long snow free season and good for cross country skis when it does snow. Even open when all other areas close down due to fire danger.

The 5 mile loop has two good climbs and some fun fast descents. The tread is not too challenging so it's great for beginners. It's all marked. There is also a way bitchin' technical section called Bridge Trail that bisects the main loop. It's only 1.1 miles each way, but the added 2.2 miles can really make the whole thing a hammer fest, especially if you ride out from town via the Ft. Tuthill Urban Trail from Wal-Mart. Hats off to the crew that built Bridge Trail with us mountain bikers in mind. They left in some good roots, rocks, dips, drops and even hand built a narrow little stone bridge.

To do the whole enchilada from town adds up to about 12 miles. At high speed it may take some under an hour, but I'd allow 1.5 to 2.5 hours for most human type folks. I prefer the loop counter-clockwise because the climbs are steep and short and the descents are loooong, twisty and fast. Do not miss the Bridge Trail. Although short, it's twists, turns and wild ride are itself worth the journey.

DIRECTIONS: Find the Flagstaff Wal-Mart. Good place to park, buy corn dogs and look at strange people. Urp! Urban trail starts along the east side of the parking lot next to the Wal-Mart garden center. It is well marked with a big sign. Head south until you get to a big trailhead sign by the horse jump area at Fort Tuthill County Fairgrounds.

"The greatest risk is never taking one."
- Jackie Robinson

SUNSET TRAIL LOOP

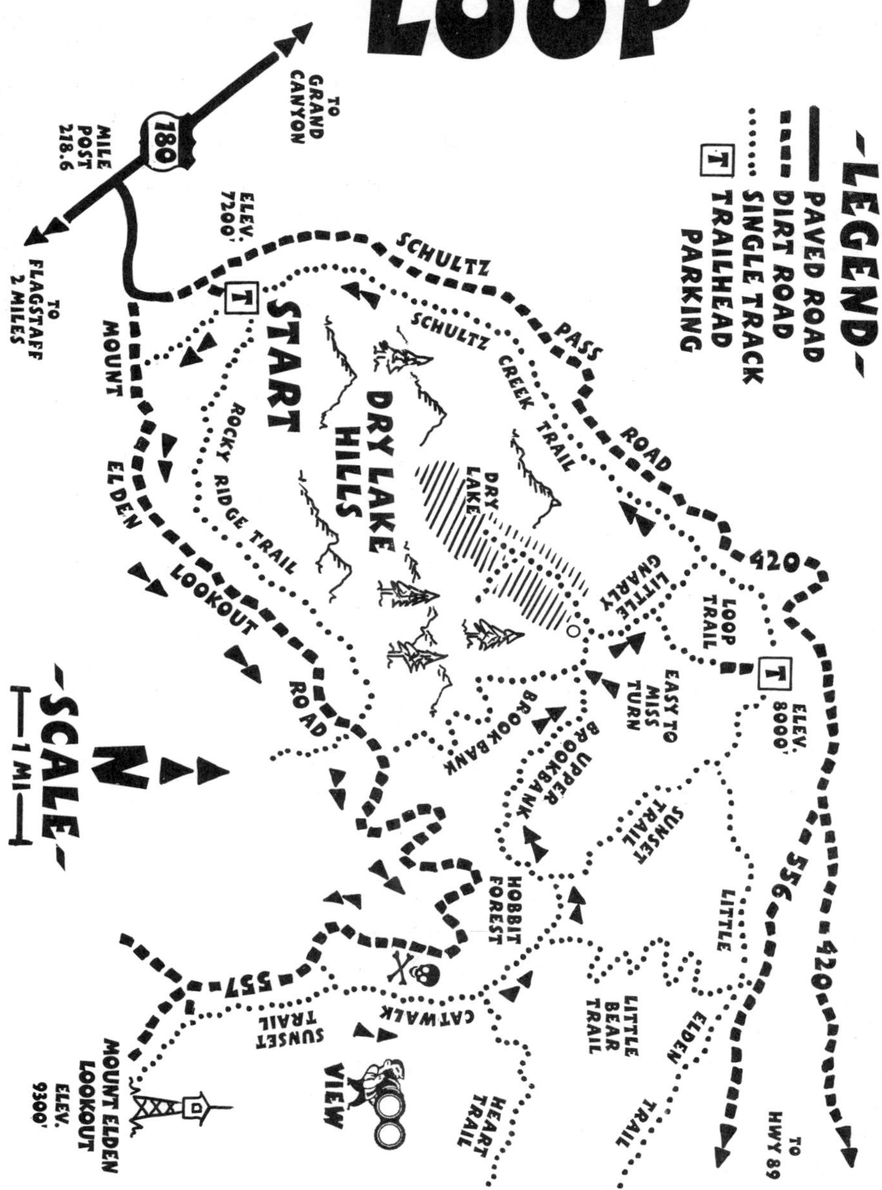

FLAGSTAFF

Flagstaff SUNSET TRAIL
THE PREMIER EPIC SINGLE TRACK LOOP

FLAGSTAFF

DISTANCE: 14.6 MILES
TIME: 2.5 to 3.5 HOURS
EFFORT: ONE LONG CLIMB
SKILL: EXPERTO
PUCK-O-METER: PUCK 8.5
"ORGAN DONOR" TRAIL IS FOR REAL.
ROUTE FINDING: EASY
SEASON: APR to NOV

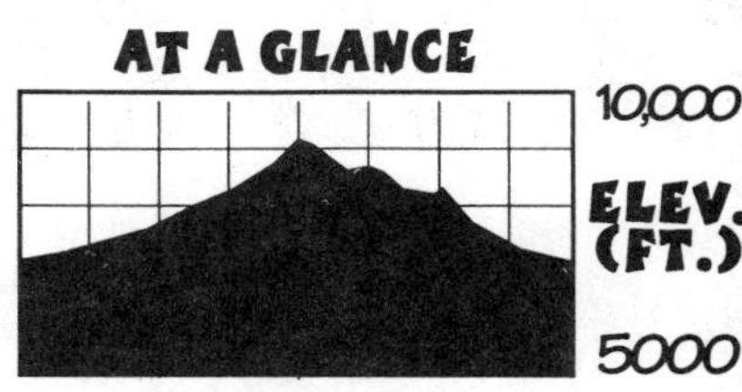

DESCRIPTION: Railing down Sunset at warp speed makes your pants dance! A super narrow, widowmaker catwalk is aptly named Organ Donor. An 8-mile single track descent through a big boulder hobbit fern forest and ultra-mondo killer, twisty-turny finish make the word epic seem pale. Whether you ride the full metal Huffy or a high dollar, full bounce Ti Dream Weenie, this ride is sweeter than that music that paints pictures. If you drove to the top so you can skank your weak butt merrily DOWN the hill, SHAME! You are a lame ass corndog. *No guts, no glory!*

MILEAGE LOG

0.0 Head up Elden Lookout Road. Figure 1 hour for the climb. (Record is 26 minutes!) Crank up the miles.
7.0 Whew and yahoo! You did it! Sign directs you up a steep trail on LEFT 50 ft. to Sunset Trail. LEFT on Sunset. The skinny catwalk, Organ Donor (no joke), is etched on the ridgeline cliff. EXTREME CAUTION!
8.8 Trail splits. Bear LEFT onto Upper Brookbank Trail. Go up a little then a way fun single track descent.
10.5 EASY TO MISS! You are enjoying a fast, rough, rocky root-infested descent when an unmarked trail heads sharply to your RIGHT to Dry Lake.
10.6 CONTINUE as you skirt the Dry Lake and head down ultra fun Little Gnarly Trail to Schultz Creek Trail.
10.8 A loop trail JUNCTION. Bear LEFT and CONTINUE.
11.6 Schultz Creek Trail. Go LEFT and enjoy one of the best single track descents in the western world.
14.6 *YES!* Back to GO. You be smilin' now.

"Moderation in all things, particularly moderation."
-*W.C. Fields*

FLAGSTAFF FALL COLORS

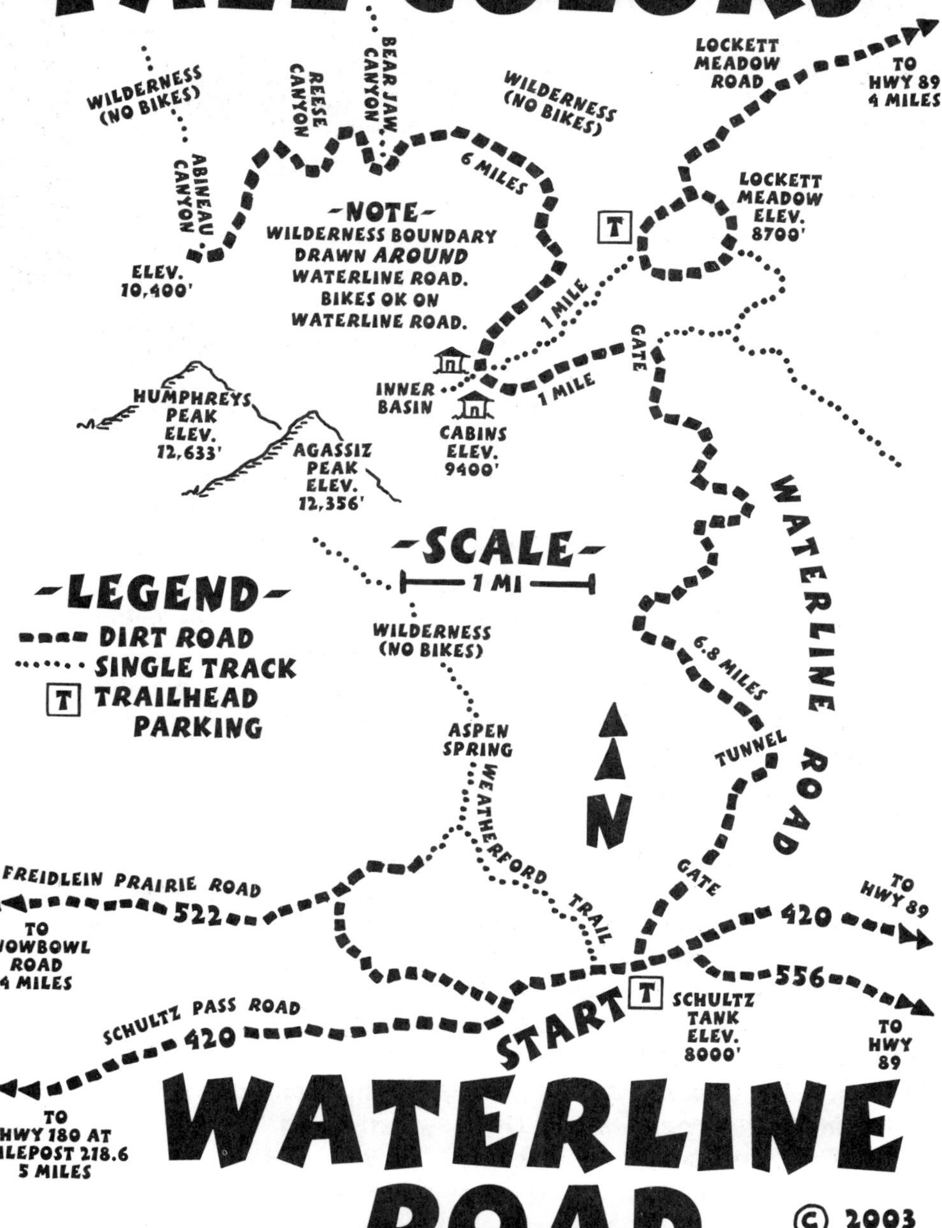
WILDERNESS (NO BIKES)
ABINEAU CANYON
REESE CANYON
BEAR JAW CANYON
WILDERNESS (NO BIKES)
LOCKETT MEADOW ROAD
TO HWY 89 4 MILES
6 MILES
-NOTE-
WILDERNESS BOUNDARY DRAWN AROUND WATERLINE ROAD. BIKES OK ON WATERLINE ROAD.
ELEV. 10,400'
LOCKETT MEADOW ELEV. 8700'
1 MILE
1 MILE
GATE
INNER BASIN
CABINS ELEV. 9400'
HUMPHREYS PEAK ELEV. 12,633'
AGASSIZ PEAK ELEV. 12,356'
-SCALE-
1 MI
-LEGEND-
DIRT ROAD
SINGLE TRACK
T TRAILHEAD PARKING
WILDERNESS (NO BIKES)
WATERLINE ROAD
6.8 MILES
ASPEN SPRING
WEATHERFORD TRAIL
TUNNEL
N
GATE
FREIDLEIN PRAIRIE ROAD
522
TO SNOWBOWL ROAD 4 MILES
TO HWY 89
420
556
TO HWY 89
SCHULTZ PASS ROAD
420
START
SCHULTZ TANK ELEV. 8000'
TO HWY 180 AT MILEPOST 218.6 5 MILES

WATERLINE ROAD

Flagstaff WATERLINE ROAD
FALL COLORS ON THE PEAKS

DISTANCE: 2 TO 25 MILES
TIME: 2 TO 7 HOURS
EFFORT: LONG CLIMB
SKILL: SPEED CONTROL
PUCK-O-METER: PUCK 7.5
VERY HIGH SPEED DESCENT
FIND ROUTE: NO PROB
SEASON: MAY to OCT

AT A GLANCE

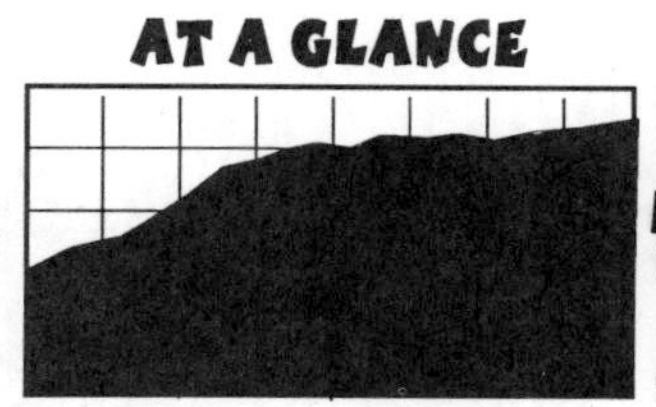

DESCRIPTION: Summer aspen shimmer silver and green. A blast of color tints the leaves around October 1, just before winter bares its skeletal bleached bark bones. Flagstaff Fall Leaf Looker is a 25 total mile *turn-and-burn* (out-and-back) all the way up Waterline Road to where it ends at Abineau Canyon. There is also a much easier route.

DIRECTIONS: Caught your attention with mention of an easy route, eh? OK, first the short cut way. Head north out of Flag on HWY 89A to Lockett Meadow Road at milepost 431.2. Drive the 4.5 miles up to Lockett Meadow. Now hop on your bike and ride a rough and tough 1 mile up to "the cabins". That's only a 2-mile out and back. See the map. Turn RIGHT at the cabins and roll out to Abineau under a canopy of red and gold. This will be a total of 14 miles out and back with little climbing except for that first mile. I've seen this road 6 inches deep in a carpet of gold. If you get a wild hair, send the car home with a sofa spud and ride 20 miles all the way downhill via Schultz Creek Trail to Flag. *That's a gas!*

BLACK CANYON

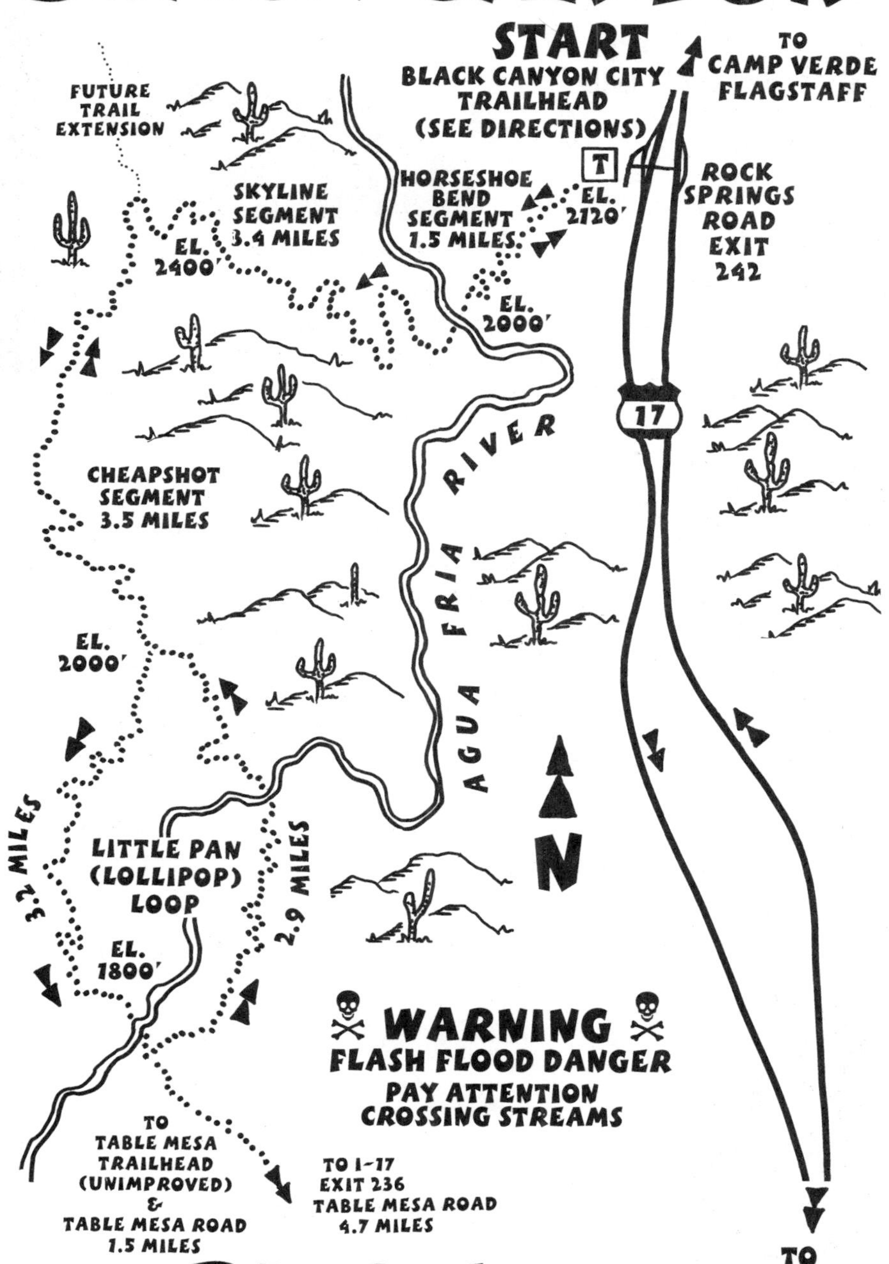

START
BLACK CANYON CITY
TRAILHEAD
(SEE DIRECTIONS)
TO
CAMP VERDE
FLAGSTAFF
FUTURE
TRAIL
EXTENSION
SKYLINE
SEGMENT
3.4 MILES
HORSESHOE
BEND
SEGMENT
1.5 MILES
T
EL.
2120′
ROCK
SPRINGS
ROAD
EXIT
242
EL.
2400′
EL.
2000′
17
RIVER
CHEAPSHOT
SEGMENT
3.5 MILES
FRIA
AGUA
EL.
2000′
N
3.2 MILES
LITTLE PAN
(LOLLIPOP)
LOOP
2.9 MILES
EL.
1800′
WARNING
FLASH FLOOD DANGER
PAY ATTENTION
CROSSING STREAMS
TO
TABLE MESA
TRAILHEAD
(UNIMPROVED)
&
TABLE MESA ROAD
1.5 MILES
TO I-17
EXIT 236
TABLE MESA ROAD
4.7 MILES
TO
PHOENIX
LOOP 101
24 MILES

PHOENIX

Phoenix BLACK CANYON TRAIL

ALL THRILLER, NO FILLER SINGLE TRACK

DISTANCE: 23 MILE LOLLIPOP
TIME: 4 TO 5 HOURS
EFFORT: HARD
SKILL: INTERMEDIATE TO EXPERT
PUCK-O-METER: PUCK 8.5
skinny trail & some wicked exposure to death
FIND ROUTE: SIGNED
SEASON: SEP to JUNE

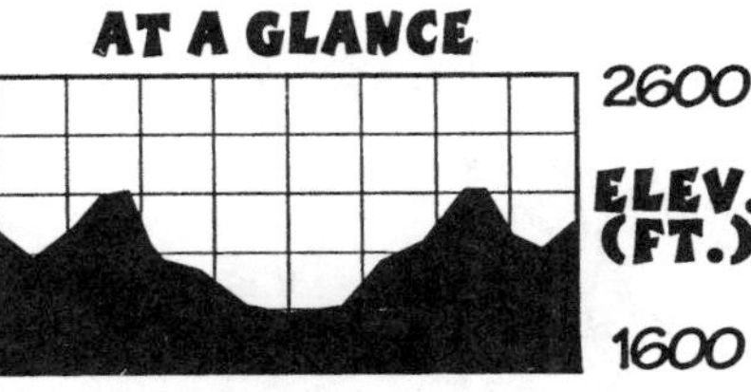

0 **TOTAL MILES** 23

PRIMO TRAIL
WORTH A JOURNEY

DESCRIPTION: I know what you like. Nice and skinny single track, hard climbs, wicked exposure, fast descents, killer views, saguaro humongo and lots of flowers. I even came upon a desert tortoise strolling the trail. Very nice.

It's *ALL* a single track, raging, roly-poly riot with some ridge riding and stream crossings, some big when running, along the way. The trail is hand made and built right. Not a wimp ride. Figure on about 3000 feet of climbing to do the entire 23 mile out & back plus lollipop loop. Less if you opt for a shorter ride.

Sock laundry stream crossings add to the fun during wet winter and spring months when desert grasses turn green and the cacti and wild flowers come into neon bloom. Summer is parched. The Agua Fria River turns dry river bed. *HOWEVER,* monsoon arrives mid-July and lasts into September. Flash floods can come roaring down the rock hard river chute any time in those months, even without a cloud overhead. Beware! Also, trail is totally exposed to sun. You can drink 5 quarts of water on a warm spring day.

DIRECTIONS: From I-17, either direction, north or south, take exit 242 (Rock Springs exit), turn WEST, proceed to stop sign, turn NORTH (RIGHT) on the frontage road, drive about 300 feet to first road on the LEFT, Warner Road, and turn LEFT. Drive to the first crossroad. Turn RIGHT and proceed to the parking area.

Food (yummy pies!) and liquid refreshment in the Rock Springs Cafe. Nothing like great pie and ice cream within two minutes after a hard ride.

CAVE CREEK

THE FASTER YOU GO, THE SMOOTHER IT GETS

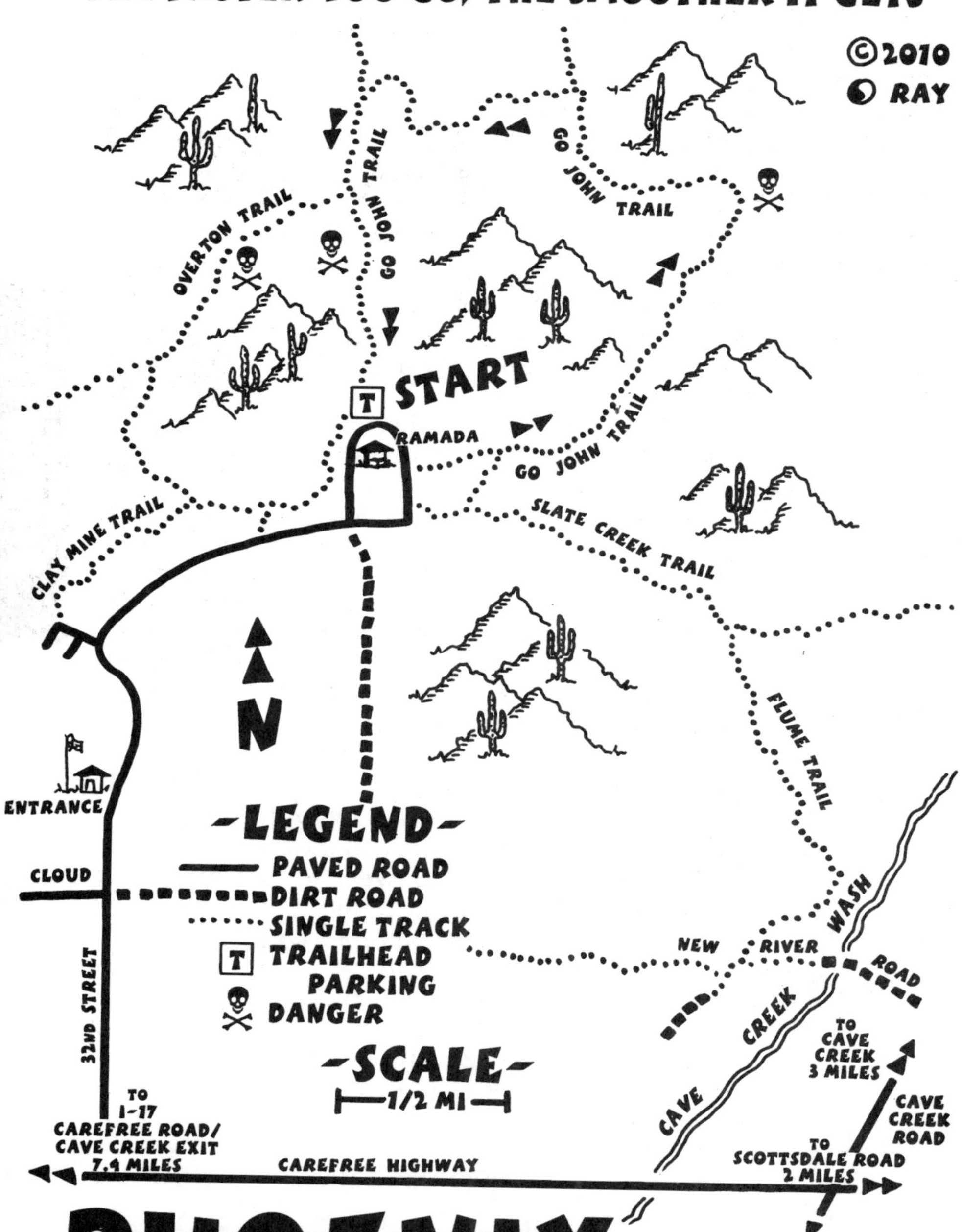

PHOENIX

Phoenix CAVE CREEK

BURLACIOUS SINGLE TRACK BUTT RUFF

DISTANCE: 6.2 MILE LOOP
TIME: 1 TO 2 HOURS
EFFORT: EASY OR TOUGH
SKILL: NOVICE TO INTERMEDIATE
PUCK-O-METER: PUCK 3 TO 8
FIND ROUTE: SIGNED
SEASON: OCT to MAY
TOO DANG HOT IN SUMMER

DESCRIPTION: The Go John Trail in Cave Creek County Park can be rough and tough as you get up higher in the park's trail system, but the lower trails have been improved and cleared to the point where they are suitable for almost any rider.

There is a climb or two, but nothing terribly severe. Helmet, body armor, full bounce suspension and some goodly tire pressure recommended for the wheel-bashing terrain up high. Other trails down on the flats and on the adjacent State Trust Land aren't quite as hard ass.

Surreal views, lots of great cactus and 6 plus miles of rugged single track will challenge and delight any rider with a tough butt, hard head and a firm grip on the bars. This is *FUN* in the most elastic sense of the word. Easily whacked out whiners, weenies and total weaklings stay home. Guaranteed to break your Huffy if you ride the top of Go John Trail.

It's well signed. You won't need a mileage log or computer. It would probably just pop off and get run over anyway. Mine sure did. Follow the map. I traced it from the county park's map, so it's pretty right on. There are more trails here, but I have outlined the most obvious loop. Getting lost is not an option as the terrain is wide open with expansive views and big landmarks.

Flat Tire Bikes (480-488-5261) in the town of Cave Creek (watch for radar cops) is very helpful and has a great topo map on the wall with all the local trails highlighted. Touristy Cave Creek also has more than its share of good eateries for breakfast or a tasty post ride lunch.

The park facility includes sparkling bathrooms with TP, picnic area, kiddie playground, ramadas, BBQs and a small fee (includes a nifty map) at the entrance. Start early AM in summer.

"Snack on danger. Dine on death."
-team mutant

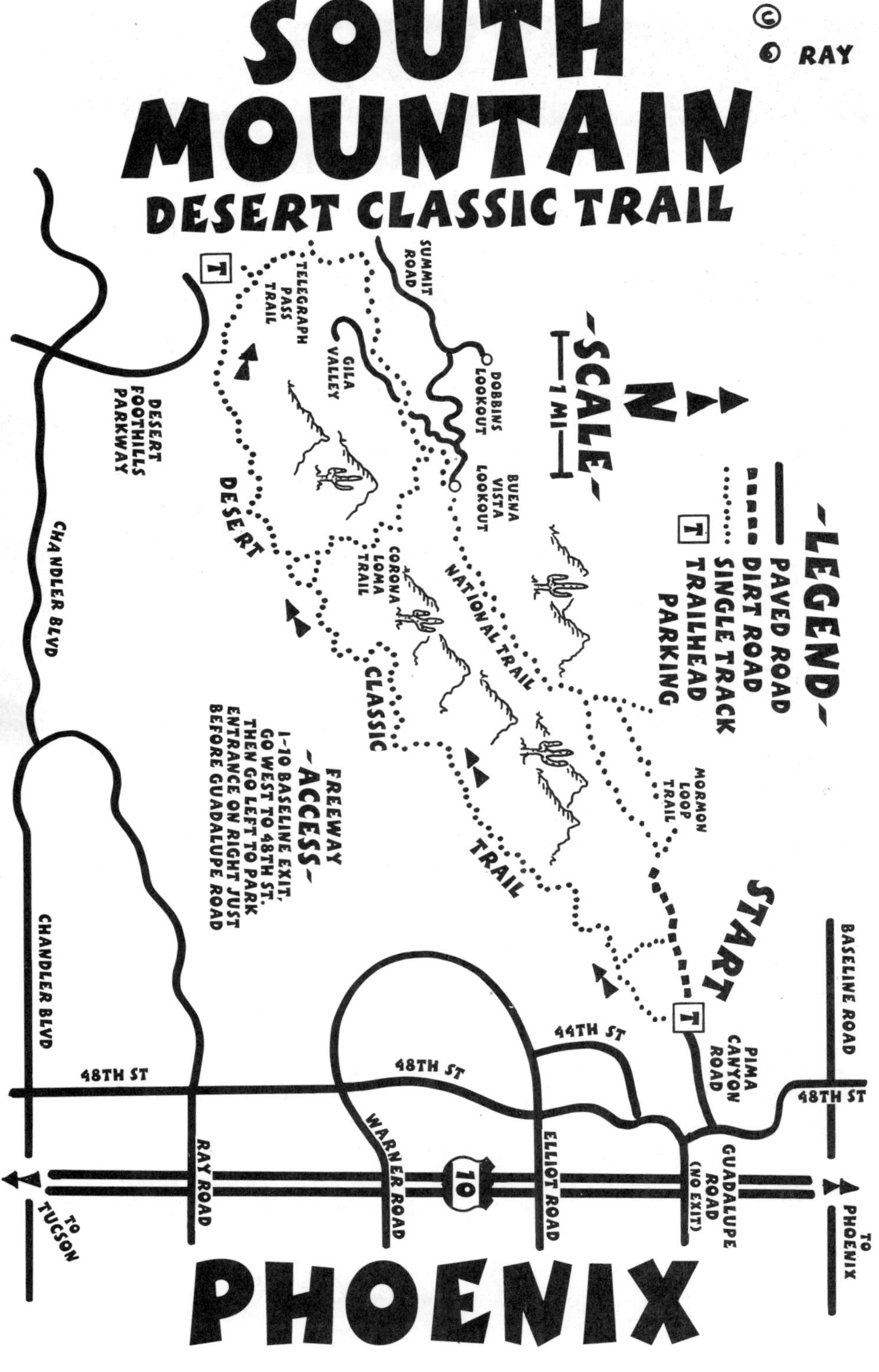

SOUTH MOUNTAIN
DESERT CLASSIC TRAIL
© RAY
-LEGEND-
PAVED ROAD
DIRT ROAD
SINGLE TRACK
TRAILHEAD PARKING
N
-SCALE-
1 MI
SUMMIT ROAD
TELEGRAPH PASS TRAIL
GILA VALLEY
DOBBINS LOOKOUT
BUENA VISTA LOOKOUT
CORONA LOMA TRAIL
NATIONAL TRAIL
MORMON LOOP TRAIL
DESERT CLASSIC TRAIL
START
DESERT FOOTHILLS PARKWAY
CHANDLER BLVD
-FREEWAY ACCESS-
I-10 BASELINE EXIT, GO WEST TO 48TH ST. THEN GO LEFT TO PARK ENTRANCE ON RIGHT JUST BEFORE GUADALUPE ROAD
44TH ST
48TH ST
PIMA CANYON ROAD
BASELINE ROAD
RAY ROAD
WARNER ROAD
ELLIOT ROAD
GUADALUPE ROAD (NO EXIT)
10
TO TUCSON
TO PHOENIX
PHOENIX

Phoenix DESERT CLASSIC TRAIL
PRIME SONORAN DESERT SINGLE TRACK

DISTANCE: 9 MILES 1-WAY
TIME: 2 to 4 HOURS
EFFORT: SOME SWEAT
SKILL: CHALLENGING FUN
PUCK-O-METER: PUCK 7
DEEP WASHES (DANGER IN THE DIPS)
FIND ROUTE: EASY
SEASON: SEP to MAY

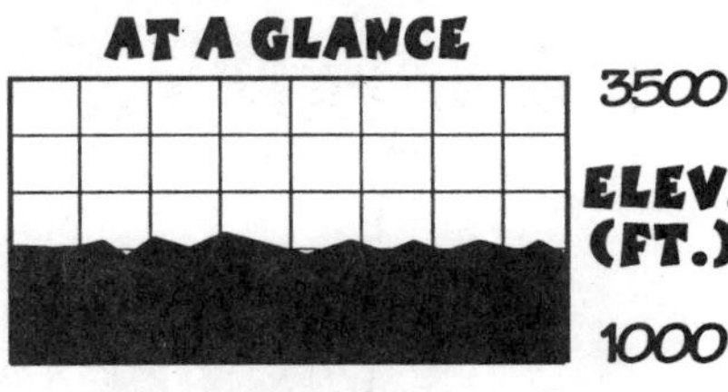

DESCRIPTION: Desert Classic delivers miles of signed South Mountain single track. START SOUTH out of Guadalupe Road lot (see map). Ahwatukee on the left, mountain on the right. Dead ahead sets a trail into the saguaro. Go.

Weekends you can't swing a cat without hitting some tool going way fast. Use care on blind cactus corners and diving into washes. They're double-skull Sid Viscous ugly when the trail comes up to smack you. After 7 miles out, a steel post marks a LEFT turn up to Old Chopper Pad. It's a tough side trip with a good view. Continue to end of Desert Classic and return unless you're a glutton. If so, where Desert Classic ends, grunt RIGHT & UP TELEGRAPH PASS TRAIL to NAT'L TRAIL at Summit Road. RIGHT to the Buena Vista parking lot via National and a great descent back down to the Guadalupe Road lot. Adds at least 1.5 hours. Whew!

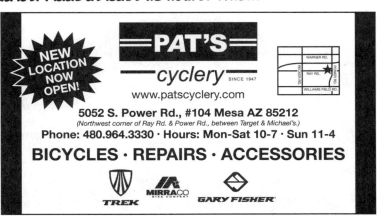

PHOENIX

PHOENIX (GOODYEAR)

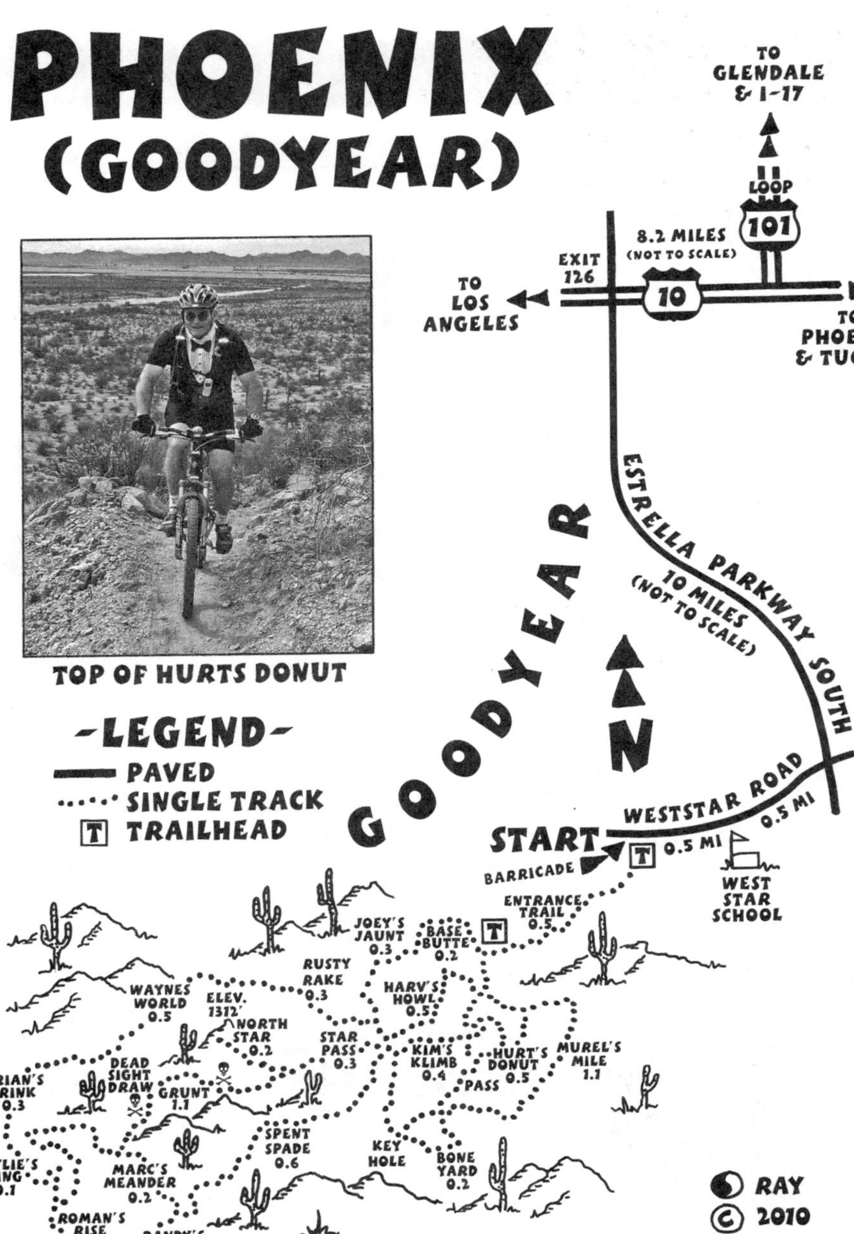

TOP OF HURTS DONUT

-LEGEND-

PAVED

SINGLE TRACK

T TRAILHEAD

F.I.N.S. TRAILS

(FANTASY ISLAND NORTH SINGLETRACK)

Phoenix F.I.N.S. TRAILS
FANTASY ISLAND NORTH SINGLETRACK

DISTANCE: 1 to 100 MILES
TIME: 2 to ? HOURS
EFFORT: EASY TO TOUGH
SKILL: EASY TO EXPERT
PUCK-O-METER: PUCK 3 to 8
ALL SKILL LEVELS
FIND ROUTE: VERY EASY
EVERY TURN SUPER WELL SIGNED
SEASON: OCT to JUN

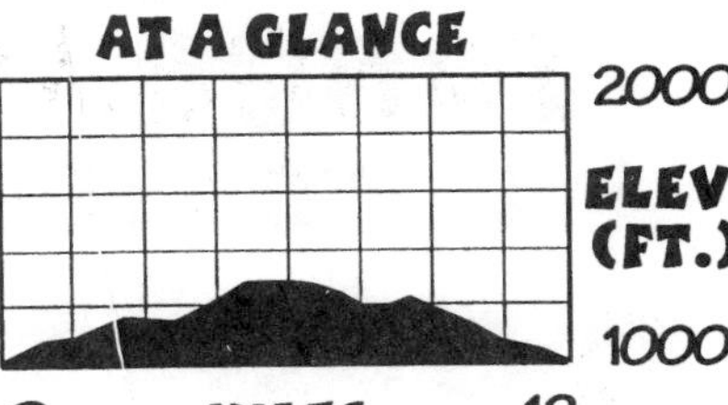

PRIMO TRAIL
WORTH A JOURNEY

DESCRIPTION: Big fun for the intermediate rider. 1300' of climbing and 12 miles to do every trail. Loads of whoop-de-doos, short climbs and tight turns. Cool signs at every turn with names and difficulty level indicated by dots. One dot is cake, two is just a bit more skill, three is gnarly, four is downright wicked. Grunt, Star Pass, Northstar and Hurts Donut rate the double skull for descent, but all trails are doable. The outer loop was built to be ridden counter-clockwise. Grunt was meant for west to east. UP Grunt, DOWN Exposure. The switchbacks just flow better. And never stop on the narrow bridge! Mucho thanks to Kim and Murel for all their kind help here.

DIRECTIONS & PARKING: From Phoenix Loop 101 head WEST on I-10 toward Los Angeles. Go 8.3 miles then take EXIT #126 Estrella Parkway South for 10 miles. Turn RIGHT on Weststar Road. Go 0.5 miles to Weststar School. Park there if it's a weekend. The trailhead is 0.5 miles further along on the LEFT on Westar Road behind the striped barricade. Weekdays, park at the trailhead barricade if there is room OR under the electric lines next to the pumping station.

McDOWELL SONORAN PRESERVE
GATEWAY LOOP

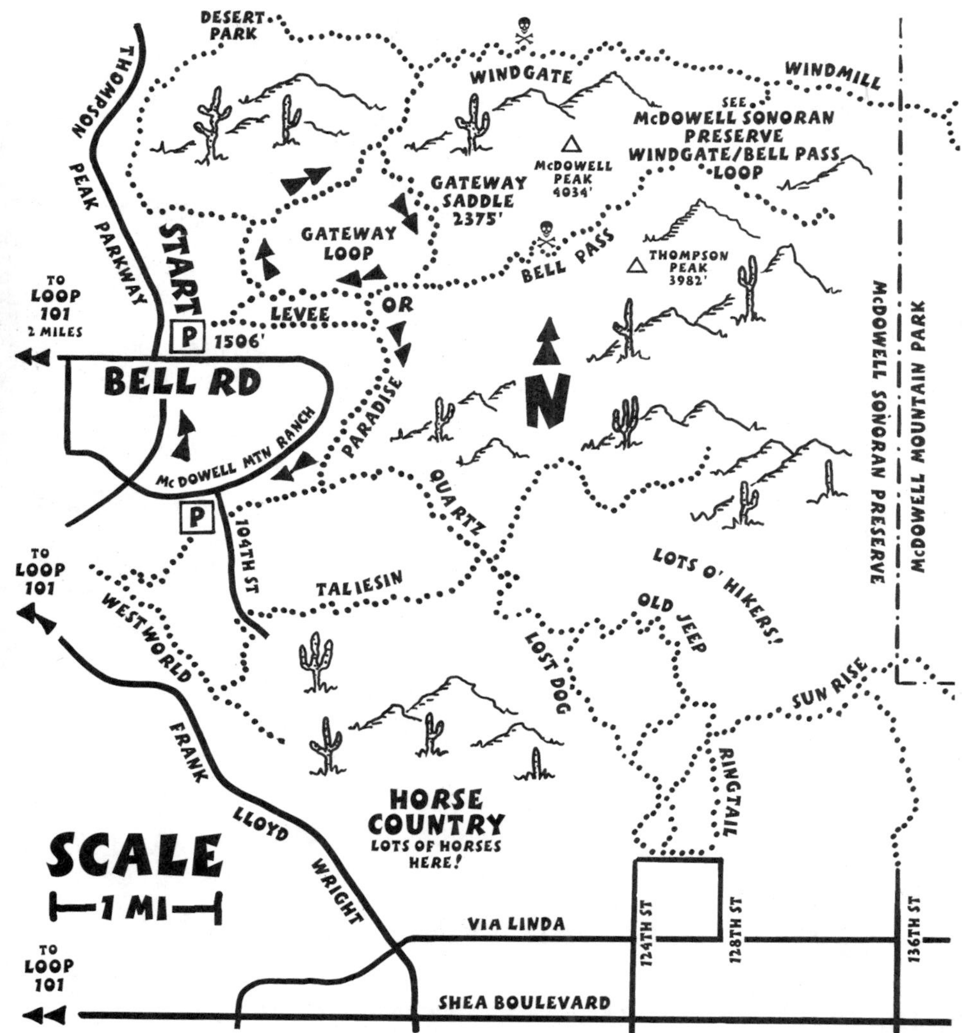
DESERT PARK
THOMPSON PEAK PARKWAY
WINDGATE
WINDMILL
SEE McDOWELL SONORAN PRESERVE WINDGATE/BELL PASS LOOP
McDOWELL PEAK 4034'
GATEWAY SADDLE 2375'
GATEWAY LOOP
START
BELL PASS
THOMPSON PEAK 3982'
TO LOOP 101 2 MILES
LEVEE
OR
1506'
P
BELL RD
N
PARADISE
McDOWELL MTN RANCH
McDOWELL SONORAN PRESERVE
McDOWELL MOUNTAIN PARK
QUARTZ
P
104TH ST
TO LOOP 101
TALIESIN
LOTS O' HIKERS!
WESTWORLD
OLD JEEP
LOST DOG
SUN RISE
FRANK LLOYD WRIGHT
RINGTAIL
HORSE COUNTRY
LOTS OF HORSES HERE!
SCALE
1 MI
VIA LINDA
124TH ST
128TH ST
136TH ST
TO LOOP 101
SHEA BOULEVARD

SCOTTSDALE

McDOWELL SONORAN PRESERVE
EXCELLENT 1-TRACK LOOP THRU THE SAGUARO

DISTANCE: 5 TO 12 MILES
TIME: 1 TO 3 HOURS
EFFORT: GOOD WORKOUT
SKILL: INTERMEDIATE
PUCK-O-METER: PUCK 5
SOME LOOSE RUBBLE-SHARP TURNS
FIND ROUTE: ALL SIGNED
SEASON: OCT to MAY

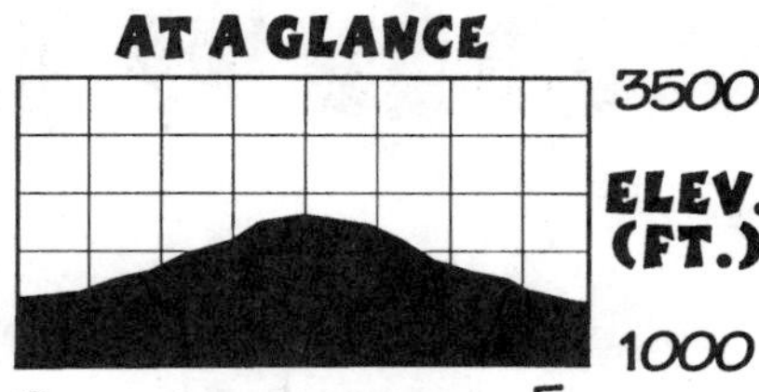

PRIMO TRAIL
WORTH A JOURNEY

PHOENIX

DESCRIPTION: Beware Phoenix developers. The party is *over!* Out past all the "McMansion For Sale" signs hanging limp in the breeze, past the last outposts of civilization is the newest gem among Phoenix Trails. McDowell Sonoran Preserve is the love child born of nearly two decades hard work from the McDowell Sonoran Conservancy and Scottsdale taxpayers.

The west side of the McDowell's features rugged but exquisitly well built single track with the best views in The Valley. There are no roads to shuttle to the top. These trails will remain the sole province of pedaling, pushing, sweating hammerheads like us. I've suggested an introductory single track loop here, but there is lots more. See the map. Trails are super well marked with steel-is-for-real bomb proof signs. No odometer or GPS needed. You can't get lost. When in doubt, just head downhill toward civilization.

Locals tell me we should stay off Sunset and Lost Dog Trails southeast of Gateway Loop on weekends or if you really want to shred. Lots of hikers, horses and blind turns on those trails make for possible trouble, especially if you ding a lawyer.

Thanks to expert rider Jim Rossi for doing the riding for me on these trails while I was on the broke-leg injured list. He did the work so you could find the ride. Thanks Jim.

DIRECTIONS: From anywhere in The Valley, get on the freeway and make your way to Loop 101. Find your way to the Bell Road Exit and head EAST 2 miles toward the McDowell Mountains. Park in the small lot on the left just EAST of Thompson Peak Parkway.

"90 % of the game is mental. The other 15% is physical."
-Yogi Berra

McDOWELL MOUNTAINS

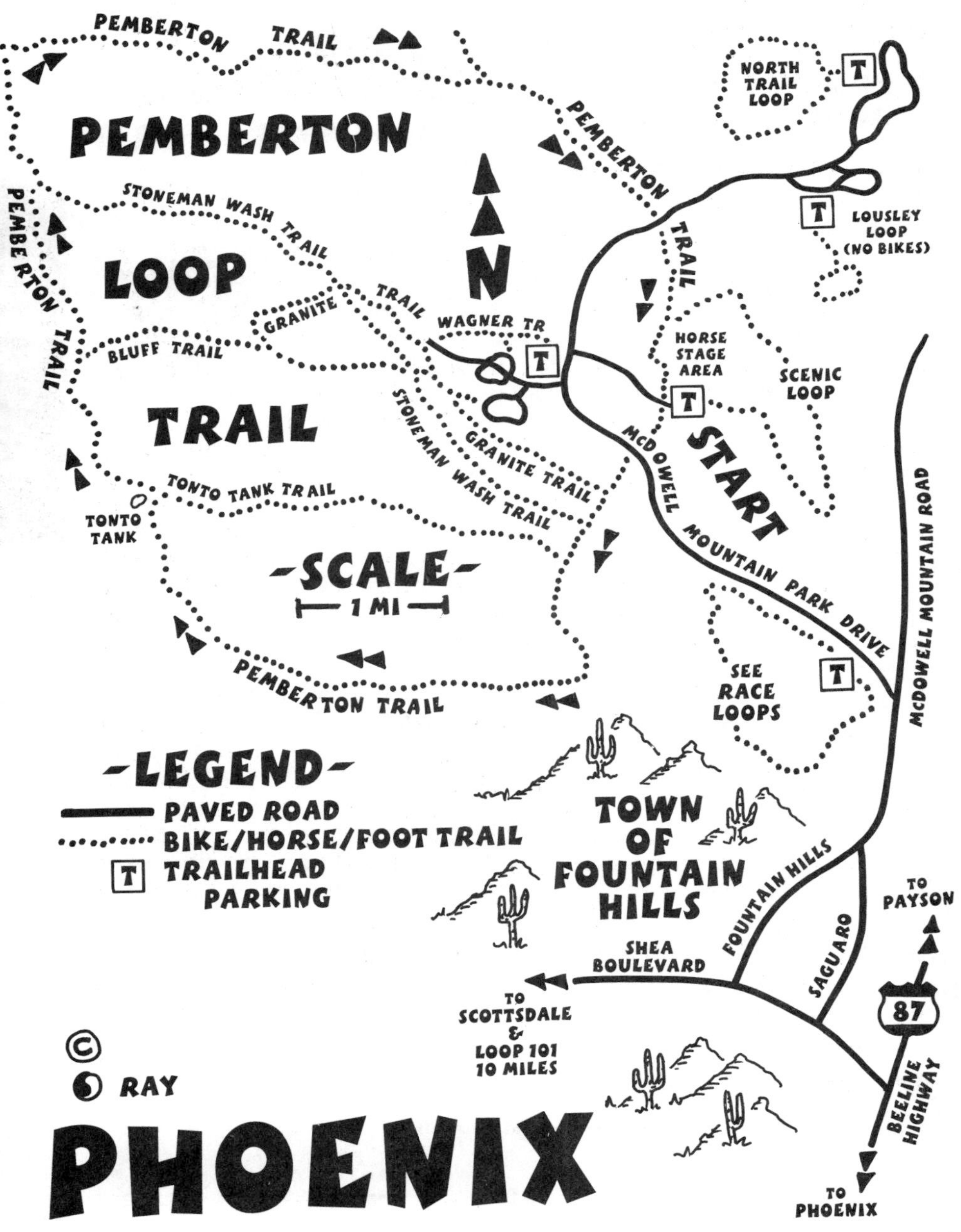

PEMBERTON TRAIL
PEMBERTON LOOP TRAIL
PEMBERTON
TRAIL
STONEMAN WASH TRAIL
GRANITE TRAIL
BLUFF TRAIL
WAGNER TR
STONEMAN WASH TRAIL
GRANITE TRAIL
TONTO TANK TRAIL
TONTO TANK
PEMBERTON TRAIL
PEMBERTON TRAIL
N
NORTH TRAIL LOOP
LOUSLEY LOOP (NO BIKES)
HORSE STAGE AREA
SCENIC LOOP
START
McDOWELL MOUNTAIN PARK DRIVE
SEE RACE LOOPS
McDOWELL MOUNTAIN ROAD
-SCALE-
1 MI
-LEGEND-
PAVED ROAD
BIKE/HORSE/FOOT TRAIL
T TRAILHEAD PARKING
TOWN OF FOUNTAIN HILLS
FOUNTAIN HILLS
SAGUARO
SHEA BOULEVARD
TO SCOTTSDALE & LOOP 101 10 MILES
TO PAYSON
87
BEELINE HIGHWAY
TO PHOENIX
© RAY
PHOENIX

Phoenix McDOWELL MOUNTAINS
PEMBERTON SINGLE TRACK LOOP

DISTANCE: 15.3 MILE LOOP
TIME: 2 HOURS
EFFORT: MODERATE
SKILL: NOVICE
PUCK-O-METER: PUCK 2
FORGIVING, SMOOTH, EASY TERRAIN
FIND ROUTE: EASY
SEASON: OCT to MAY

AT A GLANCE

DESCRIPTION: You can spy a telephoto view of the McDowells through the purple haze of Phoenix 25 miles away. Quiet, fresh clean air and miles of single track make it seem light years. Excellent, except in 1996 The McDowells were toasted by a (cactus) forest fire. Vegetation has started to recover in earnest. The trails are still there and fun as ever. Now that the new race loops near the park entrance have stolen some of the thunder, Pemberton Trail is still a great alternative if you opt for a less crowded scene. An easy climb up a smooth double track is followed by a rip rolling section of single track and ends with a fast 1-track descent. Control speed. This is a multi-use trail. Watch for horse-folk.

DIRECTIONS: From Phoenix take the Superstition Freeway HWY 60 east to Country Club exit then north as it becomes Beeline HWY. OR take Loop 101 to Shea an go east on Shea. Either way, continue to Fountain Hills then follow the map to the park entrance. Small entrance fee weekends.

"Amateurs built the ark . Experts built the Titanic."
- *Elson Miles*

PHOENIX

McDOWELL MOUNTAINS (RACE LOOPS)

SHORT LOOP
TECH LOOP
SHORT LOOP
TECH LOOP
LONG LOOP
PEMBERTON WASH
SOUTH WASH
LONG LOOP
LONG LOOP
LONG LOOP
TO PEMBERTON TRAIL & CAMPING
START
FEE $3/ CAR
PARK ENTRANCE
McDOWELL MOUNTAIN ROAD
N
SCALE
1 MI
-LEGEND-
PAVED ROAD
DIRT ROAD
SINGLE TRACK
(ONE WAY)
TRAILHEAD/ PARKING
DANGER
(BIG DROP)
TO SCOTTSDALE 10 MILES
TO LOOP 101 9 MILES
FOUNTAIN HILLS
FOUNTAIN HILLS
SAGUARO
SHEA BOULEVARD
FOUNTAIN HILLS
TO PAYSON
87
BEELINE HIWAY
TO MESA 15 MILES
© RAY

PHOENIX

Phoenix McDOWELL MOUNTAINS
BIKE RACE (*CACTUS CUP*) LOOPS

DISTANCE: 3 TO 12 MILES
TIME: 2 HOURS
EFFORT: RACE PACE
SKILL: EASY TO EXPERT
PUCK-O-METER: PUCK 5
SOME ROUGH STUFF & ONE BIG DROP
FIND ROUTE: NO SWEAT
SEASON: OCT to MAY

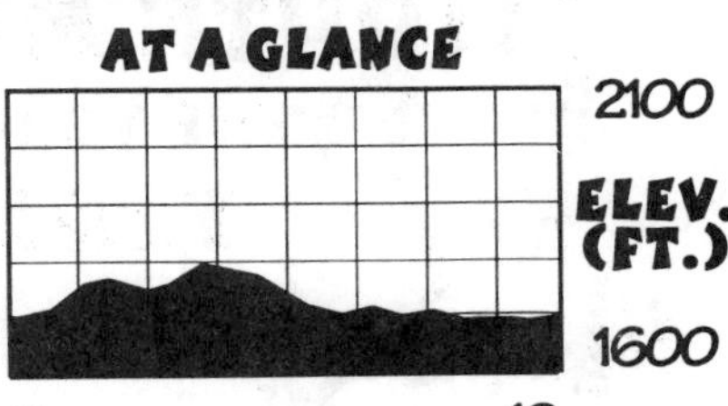

PRIMO TRAIL
WORTH A JOURNEY

PHOENIX

DESCRIPTION: Imagine a place made just for mountain bikes. The McDowell Competitive Track is the result of inspiration and perspiration by Maricopa County Parks and Rec and individuals who lent of their time and talents. We can ride at race pace on 12 miles of superb new desert trail built and set aside just for mountain bikes.

The terrain was designed for a Cactus Cup race course . Carve the trail like a slot car on speed through the giant saguaro. Cactus Cup is gone, but the track lives on.

Three single track loops roll out over this superb desert landscape. A 6-mile LONG LOOP runs up and down all over the prime real estate north of Fountain Hills. A shorter 3-mile SPORT LOOP is challenging and fast while the 3-mile TECH LOOP over T-bone Ridge is guaranteed to peg the tech-o-meter. Twisty-turny carving turns, berms, dips, jumps, and roaring fast straightaways . . . it's all here.

Besides race loops, McDowell Mountain Park has miles of other excellent intermediate mountain bike and hike trails plus camping facilities. The course is open to the public all year.

DIRECTIONS: Located 15 miles northeast of Scottsdale. From Phoenix go EAST on Superstition Freeway OR 202 to Country Club, then north as Country Club becomes Beeline Highway and continues to Fountain Hills. OR take Loop 101 to Shea, head EAST ON Shea to Fountain Hills Blvd. and turn left. There is a nominal $2 per car entrance fee that gets pumped right back into park maintenance and development, so have a couple of bucks in hand.

"Seize the day, put no trust in the 'morrow."
- ancient poet Horace

"Seize the day and throttle it."
- Calvin and Hobbs

NATIONAL LOOP

(SOUTH MOUNTAIN)

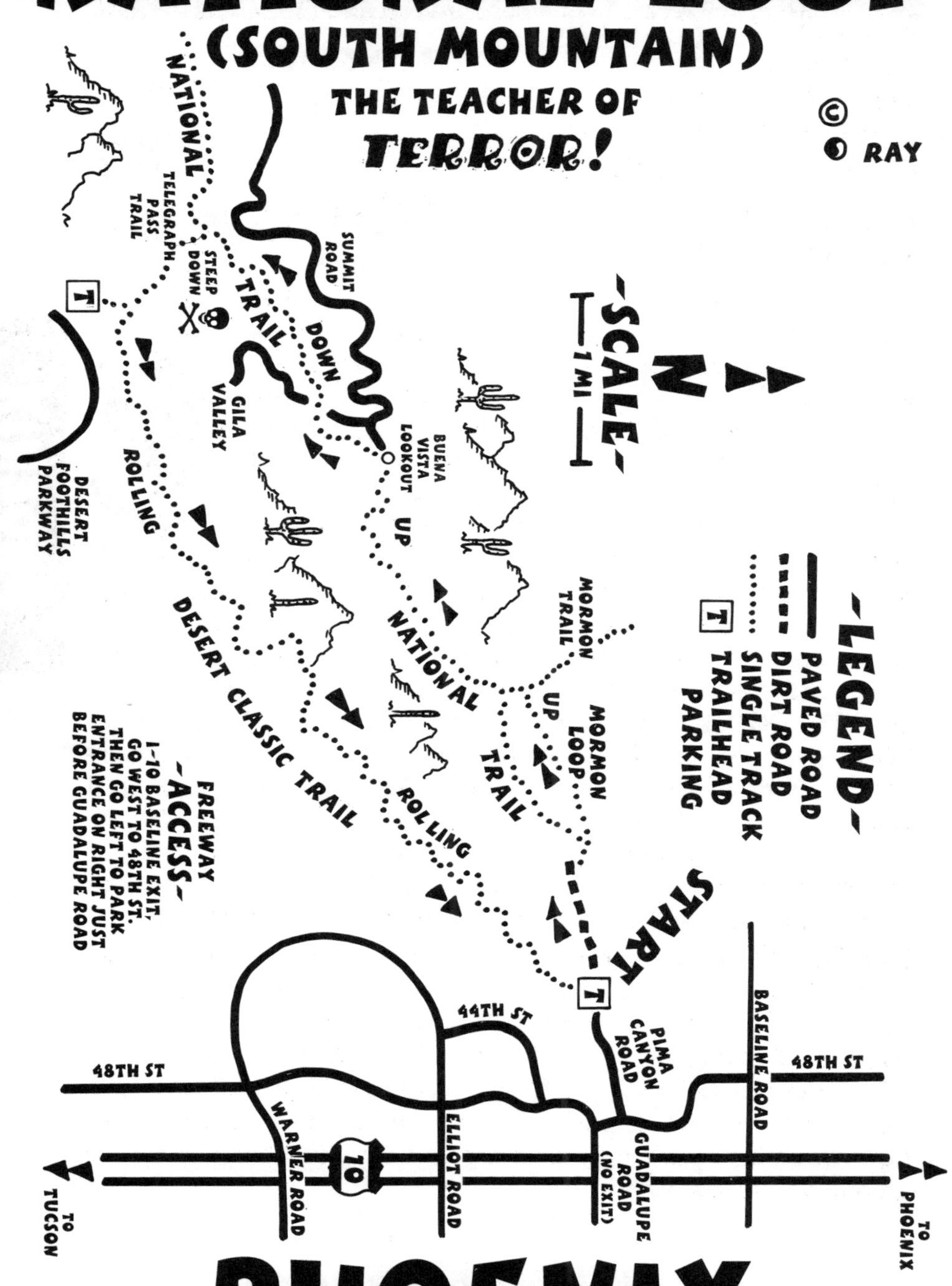

PHOENIX

Phoenix NATIONAL TRAIL LOOP
SOUTH MOUNTAIN TEACHER OF TERROR

DISTANCE: 18 MILES
TIME: 3 to 4 HOURS
EFFORT: SEVERE
SKILL: ☠NO BEGINNERS☠
PUCK-O-METER: PUCK 10
HAIRY DESCENT PLUS TECH SESSIONS
FIND ROUTE: EASY
SEASON: SEP to JUN

0 **LOOP MILES** 18

PRIMO TRAIL
WORTH A JOURNEY

DESCRIPTION: The *Teacher of Terror!* Wicked tough climb. Narrow single track along a skinny ridge. Ultra-hairball, cactus infested descent. Rolling, twisting 9-mile single track finish. Crackling cat brains! Finish up on ripping single track Desert Classic Trail whoop-de-do rollers that do anything but straight. Weekdays best. Weekends are a freak show. Whilst living so large and quick, be polite to hikers. Use the Big Head for thinking.

PHOENIX

MILEAGE LOG

0.0 START at Guadalupe/Pima Canyon parking lot. See map. Head up the dirt road through gate at west end of lot.
1.3 Dirt road dead-ends. Trail is down behind "Park Rules" sign on right. GO short quick down then up.
1.4 Trail splits. Left goes straight up for hard cores. Take the RIGHT (easier UP) .
2.8 LEFT at "T", signed "Mormon Trail".
3.6 ARRIVE at Buena Vista Lookout. Continue on National Trail. Caution here. Some hairy exposure as you go down toward the towers. Scary and fast.
7.5 Sign says Telegraph Pass Trail. Begin the ultra-postal psycho descent. Don't go over the bars like me!
9.0 Still with me? CONTINUE LEFT on Desert Classic rollers around the base of mountain on the left and Awatukee on the right. Tour de backyard! Pools and killer mutts over every fence. Where is everybody? Out diggin' up the bucks to feed mutt and mortgage! Very fun, very fast.
18.0 BACK TO GO. Happy as heck *presuming you lived!*

"The faster you go, the smoother it gets."
- *team mutant*

PAPAGO PARK

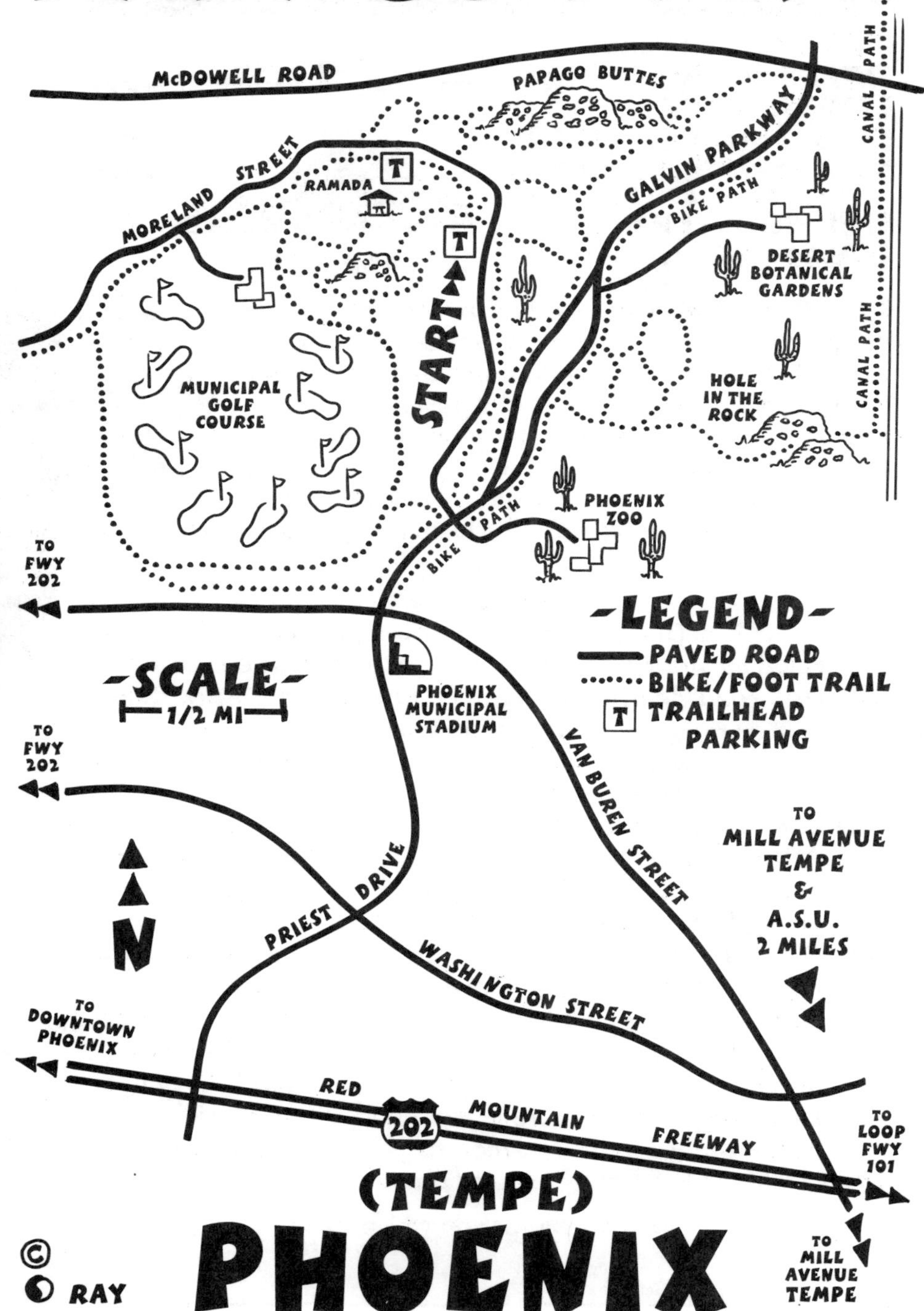

McDOWELL ROAD
PAPAGO BUTTES
CANAL PATH
GALVIN PARKWAY
MORELAND STREET
RAMADA
T
START
BIKE PATH
DESERT BOTANICAL GARDENS
MUNICIPAL GOLF COURSE
HOLE IN THE ROCK
CANAL PATH
PHOENIX ZOO
BIKE PATH
TO FWY 202
LEGEND
PAVED ROAD
BIKE/FOOT TRAIL
TRAILHEAD PARKING
SCALE
1/2 MI
PHOENIX MUNICIPAL STADIUM
TO FWY 202
VAN BUREN STREET
TO MILL AVENUE TEMPE & A.S.U. 2 MILES
N
PRIEST DRIVE
WASHINGTON STREET
TO DOWNTOWN PHOENIX
RED MOUNTAIN FREEWAY
202
TO LOOP FWY 101
(TEMPE)
PHOENIX
TO MILL AVENUE TEMPE
© RAY

Phoenix PAPAGO PARK

EASY FUN SINGLE TRACK LOOPS

DISTANCE: 1 TO 5 MILES
TIME: 1 TO 2 HOURS
EFFORT: EASY
SKILL: NOVICE
PUCK-O-METER: PUCK O
FIND ROUTE: EASY
SEASON: ALL YEAR

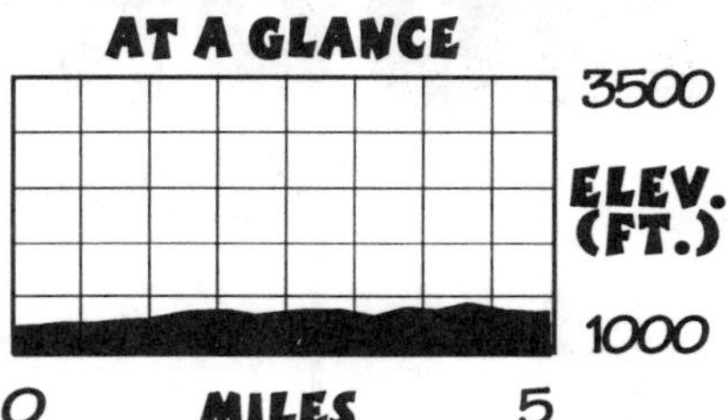

DESCRIPTION: You say to yourself, "Self, this ain't no ride. Too easy." But hey, dude or dudette, don't be mistaken. This is probably the first place you ever rode real dirt trail in Phoenix. Hundreds of riders do it here every day.

Located only a mile from downtown Tempe, Papago has a lot going for itself. There's a zoo. It's only a mile from ASU. If you're a student living at The U., it's the only ride you can ride to. Spring training is just across the street. Nearby Mill Avenue is a hub for shopping, coffee, night life, food and brew. Papago is swell for experts and beginners alike. Rookies love the smooth trails with enough whoop-de-doos to keep life worth living and even get a feel for what it's all about. Papago is also perfect for the expert who might be pressed for time and can't make it all the way to *The Teacher of Terror* at South Mountain. Just go fast enough, catch enough air and it just doesn't matter where you are. The heart will beat, the head will pound, the feet will smell . . . but I digress.

Hear tell Papago is quite agreeable to poach a night ride. Smooth trails, warm temps and a nice bright halogen light add up to some cheap thrills, but you may not park a car in the lot after dark without a hassle. Hey, I never suggest anything illegal. No sir-eee. I merely note that others have done so without regret, so take that for what it's worth. Speaking of regret, the area around The Buttes is reported to be a fave hang out for horndogs who can ill afford a room. You'd not be the first night rider to surprise an *au natural* couple *en flagrant*, if you know what I mean. Just be cool as you speed away with a hearty "Hiyo Silver, awaaayyyyy!"

"It ain't that life is so short, It's just that you're dead so freaking long."
-mountain bike wisdom

PHOENIX MOUNTAINS

TRAIL #100

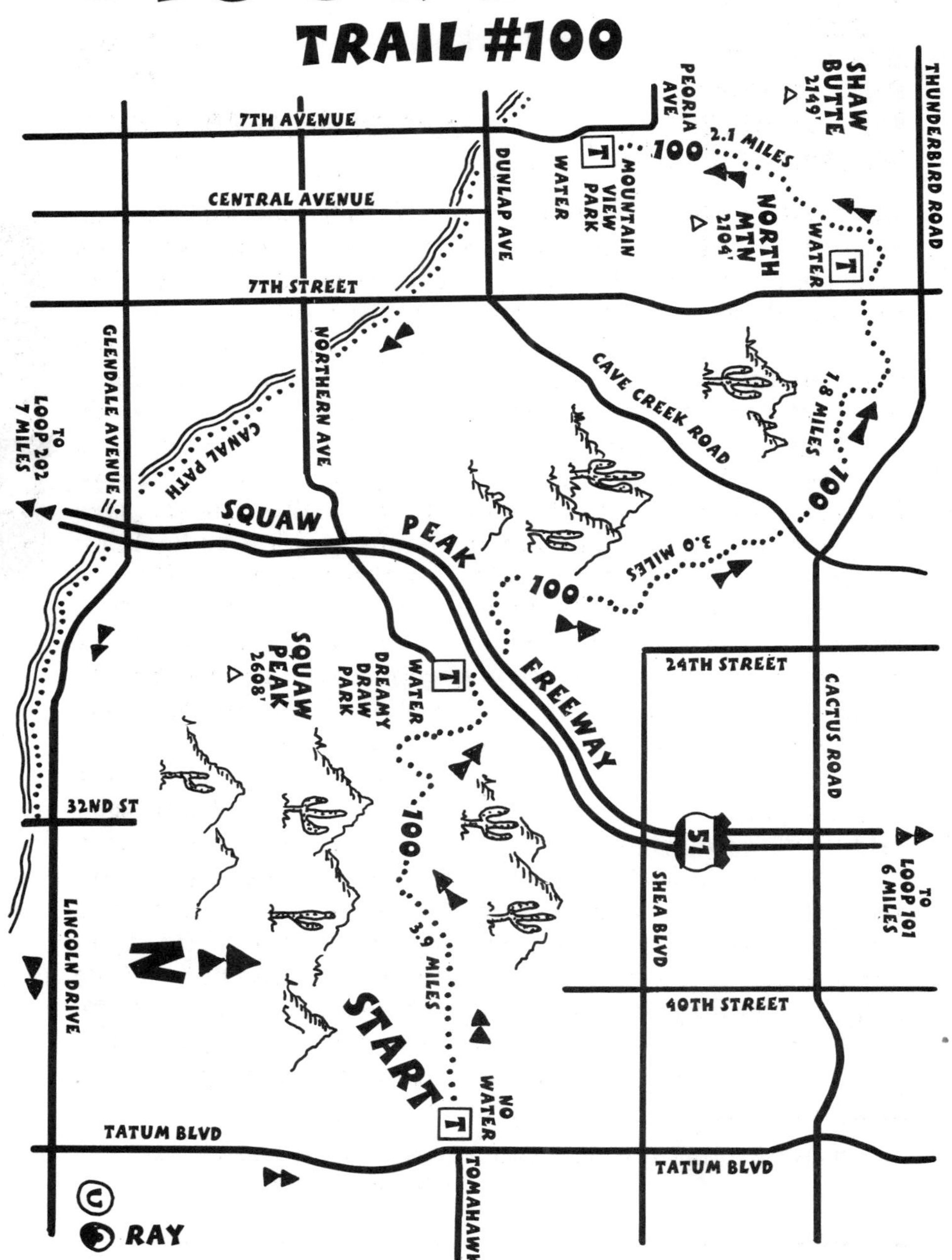

Phoenix PHOENIX MOUNTAINS
TRAIL #100 EXCELLENT SINGLE TRACK

DISTANCE: 10.7 MILES
TIME: 3 to 5 HOURS
EFFORT: VERY HARD WORK
SKILL: EXPERT
PUCK-O-METER: PUCK 7.5
SOME TECHNICAL WORK AND SPEED
FIND ROUTE: SIMPLE
SEASON: OCT to MAY

AT A GLANCE

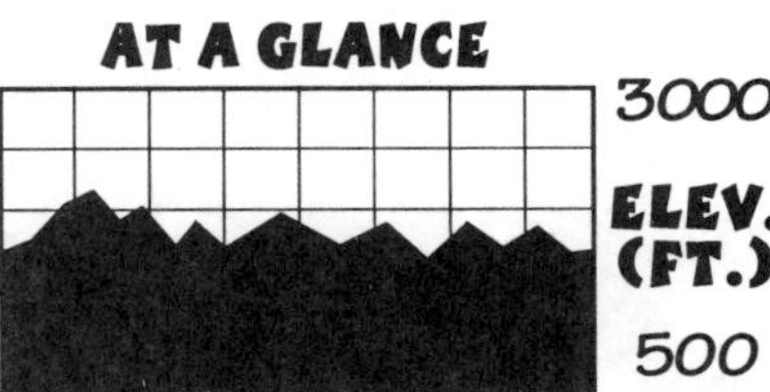

PRIMO TRAIL
WORTH A JOURNEY

DESCRIPTION: Amazes me how you can feel like you're in the middle of wilderness and yet be right in the heart of a city. Trail #100 traverses the entire east-west length of the Phoenix Mountains using tunnels under major urban arterials. Making use of the canal path you can complete a nice 20-mile loop doing the whole length of Trail #100 and then return via canal path and a short wicked bit on city streets. See the map. Be very careful on Lincoln.

Clearly marked Trail #100 passes just north of the Dreamy Draw Rec Area parking lot. The westernmost end of Trail #100 might be considered a tad bleak, but the entire rest is excellent with the area east of Dreamy Draw the best for trail and cacti.

DIRECTIONS: Access from anywhere in Phoenix is super easy via HWY 51 Squaw Peak Freeway. Take Northern Av. exit and follow signs EAST to Dreamy Draw Recreation Area. This the best place to start. Parking lot on Tatum is dinky.

PHOENIX

RED MOUNTAIN

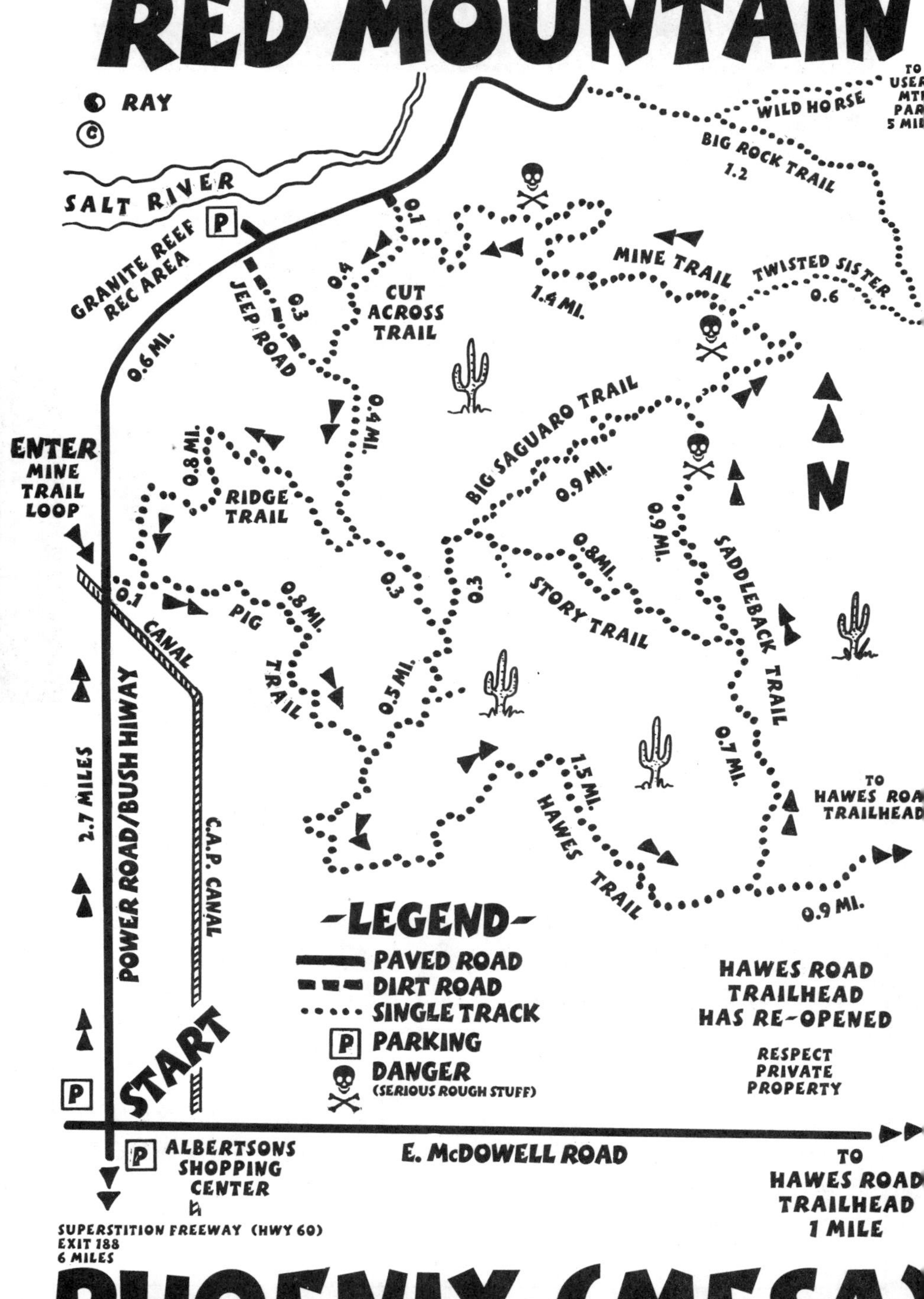

PHOENIX (MESA)

Phoenix (Mesa) RED MOUNTAIN
KICK ASS LOOP THRU PRISTINE DESERT

DISTANCE: 7.1 MILES
TIME: 1.5 to 2 HOURS
EFFORT: TOUGH
SKILL: ADVANCED
PUCK-O-METER: PUCK 9
SPEED, EXPOSURE & BOTTOMLESS PIT
FIND ROUTE: MODERATE
SEASON: OCT to MAY

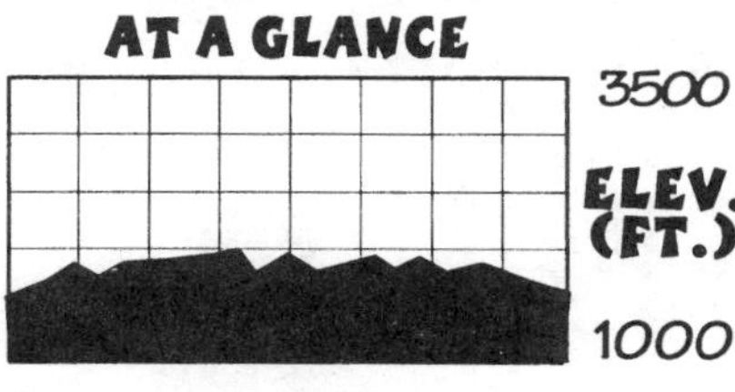

0 **LOOP MILES** 7.1

PRIMO TRAIL
WORTH A JOURNEY

PHOENIX

DESCRIPTION: The Mine/Hawes Trail Loop just might kick your bootie up around your ears. Despite the efforts of greedy, desert-spoiling, trailhead-closing developers, we can still ride *the* most excellent route in Mesa. Giant saguaro line the paths. Best in cool, wildflower months, there is danger at every turn. Watch for old mine pits just off narrow trails with steep exposure, twisty turning climbs and rapid descents. I describe my favorite loop, the Hawes/Mine Trail. Get there quickest by heading EAST from central Phoenix out the Red Mountain Freeway Loop 202 and take the E. McDowell/Power Road exit OR you can come out the Superstition Freeway HWY 60 heading EAST all the way out to Power Road then head NORTH 6 miles to E. McDowell and Power Road.

PARKING: Always a booger because of private property and smash & grab activity around isolated parking areas like the Recker Road lot. Your best bet is to park in Walgreen's lot at McDowell and Power or the giant supermarket across the street. Good for shred food too. Ride to the trailhead.

TRAILHEAD: Ride NORTH out Power Road /Bush Highway 2.7 miles to the trailhead just beyond the canal bridge. See the map. Veer right onto Pig Trail and climb. Continue up Hawes Trail and then go left on Saddleback. This makes for a great loop. Just follow the map.

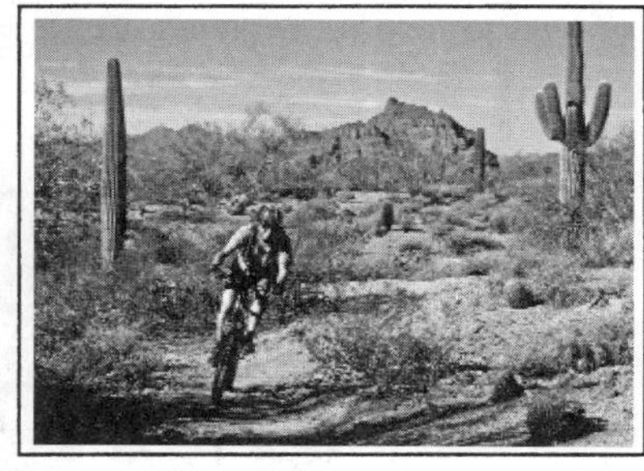

"If you done it, it ain't braggin'."

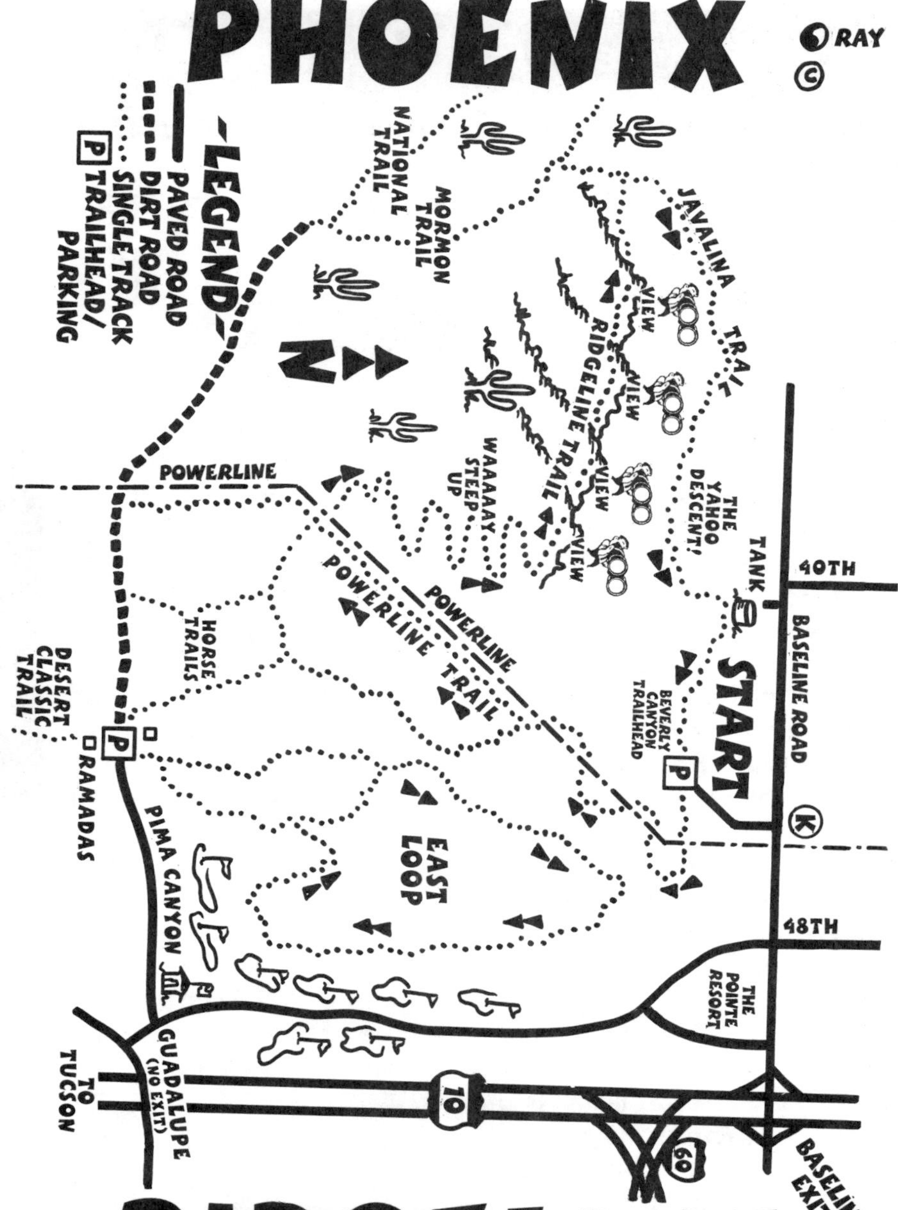

PHOENIX
© RAY
-LEGEND-
PAVED ROAD
DIRT ROAD
SINGLE TRACK
P TRAILHEAD/ PARKING
N
NATIONAL TRAIL
MORMON TRAIL
JAVALINA TRAIL
RIDGELINE TRAIL
VIEW
WAAAAAY STEEP UP
THE YAHOO DESCENT!
TANK
40TH
POWERLINE
POWERLINE TRAIL
HORSE TRAILS
DESERT CLASSIC TRAIL
RAMADAS
START
BEVERLY CANYON TRAILHEAD
BASELINE ROAD
K
EAST LOOP
PIMA CANYON
48TH
THE POINTE RESORT
GUADALUPE (NO EXIT)
TO TUCSON
10
60
BASELINE EXIT

RIDGELINE LOOPS (SOUTH MOUNTAIN)

Phoenix RIDGELINE TRAIL LOOPS
SECRET SOUTH MOUNTAIN 1-TRACK

DISTANCE: 5 to 25 MILES
TIME: 2.5 to 5 HOURS
EFFORT: TOUGH
SKILL: EXPERT
PUCK-O-METER: PUCK 8
ROUGH, STEEP DESCENTS
FIND ROUTE: TRICKY
SEASON: OCT to MAY

AT A GLANCE

PHOENIX

DESCRIPTION: TOP SECRET! Most local sprocketheads know dang little about the way cool single track area just north of the main South Mountain Trails, yet these are some of the best. I outline a short tough 5.5 mile loop, but at day's end my odometer read 25 miles to do every great side loop and trail. East Loop is really superb and fairly easy. Everything here is a mix of tough, technical, steep or smooth, but it's all secret single track.

MILEAGE LOG

0.0 Leave Beverly Cyn. lot on 1-track under power lines. Stay under power lines to avoid false turns.
1.2 Right at Ridgeline Trail sign and steep up over four little peaks and views then zip down to Javelina Trail.
3.1 Right onto Javelina and fast down to reservoir.
4.5 Sharp RIGHT up behind reservoir onto faint 1-track.
5.5 Back to Beverly. Next time try the East Loop.

McDOWELL SONORAN PRESERVE
WINDGATE/BELL PASS LOOP

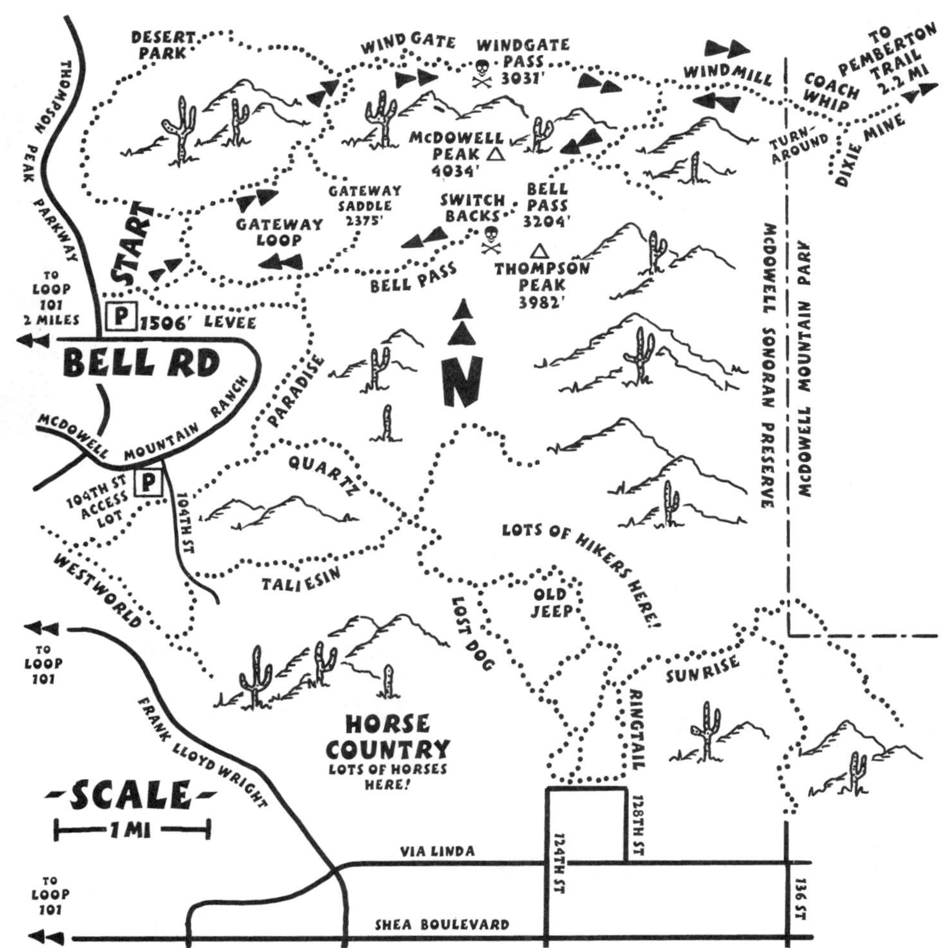
DESERT PARK
WIND GATE
WINDGATE PASS 3031'
WINDMILL
TO PEMBERTON TRAIL 2.2 MI
COACH WHIP
TURN-AROUND
DIXIE MINE
THOMPSON PEAK PARKWAY
McDOWELL PEAK 4034'
GATEWAY SADDLE 2375'
SWITCH BACKS
BELL PASS 3204'
GATEWAY LOOP
START
BELL PASS
THOMPSON PEAK 3982'
TO LOOP 101 2 MILES
P
1506'
LEVEE
BELL RD
N
PARADISE
McDOWELL MOUNTAIN RANCH
McDOWELL SONORAN PRESERVE
McDOWELL MOUNTAIN PARK
QUARTZ
104TH ST ACCESS LOT
104TH ST
WESTWORLD
TALIESIN
LOTS OF HIKERS HERE!
OLD JEEP
LOST DOG
TO LOOP 101
SUNRISE
RINGTAIL
HORSE COUNTRY
LOTS OF HORSES HERE!
FRANK LLOYD WRIGHT
-SCALE-
1 MI
128TH ST
VIA LINDA
124TH ST
136 ST
SHEA BOULEVARD

SCOTTSDALE

McDOWELL SONORAN PRESERVE
HIGH PASSES OVER THE McDOWELLS

DISTANCE: 16 MILES
TIME: 3 TO 5 HOURS
EFFORT: HERCULEAN
SKILL: EXPERTO DESPERADO
PUCK-O-METER: PUCK 10
SOME RUBBLE & BIG EXPOSURE
FIND ROUTE: WELL SIGNED
SEASON: OCT to MAY

AT A GLANCE

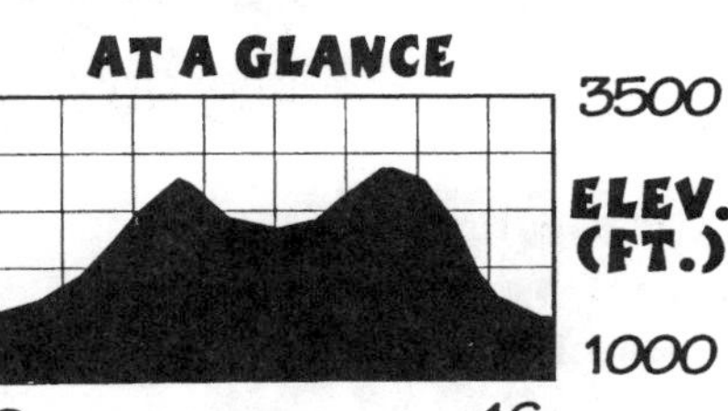

DESCRIPTION: This is the epic ride out at McDowell Sonoran Preserve. Only shred heads need apply. Don't let the reasonable mileage fool you . . . this is one mean ride. I've felt less bushwacked after a 30-mile singletrack siege in The Sierra Nevada. Be prepared.

The entire route is super well signed with names on metal posts. You can't get lost because you can always just head downhill toward civilization any time you choose.

Follow the map up Gateway Trail and keep climbing toward Windgate Pass. Windgate is a little lower than Bell Pass, but otherwise just as tough. Even strong riders will be hike-a-biking parts of Bell and Windgate. Enjoy the remote desert spin down Windmill Trail to Coachwhip and eventually Dixie Mine Trail.

Now you're in McDowell Mountain Park and there is still one serious pass back between you and your ride home. I'd say turn and burn right here, climb Bell Pass and enjoy the Puck 10 descent back to Gateway Loop and your trailhead.

PSYCHOTIC LOOP

There are those among us who might be training for an ultra-race, too tough for The Navy Seals or just plain running from the law. Roll up Gateway Trail, over Windgate Pass and use Dixie Mine to connect with Pemberton Loop in McDowell Mountain Park on the other side of The McDowells. See page 49. Then roll back up and over Bell Pass and back down to Gateway to pour your psycho ass back in your ride home. That's over 30 miles of ruffty-tuffty single track over many thousands of feet of climbing, my friends. I call that hard core.

DIRECTIONS: From anywhere in Phoenix, find Loop 101 thru Scottsdale. Take the Bell Road exit. Head EAST 2 miles toward the mountains. Just past Thompson Peak Parkway there is a cozy little trailhead lot on the left.

THANKS TO MY GOOD PAL JIM ROSSI FOR CHECKING OUT THIS RIDE WHILST I WAS BUSTED UP FROM A BAD CRASH.

UNION HILLS LOOP

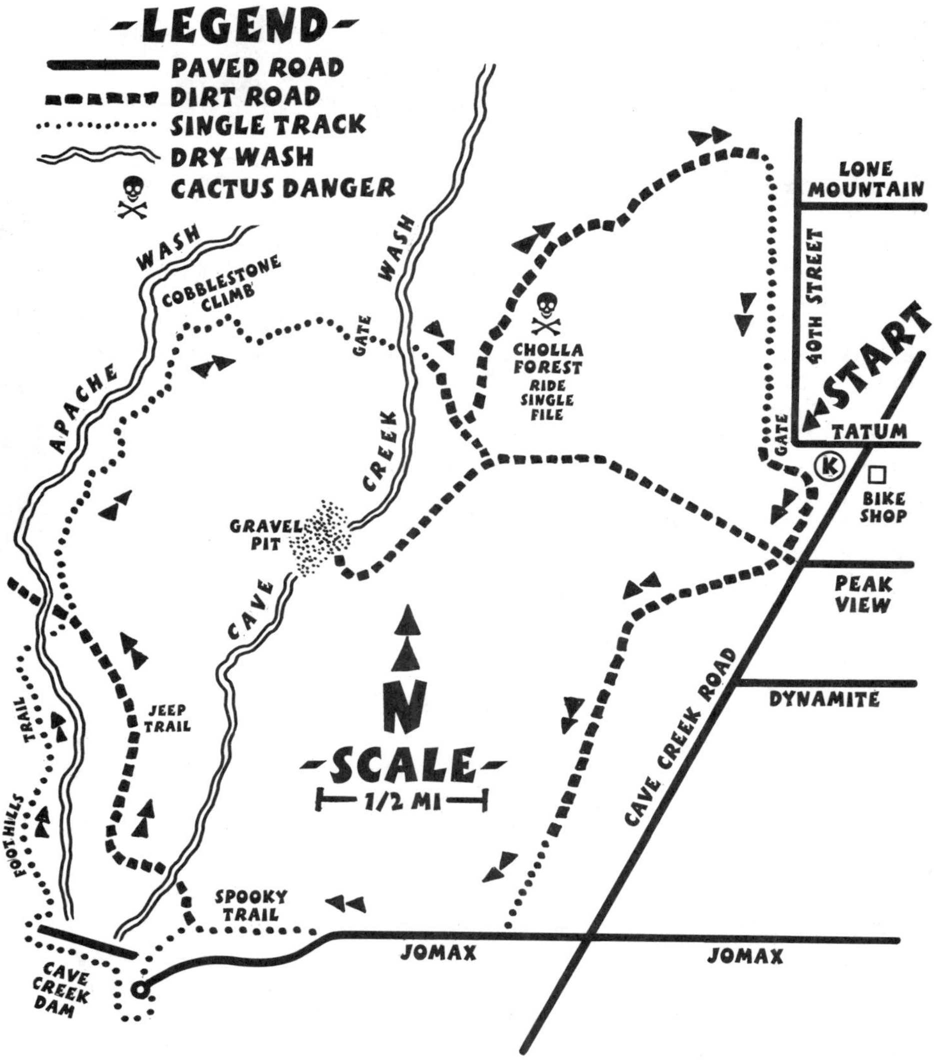

-LEGEND-

PAVED ROAD
DIRT ROAD
SINGLE TRACK
DRY WASH
CACTUS DANGER

APACHE WASH
COBBLESTONE CLIMB
GATE
CAVE CREEK WASH
CHOLLA FOREST
RIDE SINGLE FILE
LONE MOUNTAIN
40TH STREET
START
GATE
TATUM
K
BIKE SHOP
GRAVEL PIT
PEAK VIEW
DYNAMITE
JEEP TRAIL
FOOT HILLS TRAIL
N
-SCALE-
1/2 MI
CAVE CREEK ROAD
SPOOKY TRAIL
JOMAX
JOMAX
CAVE CREEK DAM

PHOENIX

Phoenix UNION HILLS LOOP

VERY FUN, FAST & EASY 12 MILE LOOP

DISTANCE: 12 MILES
TIME: 2 HOURS
EFFORT: FAIRLY EASY
SKILL: EASY
PUCK-O-METER: PUCK 2
FIND ROUTE: FLAGGED
SEASON: SEP to JUN
GOOD NIGHT RIDE IN SUMMER

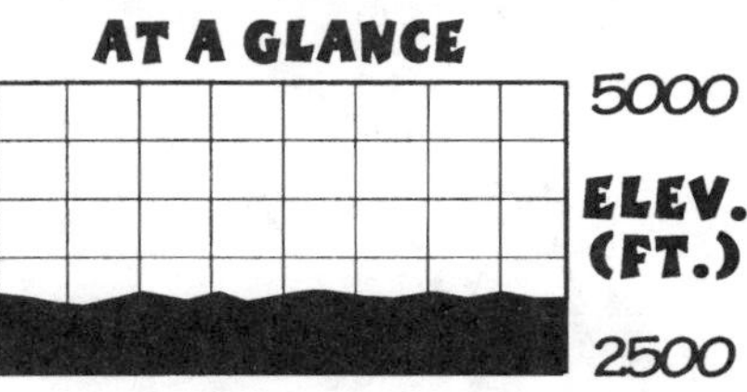

0 **LOOP MILES** 12

DESCRIPTION: Flat, roly-poly, twisting, hopping, jumping and way fast loop in North Phoenix. Soil is superb compacted crushed granite that makes an excellent ripping sound in the turns. The wide 2-track is ideal for the burning fast expert training loop or an easy, long ride for rookies. Trail surface is challenging enough with dips, hops and bumps to make it *NOT* a total putz ride. Southwest Bikes shop ride for all levels is every wednesday nite. Bring your own light. Call ahead.

Union Hills Loop is on Arizona State Trust Land. Although *usually* not strictly enforced, you need a permit to ride here. Said permits are available from Ariozona State Trust Land Department (602) 364-2753 or download one at the Arizona State Trust Land website (search on Google). The nominal fee of $15 also allows you to ride legal beagle style on the superb trails around Dynamite & Pima plus other Trust Lands around the state. Mike and the guys at Southwest Bikes are kind enough to flag the route so you won't get lost. Stop in and say thanks. Tell 'em Ray sent ya.

PHOENIX

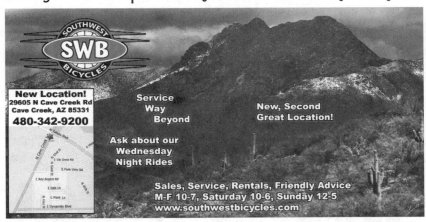

USERY PASS

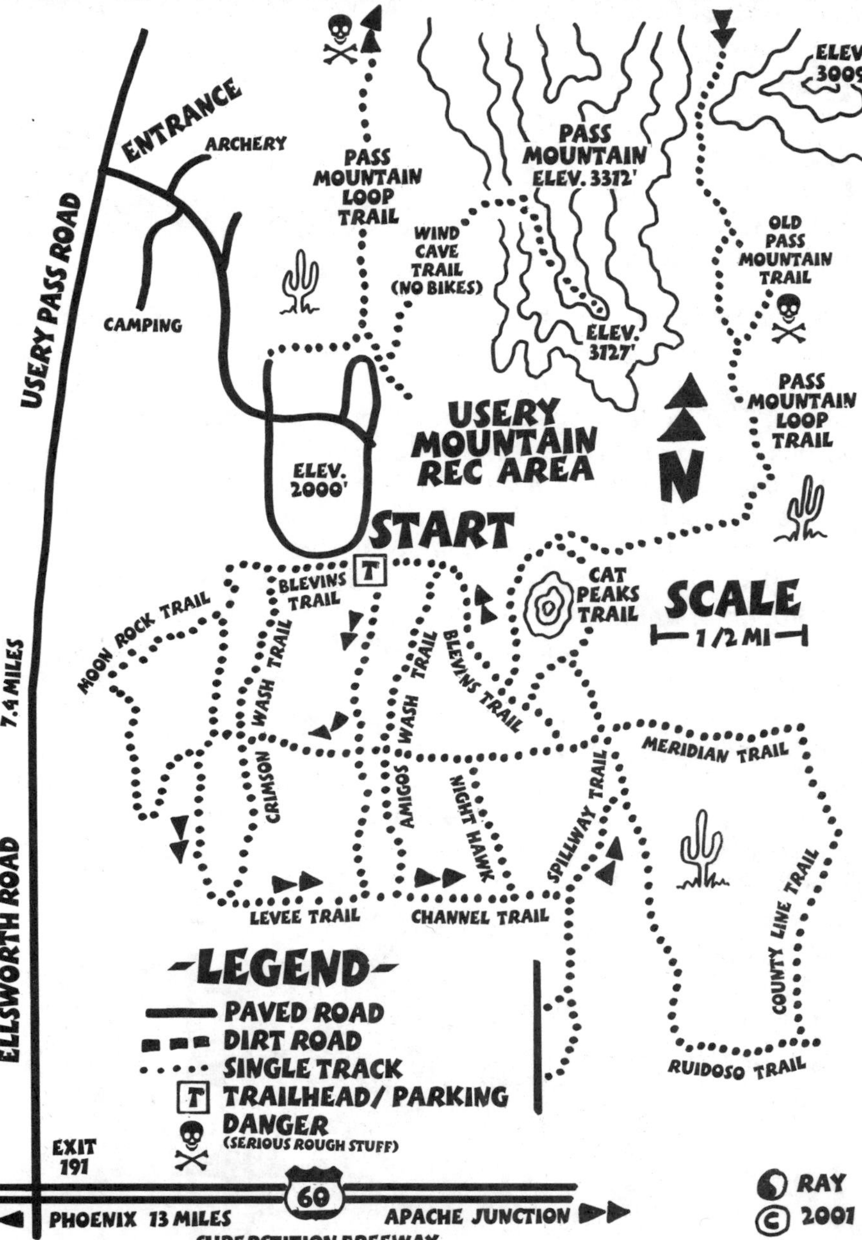

PHOENIX (MESA)

Phoenix USERY MOUNTAIN PARK
SONORAN DESERT SINGLE TRACK

DISTANCE: 5 & 8 MILE LOOPS
TIME: 2 to 4 HOURS
EFFORT: NO SWEAT
SKILL: CHALLENGING FUN
PUCK-O-METER: PUCK 5
(Some puck 10 on the long loop)
FIND ROUTE: DARN EASY
SEASON: SEP to MAY

AT A GLANCE

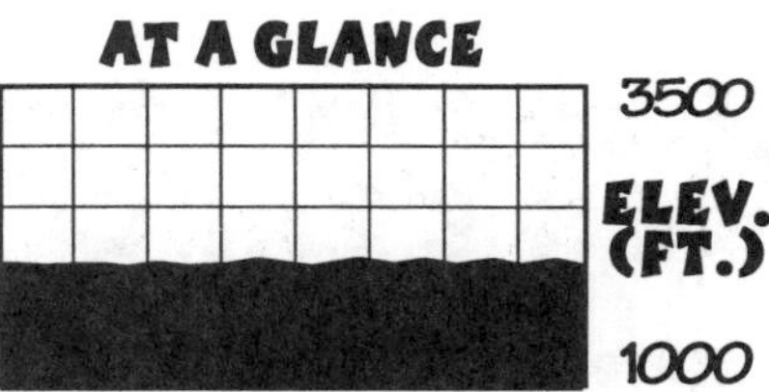

DESCRIPTION: Named for King Usery, a rancher in the 1890s. Ranching went sour. King tried robbing the Globe-Florence stage with pal Bill Blevins. Posse tracked them here to Usery Ranch. Two years later King was pardoned the rest of his seven years from Yuma territorial pen. Next, Mr. King takes up horse borrowing. Gets time back in Yuma. After release he vanished. Necktie party no doubt.

This pristine sonoran desert is best enjoyed in cooler months October to May or veeery early AM during summer inferno. The Superstitions are to the east. The Userys are just north and the McDowells sit across the Salt River northwest. Up close is Pass Mountain.

BLEVINS LOOP TRAIL, called "Usery Loves Company" by the local wig-wags, is a moderate 4.7 mile single track carve. It is signed and has virtually zero elevation gain. Great for easy exploration with no possibility of getting lost.

PASS MOUNTAIN LOOP is more the real deal ride. Tough 8 mile single track, rocky washes and sick twisted fun for the more seasoned rider. Starts off easy but gets tough quick once behind Pass Mountain. No water. No rescue.

PHOENIX

PHOENIX

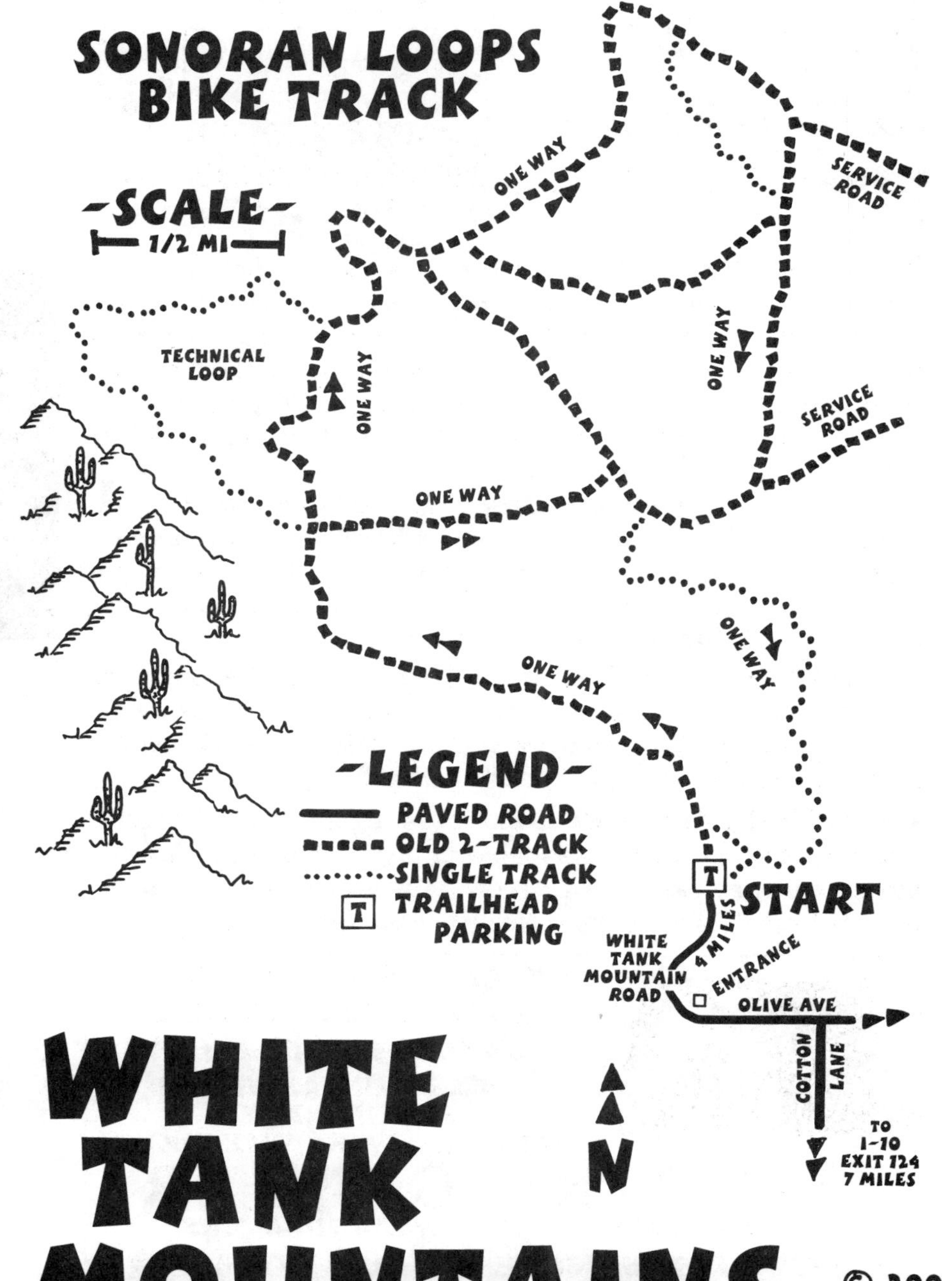

SONORAN LOOPS
BIKE TRACK
-SCALE-
1/2 MI
TECHNICAL LOOP
ONE WAY
ONE WAY
ONE WAY
ONE WAY
ONE WAY
ONE WAY
SERVICE ROAD
SERVICE ROAD
-LEGEND-
PAVED ROAD
OLD 2-TRACK
SINGLE TRACK
T TRAILHEAD PARKING
T
START
4 MILES
WHITE TANK MOUNTAIN ROAD
ENTRANCE
OLIVE AVE
COTTON LANE
TO I-10 EXIT 124 7 MILES
N
WHITE TANK MOUNTAINS
© 2003
© RAY

Phoenix WHITE TANK MTNS.
EASY 1-TRACK AND JEEP ROAD LOOPS

DISTANCE: 5.6 MILE LOOP
TIME: 1 HOUR OR SO
EFFORT: EASY
SKILL: NOVICE
PUCK-O-METER: PUCK 2
EASY ROLLING TERRAIN, NO ALARM
FIND ROUTE: EASY
SEASON: OCT to MAY

AT A GLANCE

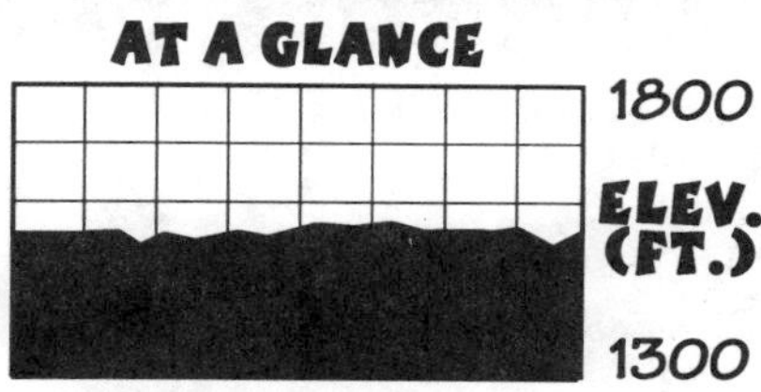

DESCRIPTION: "SONORAN LOOP TRAIL: MOUNTAIN BIKE DIFFICULTY MODERATE" reads the sign at the trailhead. Situated 15 miles due west of Peoria strip malls and traffic, Sonoran Loop is fairly flat, easy and nestled up against the base of the extremely rugged White Tank Mountains. Sonoran desert, fresh air, open sky and glorious silence replenish the soul . . . guaranteed. The White Tanks are best in cool months when the desert blooms. Cloudy, cool skies are ideal.

Interesting to note that novice friends and family won't hate you for dragging them here. The loop consists of easy jeep roads and level rolling single track with a few short excursions across sandy washes. A great place to get your trail legs going and improve wind and skills. Maricopa County has done a great job improving the single track, connecting loose ends and closing some heinously rough, rocky jeep roads that headed steep up into nowhere.

CAUTION: Mr. Western Diamondback Rattler resides here. He is one mean machine. Adults grow to 7 feet, have a heavy body with dark, diamond shaped spots and are unmistakable when aroused. Do not mess with! Observe from a distance. Only dangerous when come upon suddenly. He wishes you to leave him alone which is his right as a southwest native since before time and Arizona.

DIRECTIONS: Located 15 miles way out west of Peoria at the west end of Olive (Dunlap) Ave. The quick and easy best access is via I-10 WEST all the way to Cotton Ave. (exit 124), NORTH 7 miles to Olive and then 5 miles WEST to the park entrance. There is a small fee that includes a great new White Tank Mountain Park map.

"The more I know people, the more I like my bike."
-anonymous bike mechanic

AIRPORT MESA
CARROLL CANYON TRAILS

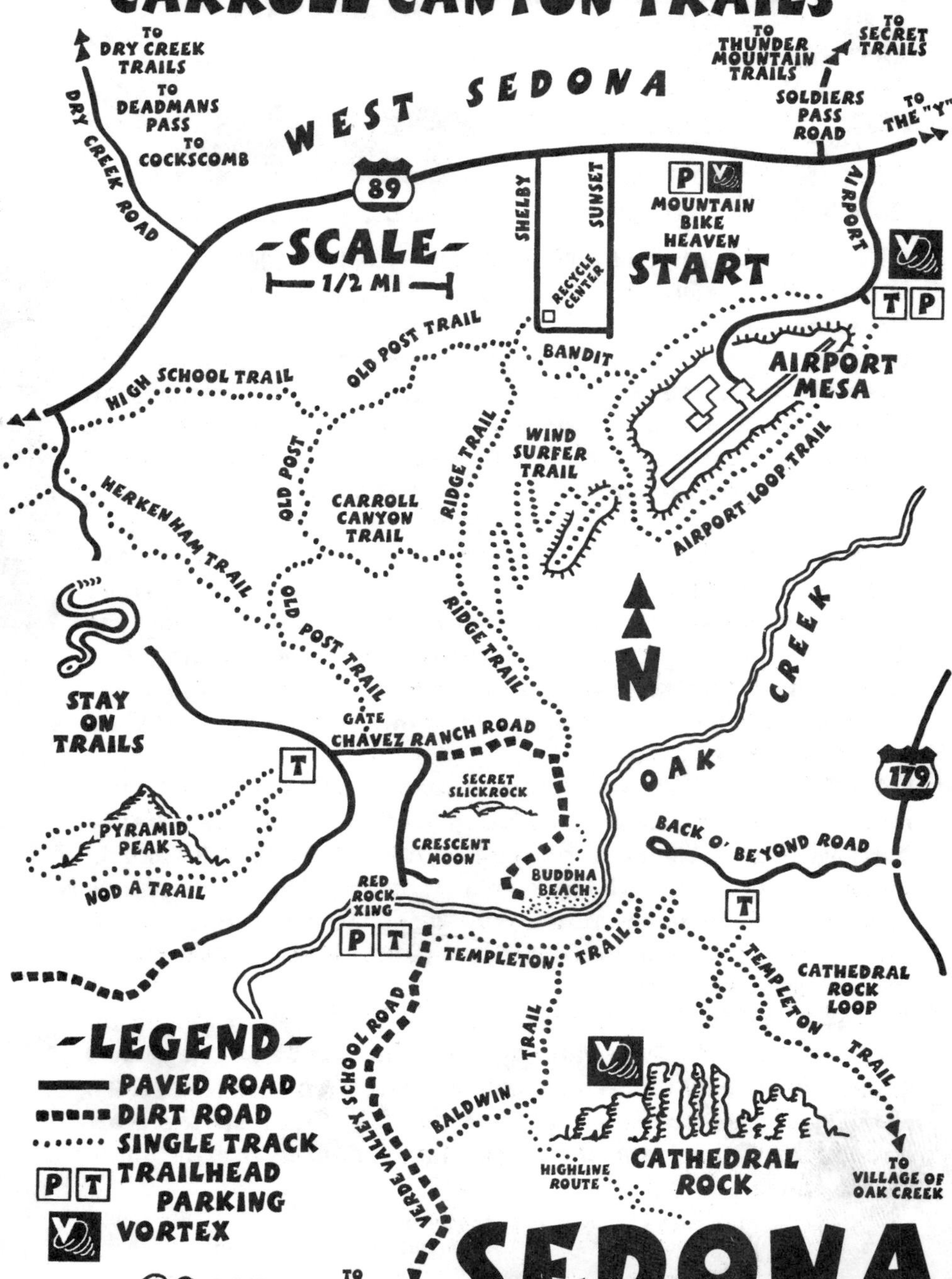

TO DRY CREEK TRAILS
TO DEADMANS PASS
TO COCKSCOMB
DRY CREEK ROAD
WEST SEDONA
89
TO THUNDER MOUNTAIN TRAILS
TO SECRET TRAILS
SOLDIERS PASS ROAD
TO THE "Y"
SHELBY
SUNSET
RECYCLE CENTER
P
MOUNTAIN BIKE HEAVEN
START
AIRPORT
T P
SCALE
1/2 MI
OLD POST TRAIL
BANDIT
AIRPORT MESA
HIGH SCHOOL TRAIL
OLD POST
RIDGE TRAIL
WIND SURFER TRAIL
AIRPORT LOOP TRAIL
HERKENHAM TRAIL
CARROLL CANYON TRAIL
OLD POST TRAIL
RIDGE TRAIL
N
OAK CREEK
STAY ON TRAILS
GATE
CHÁVEZ RANCH ROAD
T
SECRET SLICKROCK
179
PYRAMID PEAK
CRESCENT MOON
BACK O' BEYOND ROAD
NOD A TRAIL
RED ROCK XING
BUDDHA BEACH
T
P T
TEMPLETON TRAIL
TEMPLETON TRAIL
CATHEDRAL ROCK LOOP
VERDE VALLEY SCHOOL ROAD
BALDWIN TRAIL
HIGHLINE ROUTE
CATHEDRAL ROCK
TO VILLAGE OF OAK CREEK
LEGEND
PAVED ROAD
DIRT ROAD
SINGLE TRACK
P T TRAILHEAD PARKING
VORTEX
© RAY
TO VILLAGE OF OAK CREEK
SEDONA

Sedona AIRPORT MESA

SHOP CAT'S FAVORITE SINGLE TRACK SHRED

DISTANCE: 3 TO 10 MILES
GOOD SINGLE TRACK EXPLORING HERE
TIME: 2 TO 3 HOURS
EFFORT: FAIRLY TOUGH
SKILL: MEDIUM TO EXPERT
PUCK-O-METER: PUCK 8
SOME TOUGHER THAN OTHERS
FIND ROUTE: MODERATE
SEASON: SEP to JUN

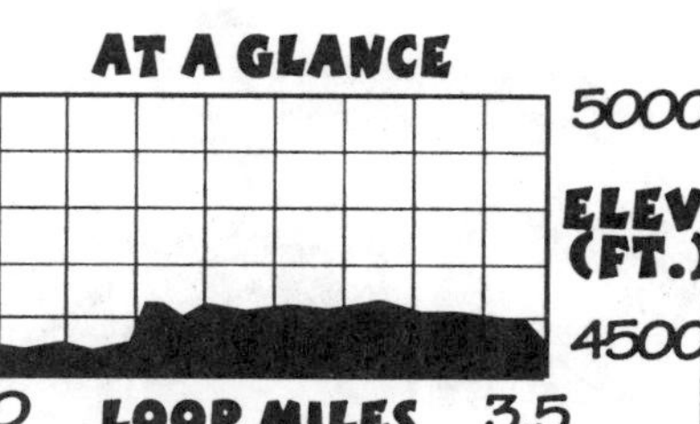

DESCRIPTION: "This is *NOT* a ride!", your homies might holler. It *is* at times rough, physical and even abusive. However, many of the trails here are merely tough rather than totally insane. A defined loop circles the mesa rim 600 feet above Sedona with killer views in every direction. It's a real test for machine and technical skills. Nice single track loops with good climbing and descending to Oak Creek. Access Cathedral Rock area across the creek over Red Rock Crossing. Check out Secret Slickrock, Buddha Beach, Pyramid Trails and much, much more.

DIRECTIONS: Easy. Best bet is to park at Mountain Bike Heaven bike shop. Say hi to the bad boys and girls there, hook up with a shop ride or just follow the map.

" When in danger, when in doubt, run in circles, scream and shout."
-NOD (G-narly old dude)

SEDONA

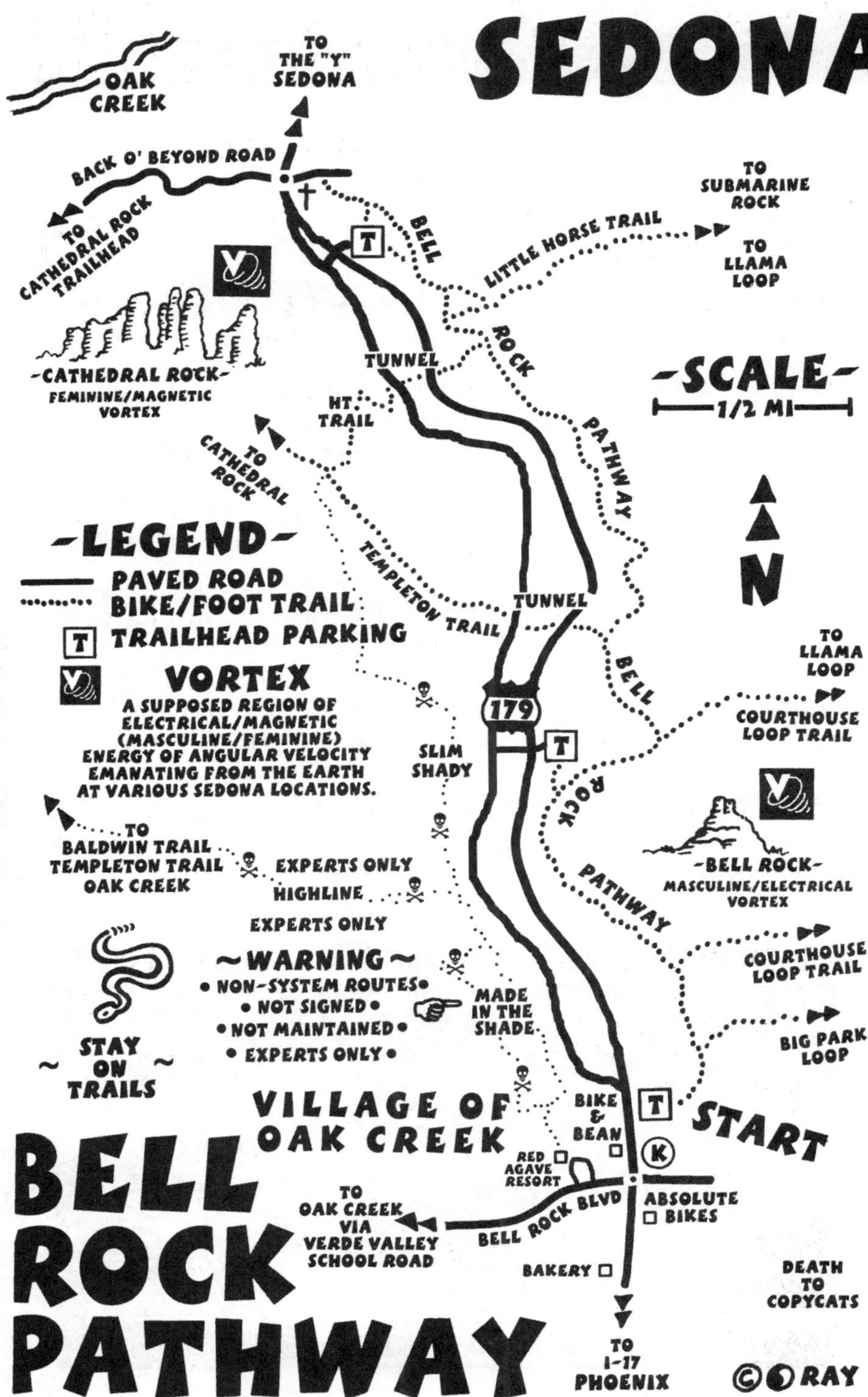
SEDONA
OAK CREEK
TO THE "Y" SEDONA
BACK O' BEYOND ROAD
TO CATHEDRAL ROCK TRAILHEAD
BELL
LITTLE HORSE TRAIL
TO SUBMARINE ROCK
TO LLAMA LOOP
ROCK
CATHEDRAL ROCK
FEMININE/MAGNETIC VORTEX
TUNNEL
HT TRAIL
SCALE
1/2 MI
PATHWAY
TO CATHEDRAL ROCK
TEMPLETON TRAIL
N
LEGEND
PAVED ROAD
BIKE/FOOT TRAIL
TRAILHEAD PARKING
VORTEX
A SUPPOSED REGION OF ELECTRICAL/MAGNETIC (MASCULINE/FEMININE) ENERGY OF ANGULAR VELOCITY EMANATING FROM THE EARTH AT VARIOUS SEDONA LOCATIONS.
TUNNEL
BELL
TO LLAMA LOOP
179
COURTHOUSE LOOP TRAIL
SLIM SHADY
ROCK
TO BALDWIN TRAIL TEMPLETON TRAIL OAK CREEK
EXPERTS ONLY
HIGHLINE
EXPERTS ONLY
BELL ROCK
MASCULINE/ELECTRICAL VORTEX
PATHWAY
COURTHOUSE LOOP TRAIL
~WARNING~
• NON-SYSTEM ROUTES •
• NOT SIGNED •
• NOT MAINTAINED •
• EXPERTS ONLY •
MADE IN THE SHADE
BIG PARK LOOP
~ STAY ON TRAILS ~
VILLAGE OF OAK CREEK
BIKE & BEAN
START
RED AGAVE RESORT
BELL ROCK BLVD
ABSOLUTE BIKES
TO OAK CREEK VIA VERDE VALLEY SCHOOL ROAD
BAKERY
DEATH TO COPYCATS
BELL ROCK PATHWAY
TO I-17 PHOENIX
©© RAY

Sedona BELL ROCK PATHWAY
WELCOME TO SEDONA!

DISTANCE: 3.5 MILES 1-WAY
7 MILES TOTAL OUT AND BACK
TIME: 1 TO 2 HOURS
EFFORT: DANG EASY
SKILL: TOTAL ROOKIE
FEAR: NO FEAR AT ALL
FIND ROUTE: EASY
SEASON: ALL YEAR

CONTOUR PROFILE

5000
ELEV. (FT.)
4000
0 1-WAY MILES 3.5

DESCRIPTION: Locals call it the "boat ramp". That's because it's the launching place for the best of what Sedona has to offer. Many of Sedona's classic loop rides begin and end here. At the same time, a beginner on a rental bike will feel totally comfortable at this modest level of difficulty.

Your best bet is to start in Village of Oak Creek just south of Sedona proper. The Village has a great bakery/coffee house called Desert Flour Bakery. There is pizza, all you can eat Chinese, Thai and more in this little tourist trap in the red rocks. A supermarket and plenty of motels round out the picture. And you can ride from your motel room door to the best single track in The Southwest.

The two bike shops at this end of town, Absolute Bikes and Bike & Bean, are both competent, friendly and have a good supply of rentals, although it is best to call ahead and reserve during the busy spring and fall season. Sedona weather is always superb and the fabulous red rock scenery is unsurpassed. Afternoons may be a little warm in summer, but if you get out for a few hours after an early breakfast, you can beat the heat. Always carry plenty of water and wear a helmet so as to be safe and not look like a total novice.

After you've mastered the basic Bell Rock Path, move up to a *real* ride. Lookit the map. Cathedral Rock Loop follows along the base contour of The Cathedral. Way cool. It leads down to Oak Creek via a set of hairball switchbacks and then back to The Village. Submarine Rock Loop is a little more expert as it follows wicked Broken Arrow single track, some nice slickrock on Subrock and finishes up with a blast down Little Horse Trail, A.K.A. Mr. Toad's Wild ride. *Yowza!*

"If at first you *DO* succeed, try not to look astonished."

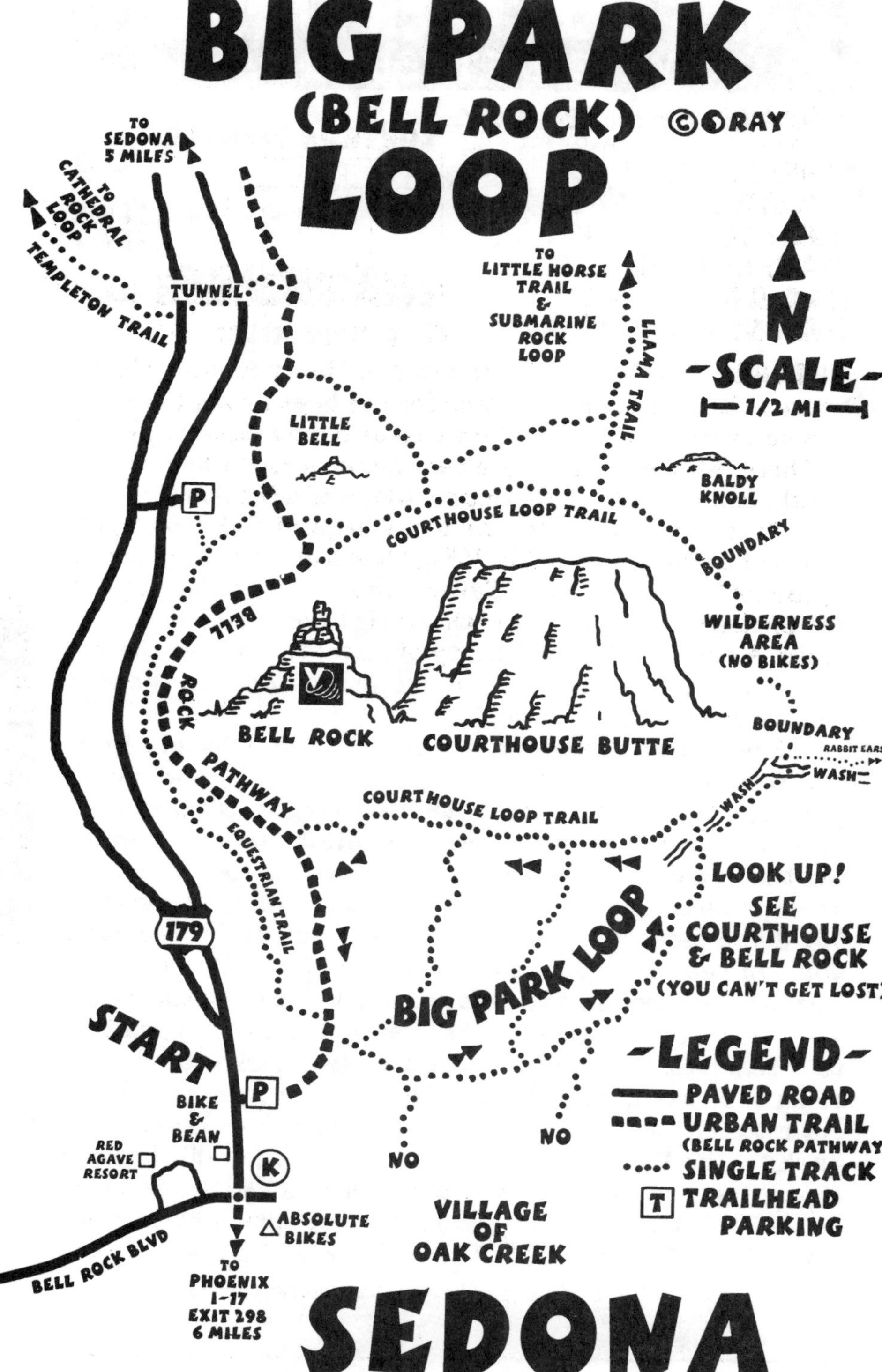
BIG PARK
(BELL ROCK)
LOOP
©RAY
TO SEDONA 5 MILES
TO CATHEDRAL ROCK LOOP
TEMPLETON TRAIL
TUNNEL
TO LITTLE HORSE TRAIL & SUBMARINE ROCK LOOP
LLAMA TRAIL
N
-SCALE-
1/2 MI
LITTLE BELL
BALDY KNOLL
COURTHOUSE LOOP TRAIL
BOUNDARY
WILDERNESS AREA (NO BIKES)
BELL ROCK PATHWAY
BELL ROCK
COURTHOUSE BUTTE
BOUNDARY
RABBIT EARS
WASH
WASH
EQUESTRIAN TRAIL
COURTHOUSE LOOP TRAIL
LOOK UP!
SEE COURTHOUSE & BELL ROCK
(YOU CAN'T GET LOST)
179
BIG PARK LOOP
START
P
P
BIKE & BEAN
RED AGAVE RESORT
K
NO
NO
-LEGEND-
PAVED ROAD
URBAN TRAIL (BELL ROCK PATHWAY)
SINGLE TRACK
T TRAILHEAD PARKING
ABSOLUTE BIKES
VILLAGE OF OAK CREEK
BELL ROCK BLVD
TO PHOENIX I-17 EXIT 298 6 MILES
SEDONA

Sedona BIG PARK TRAILS
VERY FUN SINGLE TRACK LOOPS TO VIEWS

DISTANCE: 3 MILE LOOP
(5 MILES OF LOOPS PLUS MORE)
TIME: 1 to 3 HOURS
EFFORT: INTERMEDIATE
SKILL: INTERMEDIATE
(ABOUT AS EASY AS SEDONA GETS!)
PUCK-O-METER: PUCK 6
FIND ROUTE: EASY
(LOOK UP AT THE MONUMENTS!)

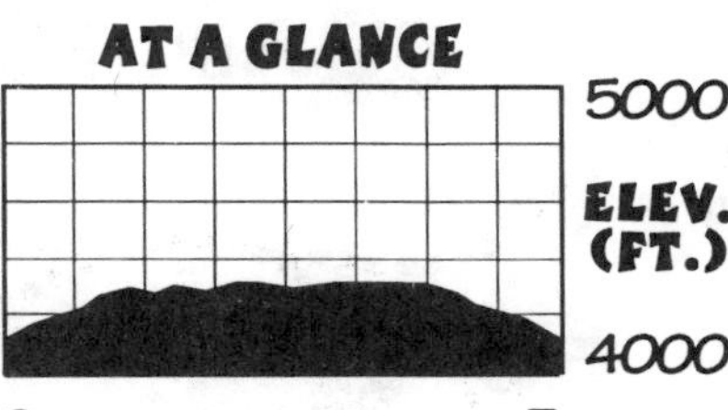

DESCRIPTION: Humongo views and superb Sedona single track with redrock monuments Bell, Courthouse and Rabbit Ears towering overhead. You won't get lost if you just look up. Trails are fun, fast and grippy with enough work to break a minor sweat.

Bell Rock Path is launch ramp to single track on either side of HWY 179. Seasoned riders zoom up to Submarine Rock Loop, Llama Loop or tunnel under HWY 179 to Cathedral Rock Loop and Buddha Beach. Trail to Rabbit Ears View is unmarked. Remember, look up.

NOTE: Do NOT follow Courthouse Loop over the saddle behind Courthouse. That short part of Courthouse Loop is tempting, but peaks out above 4400' elevation and is thus wilderness. No bikes allowed. $300 fine! Serious business.

DIRECTIONS: Take I-17 Exit #298 to Village of Oak Creek. Park free in one of the bike shop parking lots.

SEDONA

BOYNTON PASS

ROAD TO RUINS

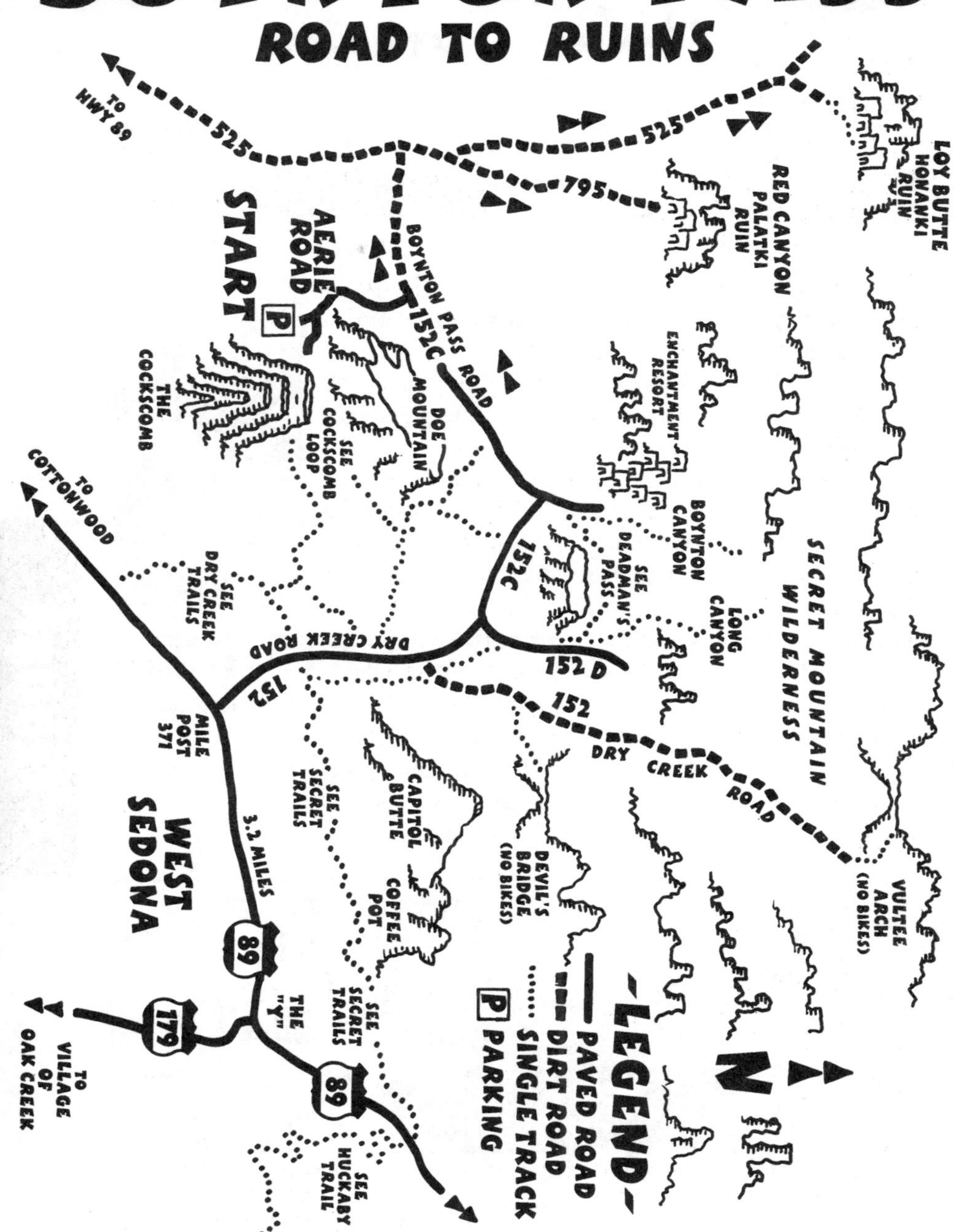

TO HWY 89
525
795
START
AERIE ROAD
BOYNTON PASS ROAD
152C
THE COCKSCOMB
DOE MOUNTAIN
SEE COCKSCOMB LOOP
RED CANYON PALATKI RUIN
LOY BUTTE HONANKI RUIN
ENCHANTMENT RESORT
BOYNTON CANYON
SEE DEADMAN'S PASS
LONG CANYON
SECRET MOUNTAIN WILDERNESS
TO COTTONWOOD
SEE DRY CREEK TRAILS
DRY CREEK ROAD
152
152 D
MILE POST 371
SEE SECRET TRAILS
CAPITOL BUTTE
COFFEE POT
DEVIL'S BRIDGE (NO BIKES)
DRY CREEK ROAD
VULTEE ARCH (NO BIKES)
WEST SEDONA
3.2 MILES
89
179
THE "Y"
TO VILLAGE OF OAK CREEK
SEE SECRET TRAILS
SEE HUCKABY TRAIL
-LEGEND-
PAVED ROAD
DIRT ROAD
SINGLE TRACK
P PARKING
N
SEDONA

Sedona BOYNTON PASS ROAD
EASY DIRT ROAD TO RUIN(S)

DISTANCE: 10 MILES
TIME: 2 to 3 HOURS
EFFORT: EASY ROLL
SKILL: NOT MUCH NEEDED
PUCK-O-METER: PUCK 2
SOME CARS ON DIRT ROAD
FIND ROUTE: EASY
SEASON: SEP to MAY

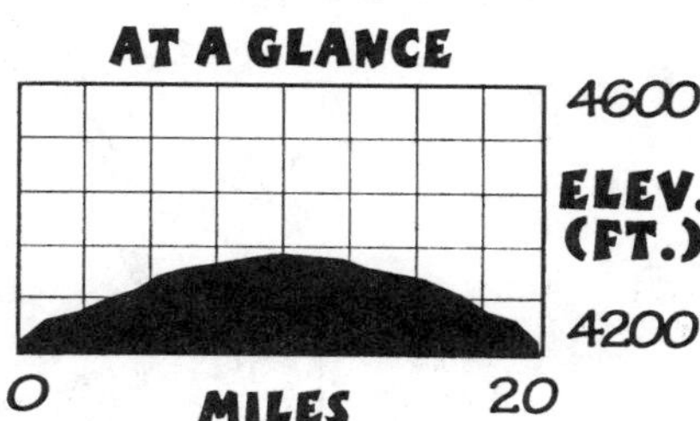

DESCRIPTION: Red dirt roads and gentle climbs roll through pinon and juniper with the red rock buttes of Secret Mountain Wilderness overhead. Ancient ruins, optional hikes and patented technicolor Sedona scenery make this one unforgettable day for those who like easy dirt road rides.

LOY BUTTE (HONANKI RUIN)

It's fairly smooth dirt road to the ruins although weekends may have some cars sharing the road. PARK in the Forest Service lot at the end of Aerie Road. See the map. Head back out to Boynton Pass Road and follow the map to FS 525 and Honanki Ruin. Do not disturb the ruins. Do not pick up anything. Do not touch the petroglyphs. Dirt and oil from many hands over time do great damage. Think about the time before time and those who lived here then. Avoid dusty tourist traffic. Ride early. Carry food, water and kit.

RED CANYON (PALATKI RUIN)

Same directions as Honanki only BEAR RIGHT on FS 525 onto FS 795. Then it's 2 easy miles out to the ruins all on smooth dirt road. Enjoy the ruins with your eyes only. Do not pick up or disturb any artifacts you may find. Do not ride close to the ruin.

NOTE: It is said that the 5000 or so archeological sites around Sedona are protected not only by law, but also by evil curse. No joke. Do not be so foolish as to tempt the ancients with bad ju-ju. Respect those who have gone before you. They may be waiting in the next life!

"As far as possible without surrender be on good terms with all."
- *popular wisdom*

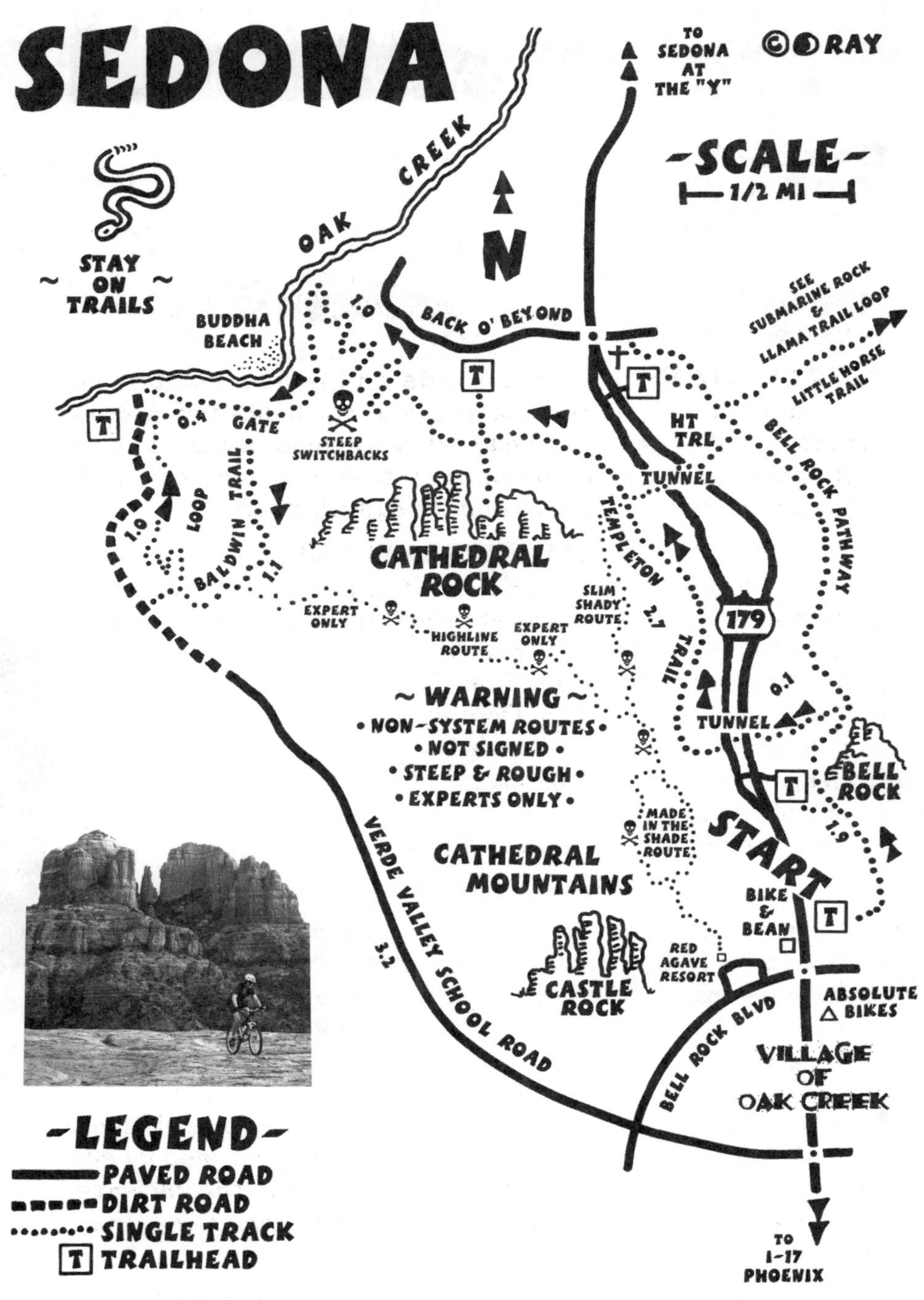
SEDONA
TO SEDONA AT THE "Y"
©☺RAY
OAK CREEK
STAY ON TRAILS
N
SCALE
1/2 MI
BUDDHA BEACH
1.0
BACK O' BEYOND
SEE SUBMARINE ROCK & LLAMA TRAIL LOOP
LITTLE HORSE TRAIL
0.4
GATE
STEEP SWITCHBACKS
HT TRL
BELL ROCK PATHWAY
TUNNEL
1.0
LOOP
BALDWIN TRAIL
1.1
TEMPLETON
CATHEDRAL ROCK
SLIM SHADY ROUTE
2.7
EXPERT ONLY
HIGHLINE ROUTE
EXPERT ONLY
179
TRAIL
~ WARNING ~
• NON-SYSTEM ROUTES •
• NOT SIGNED •
• STEEP & ROUGH •
• EXPERTS ONLY •
0.1
TUNNEL
BELL ROCK
START
1.9
MADE IN THE SHADE ROUTE
CATHEDRAL MOUNTAINS
VERDE VALLEY SCHOOL ROAD
3.2
BIKE & BEAN
RED AGAVE RESORT
CASTLE ROCK
ABSOLUTE BIKES
BELL ROCK BLVD
VILLAGE OF OAK CREEK
LEGEND
PAVED ROAD
DIRT ROAD
SINGLE TRACK
T TRAILHEAD
TO I-17 PHOENIX

CATHEDRAL LOOP

Sedona CATHEDRAL ROCK LOOP
SINGLE TRACK VIA BUDDHA BEACH

DISTANCE: 11 MILES
TIME: 2 HOURS OR SO
EFFORT: MODERATE
SKILL: ADVANCED
PUCK-O-METER: PUCK 8
ONE BIG DROP PLUS EXPOSURE
FIND ROUTE: MODERATE
SEASON: SEP to JUN

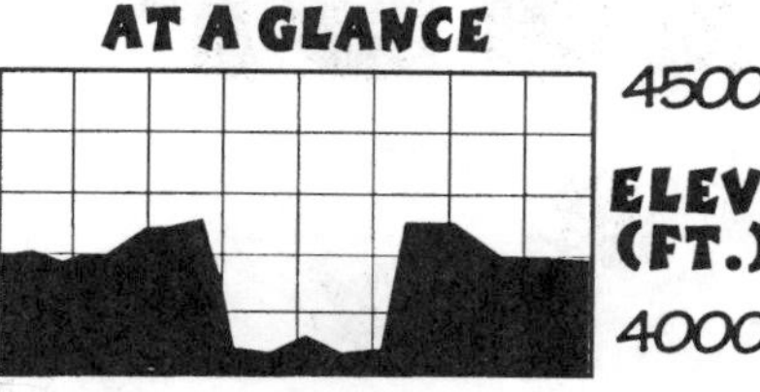

DESCRIPTION: Cathedral/Baldwin Loop has it all. Views, slickrock, single track *AND* a swimming hole. Plenty of technical fun and it links up with other trails. One of Sedona's best . . . a lollipop . . . ride out to a thriller 2-mile lollipop loop then ride back.

PRIMO TRAIL
WORTH A JOURNEY

MILEAGE LOG

0.0 Start at the trailhead next to Circle K in Village of Oak Creek. Avoid the stinkeye and make nice with hikers. Roll north on Bell Rock Pathway to the "Templeton Trail" sign.

1.9 LEFT at Templeton Trail thru tunnels under HWY 179. Follow Templeton all the way around Cathedral Rock, down the switchbacks and along Oak Creek. See map.

5.7 LEFT thru gate onto Baldwin Trail. Fun stuff here. Do the entire Baldwin Loop. It's fairly short with some very amusing technical thrills.

7.8 Back to where you started the Baldwin Loop. RIGHT turn back along the creek and return the way you came.

13.9 Back to Start. Now try some of the other nearby loops.

SEDONA

COCKSCOMB LOOP

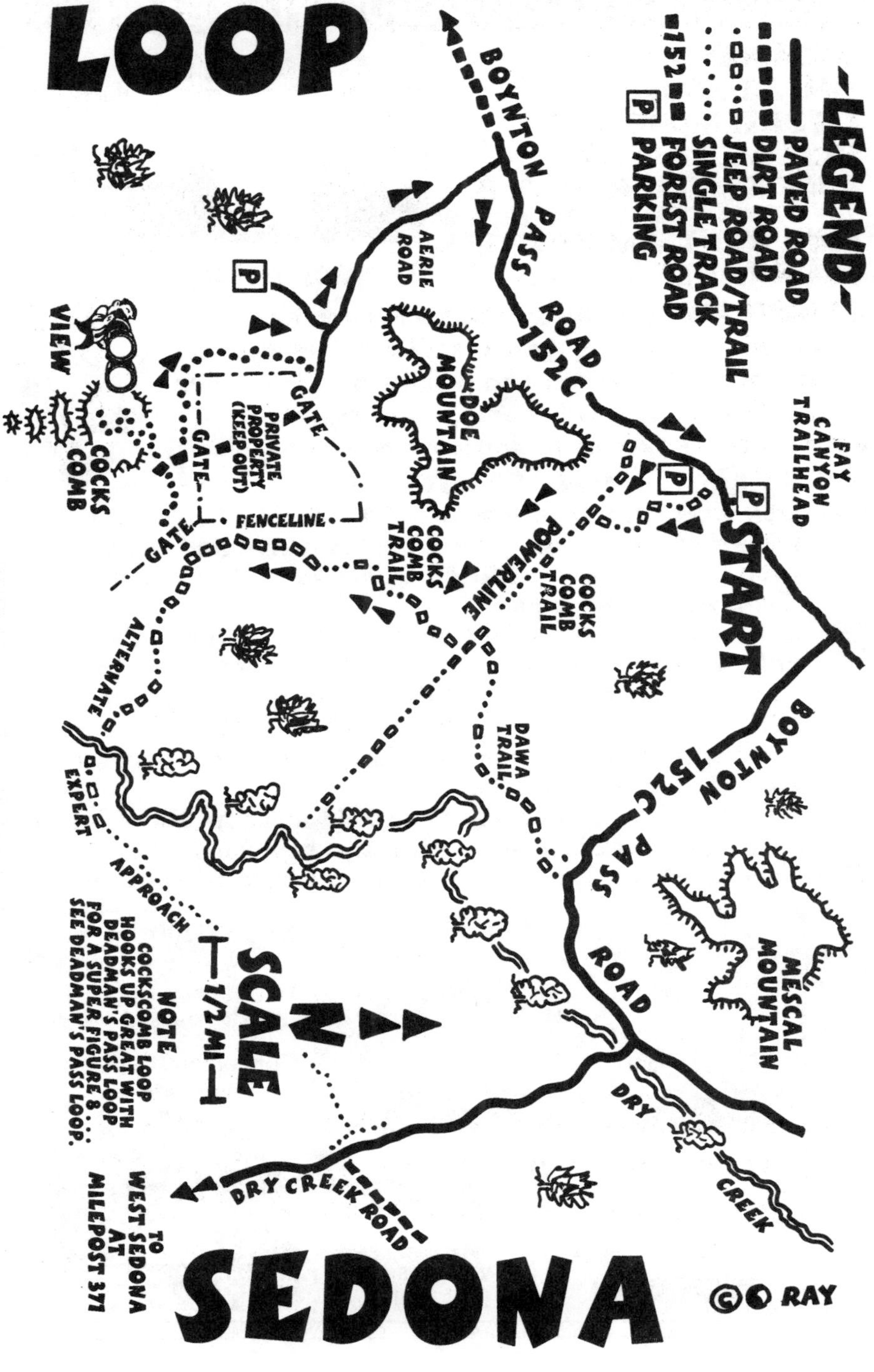

-LEGEND-
PAVED ROAD
DIRT ROAD
JEEP ROAD/TRAIL
SINGLE TRACK
152 FOREST ROAD
P PARKING

BOYNTON PASS ROAD 152C
AERIE ROAD
FAY CANYON TRAILHEAD
DOE MOUNTAIN
PRIVATE PROPERTY (KEEP OUT)
GATE
GATE
GATE
FENCELINE
COCKSCOMB VIEW
COCKS COMB
COCKS COMB TRAIL
POWERLINE
COCKS COMB TRAIL
START
ALTERNATE
DAWA TRAIL
BOYNTON 152C PASS ROAD
MESCAL MOUNTAIN
EXPERT
APPROACH
SCALE
1/2 MI
N

NOTE
COCKSCOMB LOOP HOOKS UP GREAT WITH DEADMAN'S PASS LOOP FOR A SUPER FIGURE 8... SEE DEADMAN'S PASS LOOP.

DRY CREEK
DRY CREEK ROAD
TO WEST SEDONA AT MILEPOST 371

SEDONA

Sedona COCKSCOMB LOOP
BIG FUN TRAIL TO SEDONA SPIRES

DISTANCE: 6.1 MILES
TIME: 1 to 2 HOURS
EFFORT: MEDIUM WORK
SKILL: NOT TOO TRICKY
PUCK-O-METER: PUCK 6
BE CAREFUL HIKING UP THE COCKSCOMB
FIND ROUTE: A BIT TRICKY
LOOK AT THE MAP & LOOK UP
SEASON: SEP to JUN

AT A GLANCE

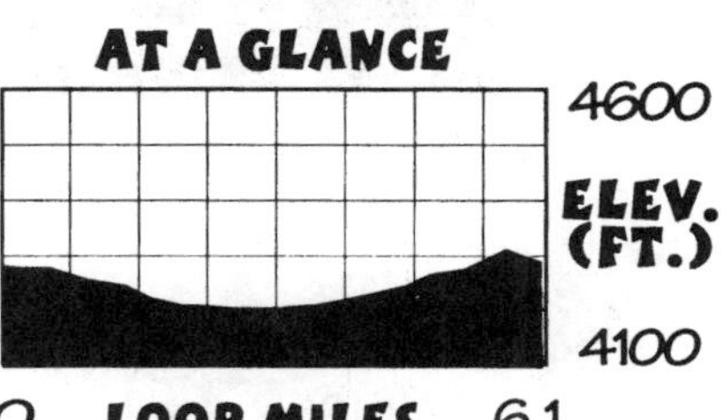

DESCRIPTION: Cockscomb's red spires invite you like a redrock Emerald City of OZ as you cruise west thru Sedona. Ride the red dirt to the base then scramble up top on foot for the best 420 degree view in these parts.

MILEAGE LOG

0.0 Follow the map and find your way to the Fay Canyon/ Cockscomb Trailheads on Boynton Pass Road. The loop begins at the powerline.

0.3 Connect with the powerline and follow it downhill.

1.0 HEADS UP! Dawak Trail goes left. You go STRAIGHT.

1.2 RIGHT first chance after Dawa junction and head away from the Powerline Trail on Cockscomb Trail.

2.1 You come upon a fence and an area of deciduous trees. Take a single track on RIGHT thru gate in fence. Look up. The Cockscomb comes into view.

2.4 The 1-track crosses a jeep road. Continue straight on the trail for a bit then stash your bike, but don't forget where you left it. You'll need it later! Look for cairns. Follow them up a steep trail on foot. It leads you to the very top of The Cockscomb, a spire 400 feet off the pinon and juniper deck. Be very careful. If your hiking route does not look like a trail, it probably is not. After the view session return to your bike and the jeep road at the bottom. There is a gate in the fence. Don't go thru it. A trail leads LEFT along the fence. See the map.

3.1 Go LEFT downhill on paved Aerie Road.

4.1 Paved Boynton Pass Road. Go RIGHT back to the Start.

6.1 Back to GO. Now turn the pages to Deadman's Pass Loop and double your fun.

DEADMAN'S PASS LOOP

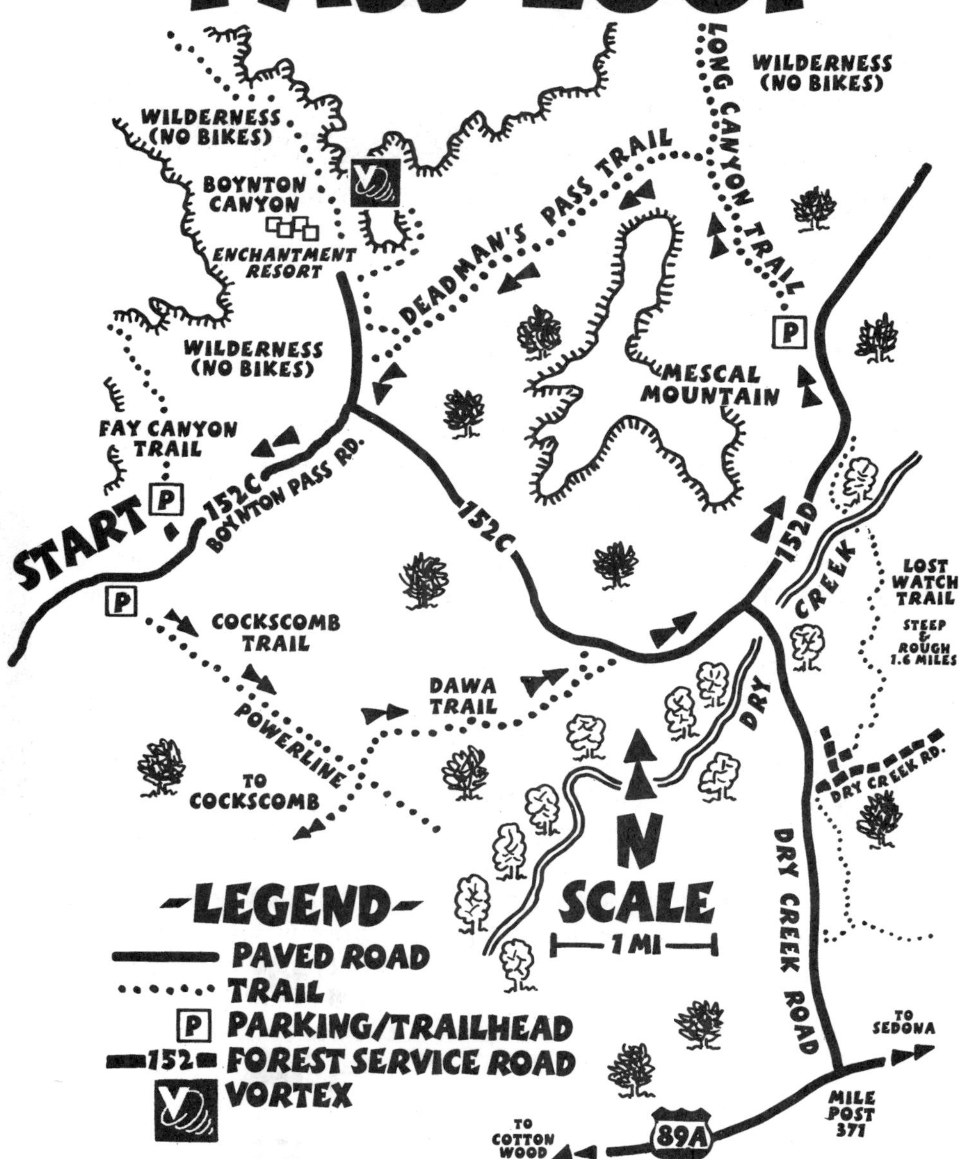

SEDONA

Sedona DEADMAN'S PASS LOOP
QUICK FUN SINGLE TRACK LOOP

DISTANCE: 6.4 MILE LOOP
TIME: 1 HOUR
EFFORT: MODERATE
SKILL: INTERMEDIATE
PUCK-O-METER: PUCK 7
BLIND DITCH AND FAST DESCENTS
FIND ROUTE: JUST A BIT TRICKY AT FIRST
SEASON: SEP to JUN

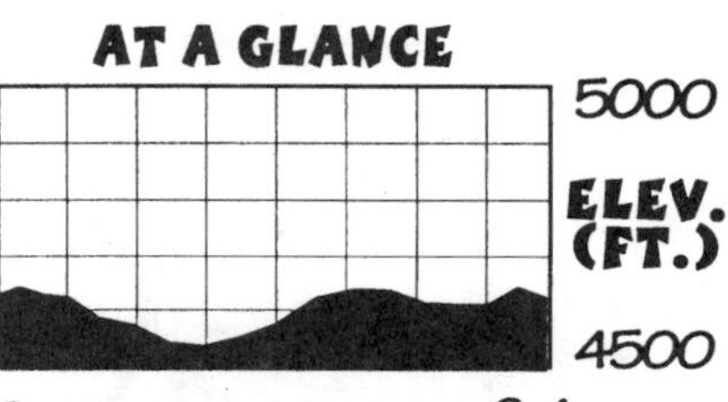

DESCRIPTION: Kicks off with a red dirt, wicked fun single track line down an old powerline 2-track. Lots of rolling drops and dips. Head back up a combination of dirt trail and a short paved bit. Finally, rock and roll down Deadman's Pass Trail behind Mescal Mountain for your daily crazy fun fix. Don't forget to check out Boynton Canyon Vortex. It lives at the foot of Kachina Woman formation at the entrance to Boynton Canyon. See the map. Follow the tourists.

Want more? Deadman's Pass Loop links up nicely with six-mile Cockscomb Loop for a mighty fine figure 8.

MILEAGE LOG

- 0.0 Check out the map and make your way to the START just across from Fay Canyon Trailhead on Boynton Pass Road. The trail begins just across the road from the parking lot. It's not too tricky if you follow the bike tracks.
- 0.3 Follow the powerline Cockscomb Trail downhill.
- 1.1 Go LEFT on Dawa Trail. More rollers and fun stuff while connecting back to paved Boynton Pass Road.
- 2.1 Boynton Pass Road pavement. Go RIGHT.
- 2.7 Continue LEFT onto Long Canyon Road FS 152D.
- 3.3 Long Canyon Trailhead on LEFT. Take it.
- 4.3 LEFT onto signed Deadman's Pass Trail. Hold on!
- 5.7 Pavement. Boynton Canyon Road. See the map. Look for tourists looking for the vortex. Impress them with the knowledge that it resides beneath the Kachina Woman. Now LEFT back to Boynton Pass Road.
- 5.8 Boynton Pass Road. CONTINUE.
- 6.4 Back to go at Fay Canyon/Cockscomb Trailheads parking lots where you began. Flip the page to nearby Cockscomb Loop and give it a go.

DRY CREEK

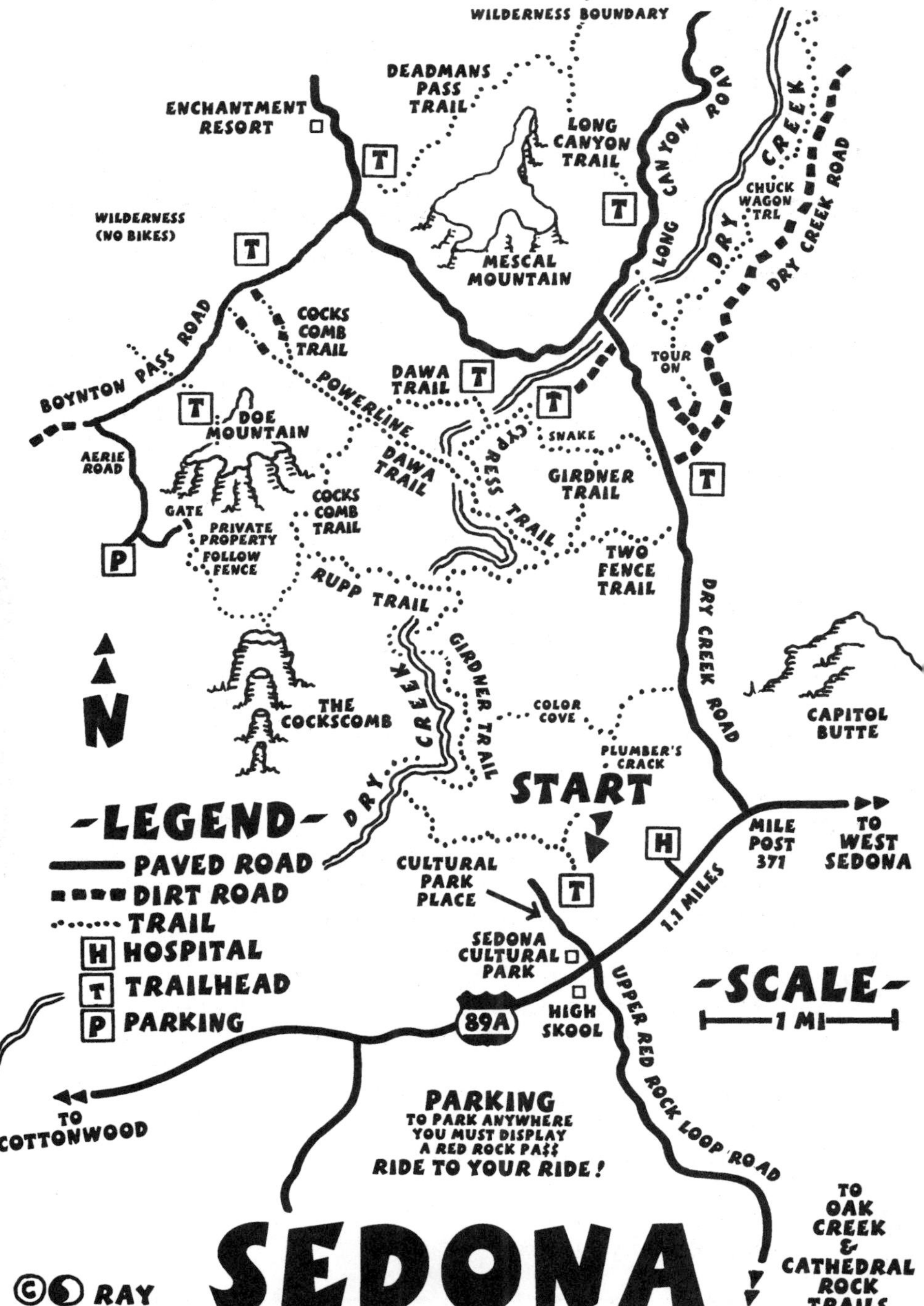

SEDONA

DRY CREEK TRAILS
WEST SEDONA SINGLE TRACK

DISTANCE: 3 TO 10 MILES
TIME: 2 to 3 HOURS
EFFORT: MODERATE
SKILL: INTERMEDIATE
PUCK-O-METER: PUCK 5
NO BIG DROPS, BUT SOME ROUGH STUFF
FIND ROUTE: SOME SIGNS
SEASON: SEP to MAY

AT A GLANCE

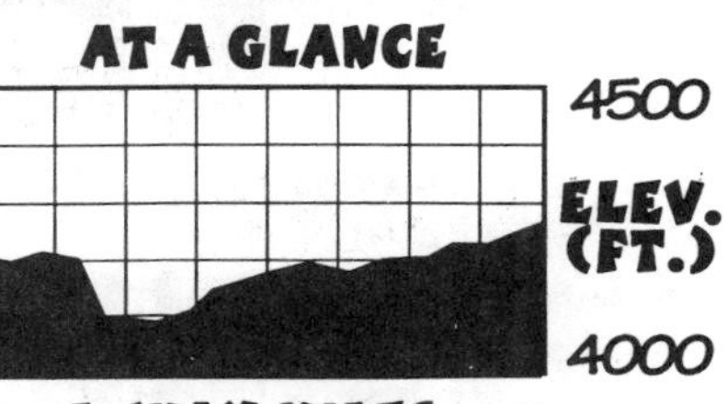

DESCRIPTION: The Forest Service has recently named and signed the maze of trails just west of Dry Creek Road known collectively as Dry Creek Trails. Colorful names like Compactor and Private Idaho have fallen by the wayside in favor of Girdner and Rupp. This is progress? Two-Fence Trail remains, well, Two Fence. Color Cove and Plumber's Crack are unsigned and new non-system trails. Signs are nice, but if you should get lost anyway, look up. Monuments like Cockscomb and Capitol Butte make good landmarks. Dry Creek runs through here at infrequent times, but mostly drier than a popcorn fart. The soil is sandy and granular, especially when you are riding directly *in* Dry Creek Wash, so you never have to worry about mud, even when the rest of Sedona is bogged down in red goo. There is no set route, just a good system of trails to explore. Pick your own route. Besides being a fine beginner ride, Dry Creek Trails serve as alternate access to more well known West Sedona loop trails like The Cockscomb and Deadman's Pass as well as Boynton Pass Road.

DIRECTIONS: There is a new Dry Creek Red Rock Pass Trailhead in West Sedona, but if you do not wish to pay the fee just to park your car, you can ride to the ride. In which case, no permit needed. There is a bike path along HWY 89 from West Sedona to the trailhead turnoff. Go west on Highway 89. Just before you leave Sedona there is one last stoplight at the High School intersection of HWY 89 and Upper Red Rock Loop Road/Cultural Park Place. Go RIGHT into the Sedona Cultural Park and just keep straight ahead. You'll see the parking area/trailhead out back.

"Chaos, panic and disorder. My work here is done."
-I think I said that, but I forget.

HUCKABY LOOP

RAY
©2009

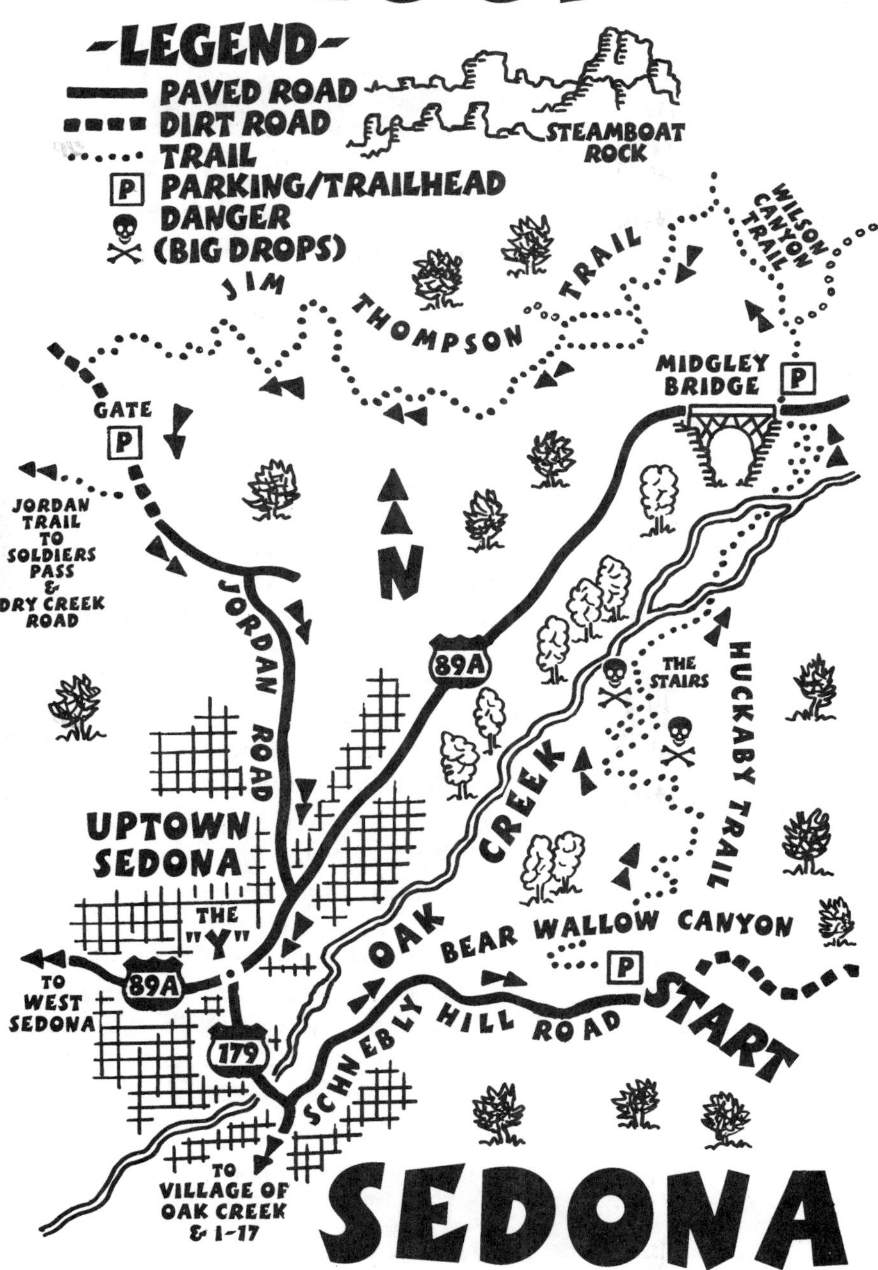

-LEGEND-
PAVED ROAD
DIRT ROAD
TRAIL
P PARKING/TRAILHEAD
DANGER
(BIG DROPS)
STEAMBOAT ROCK
JIM THOMPSON TRAIL
WILSON CANYON TRAIL
MIDGLEY BRIDGE
GATE
JORDAN TRAIL TO SOLDIERS PASS & DRY CREEK ROAD
N
JORDAN ROAD
89A
THE STAIRS
HUCKABY TRAIL
OAK CREEK
UPTOWN SEDONA
THE "Y"
BEAR WALLOW CANYON
TO WEST SEDONA
179
SCHNEBLY HILL ROAD
START
TO VILLAGE OF OAK CREEK & I-17
SEDONA

Sedona HUCKABY TRAIL LOOP

TOUGH SCENIC LOOP ALONG OAK CREEK

DISTANCE: 8.5 MILES
TIME: 1.5 TO 3 HOURS
EFFORT: HARD
SKILL: EXPERT
PUCK-O-METER: PUCK 9
WICKED EXPOSURE, BIG DROPS, STAIRS
FIND ROUTE: SIGNED
SEASON: SEP to JUN

AT A GLANCE

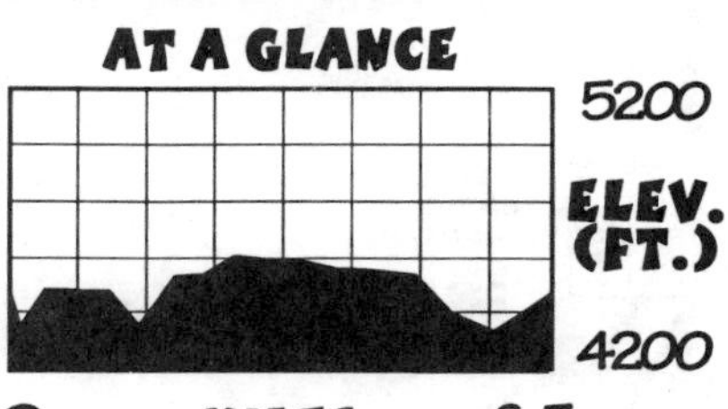

DESCRIPTION: *Very fun from the get-go down rough, winding single track into Bear Wallow Canyon and back up the other side. Follows along above Oak Creek often on cliff's edge. Great views if you dare look. Down the stairs from hell to the creek for a double wet crossing then up to Midgley Bridge. Head up Wilson Canyon Trail and over rough as heck Jim Thompson Trail before downhill finish.*

NOTE: THIS LOOP NOT POSSIBLE DURING HIGH WATER IN OAK CREEK . . . INQUIRE LOCALLY.

MILEAGE LOG

0.0 START at parking lot on left just as paved Schnebly Hill Road turns dirt. Trail begins at lower end of open area below the paved parking lot. Huckaby crosses Bear Wallow Canyon then back up along cliffs above the creek. Beware big drops and The Stairs just before the creek.

1.8 Cross Oak Creek, cross again then climb up steep switchbacks to Midgley Bridge.

2.6 Cross the parking lot and head up Wilson Canyon Trail . Trail crosses dry Wilson Creek and soon meets the sign for Jim Thompson Trail.

3.3 Grind uphill as Jim Thompson single track finds its way leading up through rocky climb.

3.6 Go RIGHT when Jim Thompson meets a short loop.

6.0 LEFT when Jim Thompson meets a gravel road then take pavement through Sedona back to GO.

8.5 Back to go on Schnebly Hill Road.

"If you ride fast and crash, you are a bad rider.
If you ride slow and crash, you are a bad rider.
And if you are a bad rider, you should not ride motorcycles."
-Dr. Hunter S. Thompson

SEDONA

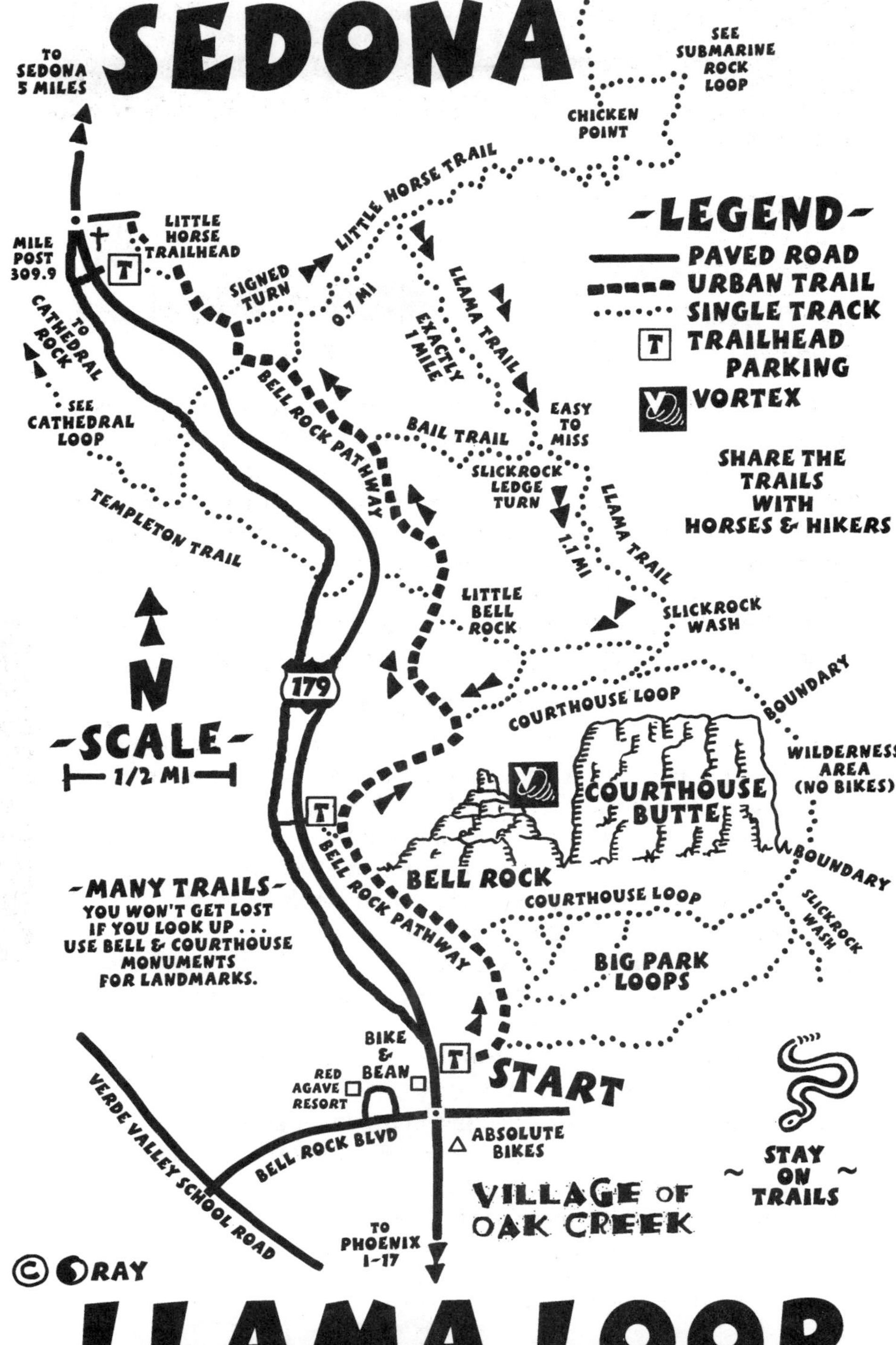

LLAMA LOOP

Sedona LLAMA TRAIL LOOP
WICKED FUN SEDONA SINGLE TRACK

DISTANCE: 8 MILE LOOP
TIME: 2 TO 2.5 HOURS
EFFORT: HARD
SKILL: SERIOUS
PUCK-O-METER: PUCK 8
FIND ROUTE: NOT EASY
(ODOMETER WOULD BE HELPFUL)
SEASON: SEP to JUN

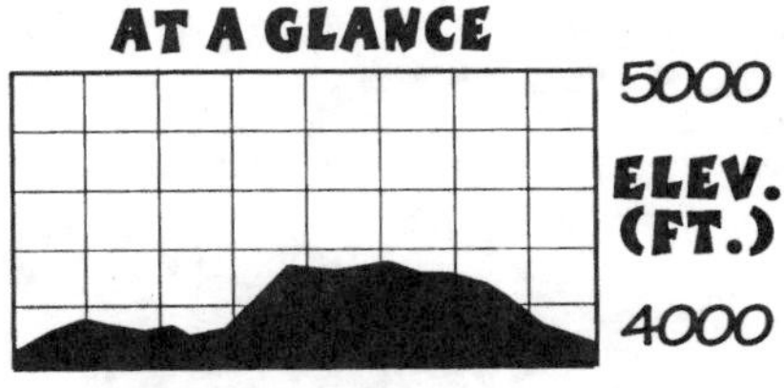

DESCRIPTION: If you could pop Llama Loop into your DVD player, you might term it a "riotous, edgy thriller". Killer views and twisty-fast-then-suddenly-technical single track are its trademark. Carvy slotcar turns become suddenly technical enough to peg the trick-o-meter.

Monuments Bell and Courthouse tower overhead. Catch postcard glimpses of Cathedral Rock, Thumb Butte, Twin Buttes, Rabbit Ears and even Cockscomb's spires way far in the purple distance. You can't get lost if you just look up at the monumental faces of Bell and Courthouse. Learn them. Permanently and indelibly inscribe them upon the fleshy tablets of your memory. You will never be lost again.

Formerly a secret, Llama Trail is now at last a "system" trail. It is just below that magic 4400' elevation contour making it non-wilderness and thus legal for mountain bikes. It is the higher, gnarlier and parallel twin to the weenie Bell Rock Pathway urban trail. Llama separates serious and often high speed, thrill seeker bike traffic from urban trail rookies and tourist foot traffic. It is marked. STAY ON THE TRAIL. Don't be tempted to ride the saddle behind Courthouse. STAY OUT OF THE WILDERNESS. $300 fine for violations!

DIRECTIONS: Take I-17 exit 298 to the Village of Oak Creek. Park in Bell Rock Pathway urban trail lot on HWY 179 next to the Circle K OR you are welcome to park free in one of the bike shop lots. Try easier Bell Rock Loops first. Bell Rock Path is the "launch ramp" to single track on both sides of HWY 179. Llama connects Submarine Rock Loop and Bell Rock/Courthouse Loops bypassing the urban trail. Shred Submarine Rock Loop then tunnel under HWY 179 via Templeton Trail to Cathedral Rock Loop and Buddha Beach. See the map.

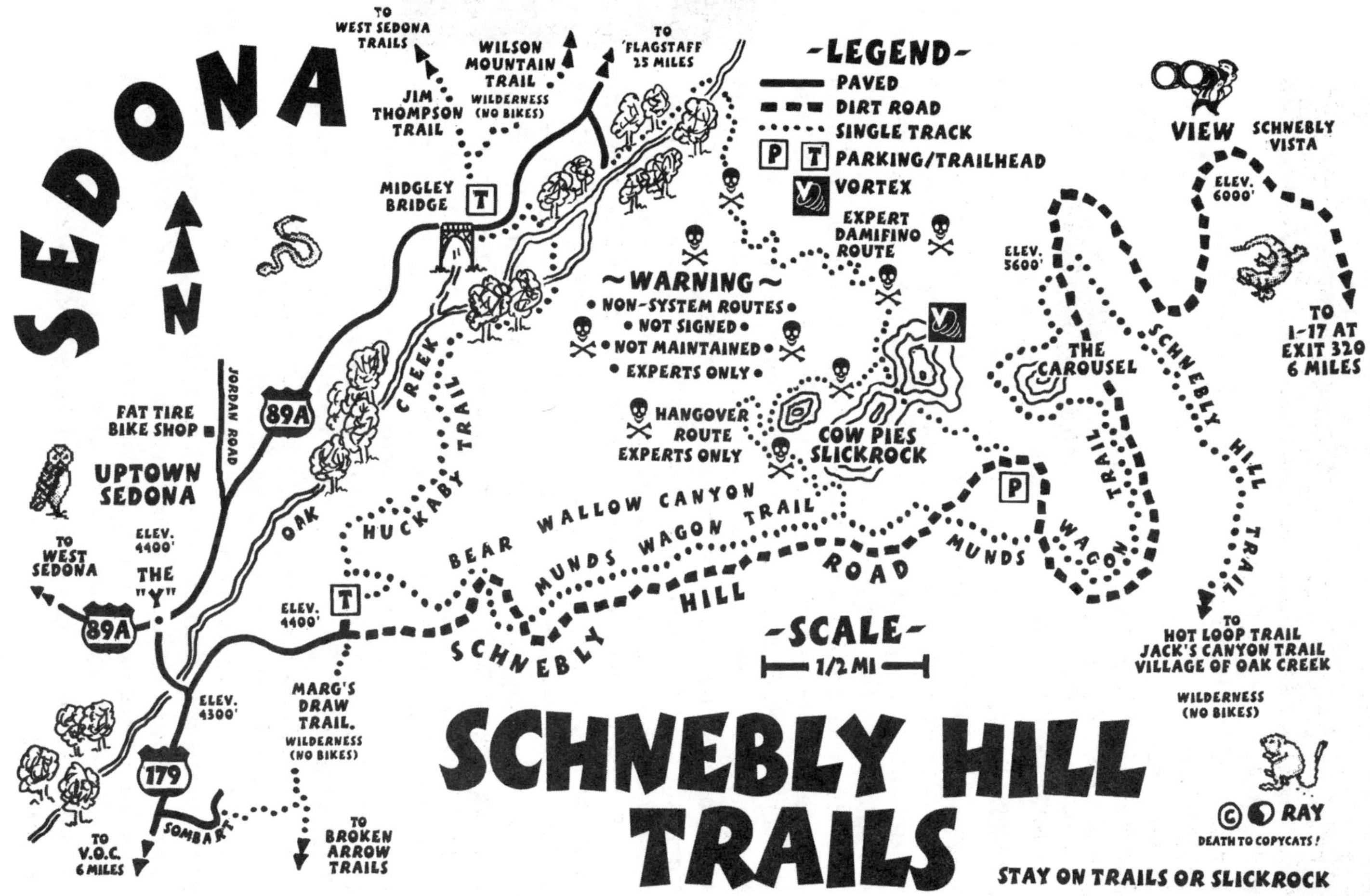
SEDONA
N
SCHNEBLY HILL TRAILS
-LEGEND-
PAVED
DIRT ROAD
SINGLE TRACK
P T PARKING/TRAILHEAD
VORTEX
~WARNING~
• NON-SYSTEM ROUTES •
• NOT SIGNED •
• NOT MAINTAINED •
• EXPERTS ONLY •
TO WEST SEDONA TRAILS
JIM THOMPSON TRAIL
WILSON MOUNTAIN TRAIL
WILDERNESS (NO BIKES)
TO FLAGSTAFF 25 MILES
MIDGLEY BRIDGE
EXPERT DAMIFINO ROUTE
HANGOVER ROUTE EXPERTS ONLY
COW PIES SLICKROCK
THE CAROUSEL
ELEV. 5600'
ELEV. 6000'
VIEW
SCHNEBLY VISTA
TO I-17 AT EXIT 320 6 MILES
SCHNEBLY HILL TRAIL
MUNDS WAGON TRAIL
BEAR WALLOW CANYON TRAIL
MUNDS WAGON TRAIL
SCHNEBLY HILL ROAD
HUCKABY TRAIL
OAK CREEK
JORDAN ROAD
FAT TIRE BIKE SHOP
UPTOWN SEDONA
89A
TO WEST SEDONA
ELEV. 4400'
THE "Y"
ELEV. 4400'
ELEV. 4300'
MARG'S DRAW TRAIL. WILDERNESS (NO BIKES)
179
SOMBART
TO V.O.C. 6 MILES
TO BROKEN ARROW TRAILS
-SCALE-
1/2 MI
TO HOT LOOP TRAIL JACK'S CANYON TRAIL VILLAGE OF OAK CREEK
WILDERNESS (NO BIKES)
© RAY
DEATH TO COPYCATS!
STAY ON TRAILS OR SLICKROCK

Sedona SCHNEBLY HILL TRAILS
RIP & RAIL A HUGE 1-TRACK DESCENT

DISTANCE: 8 PLUS MILES
TIME: 2 TO 3 HOURS
EFFORT: A GOOD SWEAT
STEADY & NOT TOO STEEP CLIMBS
SKILL: INTERMEDIATE
IF YOU WALK THE BIG DROP SCARY STUFF
PUCK-O-METER: PUCK 8
EDGY FAST DESCENTS & BIG DROPS
FIND ROUTE: EASY
SEASON: SEP to JUN

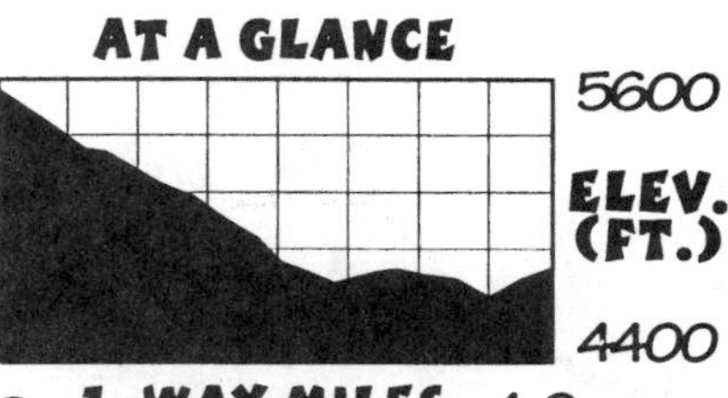

DESCRIPTION: Descending is a perilous, delirious drop into a kodachrome fantasy world of monuments, spires, hoodoos, carousels and slickrock vortices. Views are Sedona exquisite extraordinare. The hand made trail is ace perfect brilliant where the climbs are all do-able and you can remain every-hair-in-place good looking all the way up.

Munds Wagon Trail follows along Schnebly Hill Road up 4 miles and 1200 feet elevation gain. The mostly small ring ascent takes about an hour, although it gets to be a bit of a smackdown on a single speed near the top.

The climb features a twisting route up through a verdant redrock wash, sheer drops around a fantasy carousel of humongo redrock hoodoos, a slickrock detour to a vortex site and ends with a view to a thrill. Yowza! Or try the new sick, sick, sick (but legal) descent down outlaw Damifino. See map.

DIRECTIONS: Start at the tourist trailhead just where Schnebly Hill Road turns dirt. Pay $5 to park or beat the fee, park in town and ride to the ride. Builds character!

SECRET TRAILS

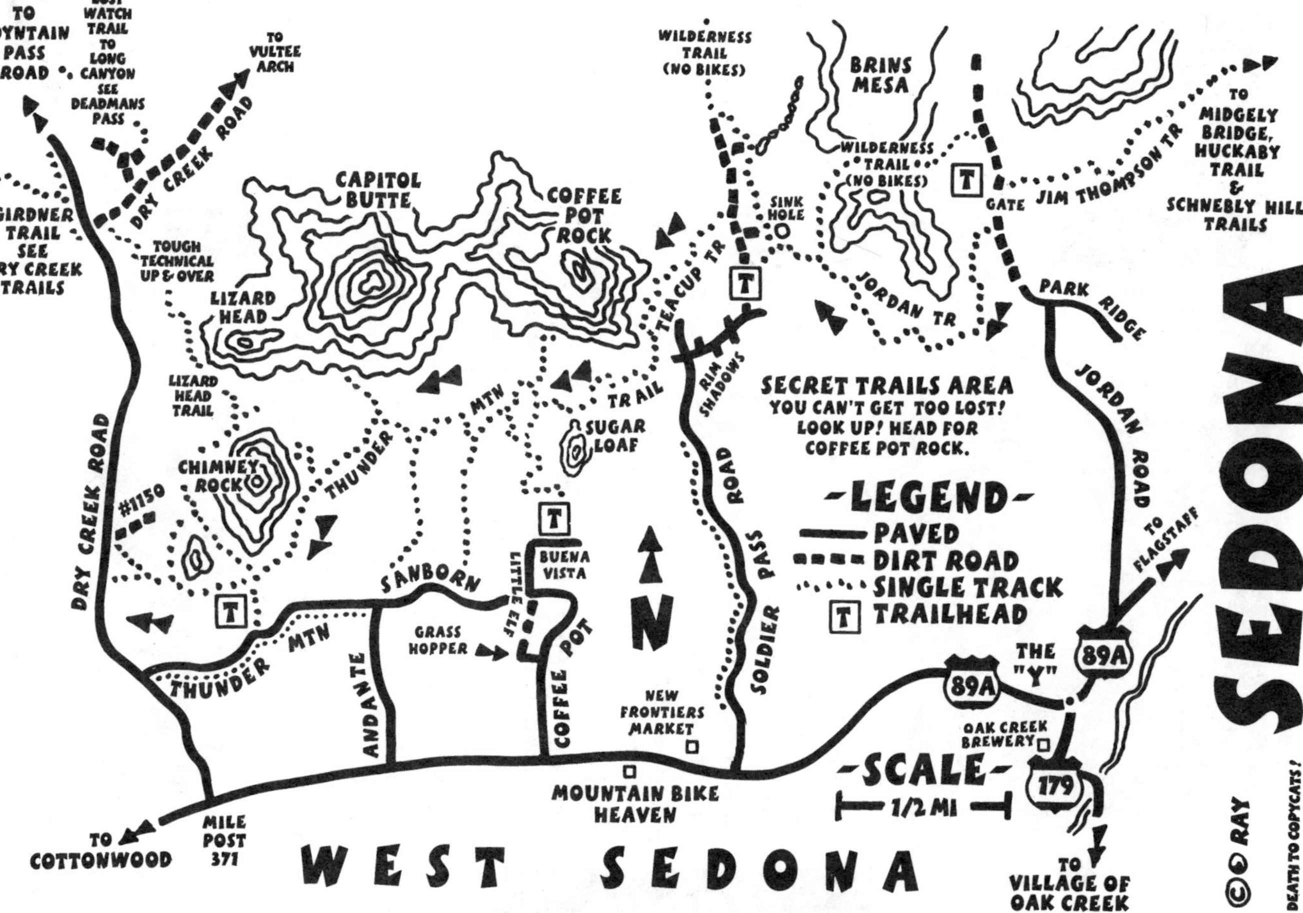

SEDONA

Sedona SECRET TRAILS
WAY FUN HIDDEN SINGLE TRACK

DISTANCE: 10 PLUS MILES
TIME: 2 to 3 HOURS
EFFORT: TOUGH
SKILL: ADVANCED
PUCK-O-METER: PUCK 8
SOME EXPOSURE AND BIG DROPS
ROUTE: MOST SIGNED
SEASON: SEP to JUN

DESCRIPTION: A helter-skelter welter of single-track trails are linked, signed and cairned to connect all the way across North Sedona from Schnebly Hill Road to Dry Creek Rd. From the Schnebly Hill Trailhead (see Schnebley Hill map), Huckaby Trail hugs along a cliff, dives down a wicked skinny single track with a big-drop set of stairs near the bottom, crosses Oak Creek via a foot bridge and back up to 89A at Midgley Bridge. There you connect with Jim Thompson Trail to climb over Uptown Sedona. If the set of stairs appears to be out of your league, they are walkable. Live to ride another day . . . or not. See "Huckaby Trail" for map details.

Next, Jordan Trail's excellent challenging single-track roller coasters along the base of Brin's Mesa then flushes you out at a deep sinkhole (Don't fall in!) in Devils Kitchen where you find signs to Teacup Trail just under Coffee Pot Rock.

If you crave exposure to ledge death risk, Teacup Trail will be just your cup of tea. Later, up on top where Teacup leads, you'll spy a power line and follow it to Chimney Rock as you hit Thunder Mountain Trail which dumps you out on paved Dry Creek Road. Pick up Lizard Head Trail (see map) and head to Long Canyon for Deadman's Pass Trail. See "Deadman's Pass" and "Cockscomb Loop". Or you can just hop across Dry Creek Road and jump a few more pages to sample all the "Dry Creek Trails".

Many trails are signed and often marked with cairns, but not always. There are trails everywhere, so stay on trail. LOOK UP! Stay un-lost Sedona style. Eyeball monuments, especially Coffee Pot Rock, Capitol Butte and Chimney Rock to keep your bearings.

SUBMARINE ROCK LOOP
-LEGEND-
PAVED ROAD
JEEP ROAD
SINGLE TRACK
CAIRNS
TRAILHEAD/ PARKING
~ WARNING ~
• ROUTES ARE NON-SYSTEM •
• NOT SIGNED •
• STEEP & ROUGH •
• EXPERT ONLY •
TO FLAGSTAFF
THE "Y"
89A
89A
TO WEST SEDONA
OAK CREEK
179
N
SCALE
1/2 MI
MORGAN ROAD
START
WILDERNESS BOUNDARY
SLICK ROCK
(EXPERT) HOG WASH ROUTE
PIG TAIL ROUTE
MYSTIC TRAIL
BATTLEMENT MESA
SINK HOLE
SLICK ROCK
GREEN BOX
179
STAY ~ ON ~ TRAILS
HOG HEAVEN ROUTE (EXPERT)
THE STAIRS
CHAPEL
SUBMARINE ROCK
CHAPEL ROAD
SLICK ROCK
SLICK ROCK
ANTELOPE
TWIN BUTTES
EASIER ROUTE
SHIRLEY
BADGER
LYNX
BACK O' BEYOND
CHAPEL TRAIL
INDIAN CLIFFS
WILDERNESS BOUNDARY
LITTLE HORSE TRAIL (MR. TOAD'S WILD RIDE) 2.0 MILES
NUNS
CHICKEN PT.
BELL ROCK PATHWAY
0.8 MI.
LLAMA TRAIL TO COURTHOUSE LOOP 2.3 MILES
TO VILLAGE OF OAK CREEK & I-17
TO BELL ROCK 3 MILES
SEDONA
©
RAY

SUBMARINE ROCK LOOP
SEDONA'S PREMIER SHRED

DISTANCE: 10 MILE LOOP
TIME: 2 to 3 HOURS
EFFORT: HARD WORK
SKILL: EXPERT
PUCK-O-METER: PUCK 9
SPEED, BIG DROPS AND "THE STAIRS"
FIND ROUTE: MODERATE
SEASON: SEP to MAY

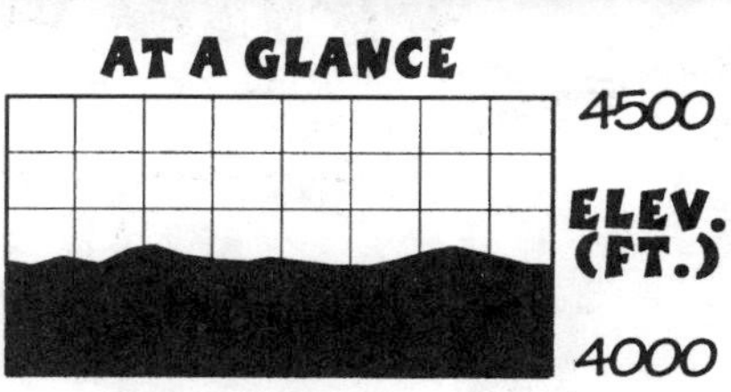

PRIMO TRAIL WORTH A JOURNEY

DESCRIPTION: The most bang for your Sedona biking buck. Slickrock, single track, stairs and even a Mr. Toad's wild ride. Danger lurks around every turn in the trail. If you've got time for just one Sedona ride, this is it.

The basic loop begins with a rough jeep road at the end of Morgan Road. See the map. Across the road from the parking area is a well marked, way fun Broken Arrow Trail single track following a higher and tougher route to Chicken Point. Be sure to visit the Devil's Kitchen sinkhole, The Stairs, and of course, Submarine Rock. Be polite to all Pink Jeeps.

Eventually you wind up at Chicken Point. From Chicken, back up 50 feet and you'll find the hidden single track down to Little Horse Trail. This 2 mile stretch is called Mr. Toad's Wild Ride and is well marked with giant bomber cairns, a.k.a. rocks in a basket. Watch out for steep drops as this little beauty screams and careens downhill almost all the way.

OPTIONS: 0.8 miles after you leave Chicken Point, signed, well worn and legal Llama Trail veers off toward Courthouse Butte. You can continue following the map to finish the *Submarine Rock Loop* or go LEFT on Llama Trail to *Courthouse Loop Trail* and connect with *Cathedral Rock Loop.* (See the Cathedral Loop Map.)

DIRECTIONS: Drive HWY 179 or ride the Bell Rock Pathway to the Morgan Road start. Morgan Road is easy to find on HWY 179 at milepost 312.1. If the Morgan Road lot is full, park and start at Little Horse trailhead at milepost 309.9.

"Don't take life seriously or you won't get out alive, Doc."
-Bugs Bunny

50 YEAR TRAIL (THE CHUTES)

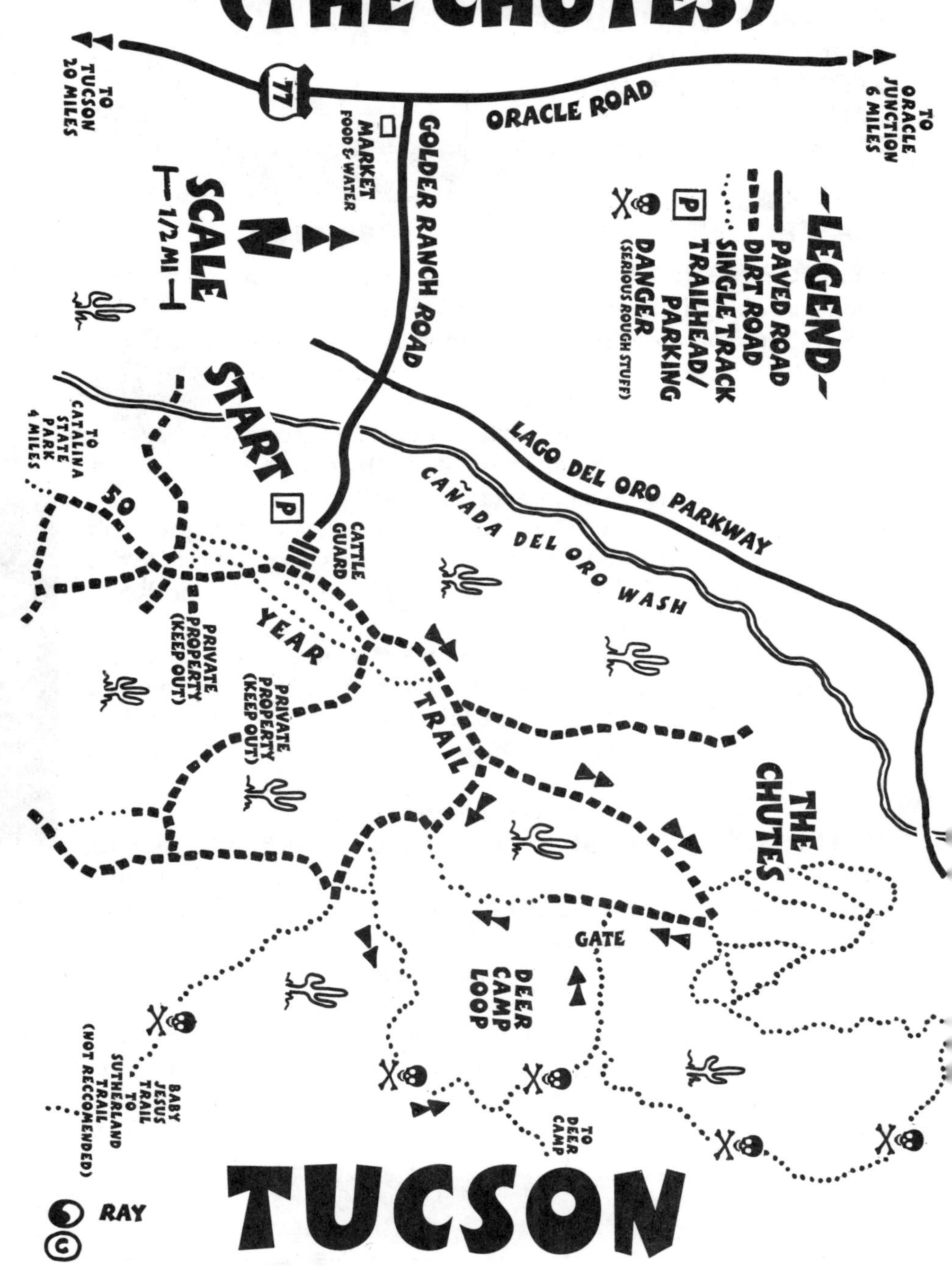

Tucson **50 YEAR TRAIL**
EXCELLENT CHUTES & SINGLE TRACK

DISTANCE: 10 MILES PLUS
TIME: 2 TO 3 HOURS
EFFORT: A GOOD SWEAT
SKILL: INTERMEDIATE TO ADVANCED
PUCK-O-METER: PUCK 7
SPEED THRU TECHNICAL SECTIONS
FIND ROUTE: MODERATE
SEASON: SEP to JUN

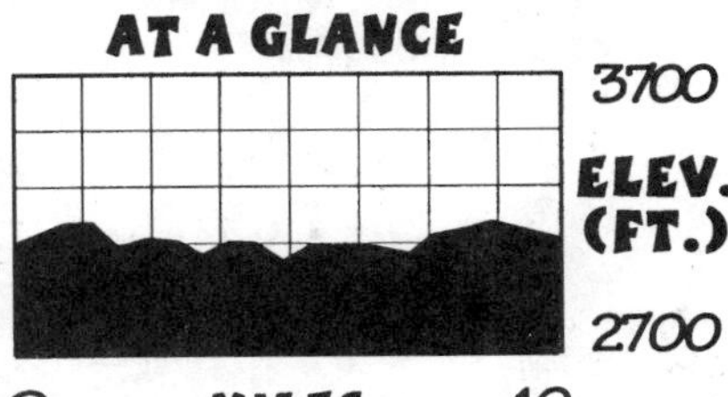

PRIMO TRAIL
WORTH A JOURNEY

DESCRIPTION: Rolling single track horse trails and jeep roads run amuck all over this prime Sonoran Desert in the western foothills of the Santa Catalina Mountains just north of Tucson. The trails roll, climb, shred, rip, jump, twist and shout through a scatter of saguaro standing tall amid lush desert vegetation. Best in cool months when everything is green and creeks are running, but good all year except in the heat of a summer afternoon. Ride early morning then.

Twist up some good loops from the map. Near the mountains to the east, the terrain gets tougher and rougher. DO NOT MISS THE CHUTES . . . a cactus lined roller coaster of twisty-turny trails that'll make you holler.

DIRECTIONS: Head due north out of Tucson on State Highway Route 77 (Oracle Road) toward Oracle Junction. It's about 20miles to the Golder Ranch Road turn. There is a mini-mart on the corner to load up on pop-tarts (just kidding!) before you hit the trail. Go to the end of Golder Ranch to where it turns dirt. Park in the lot. Get on your bike, cross the cattleguard and get on the singletrack heading north. Follow "50 YEAR TRAIL" signs, consult the map from time to time and not to worry about getting lost. The Catalinas are always overhead to the east.

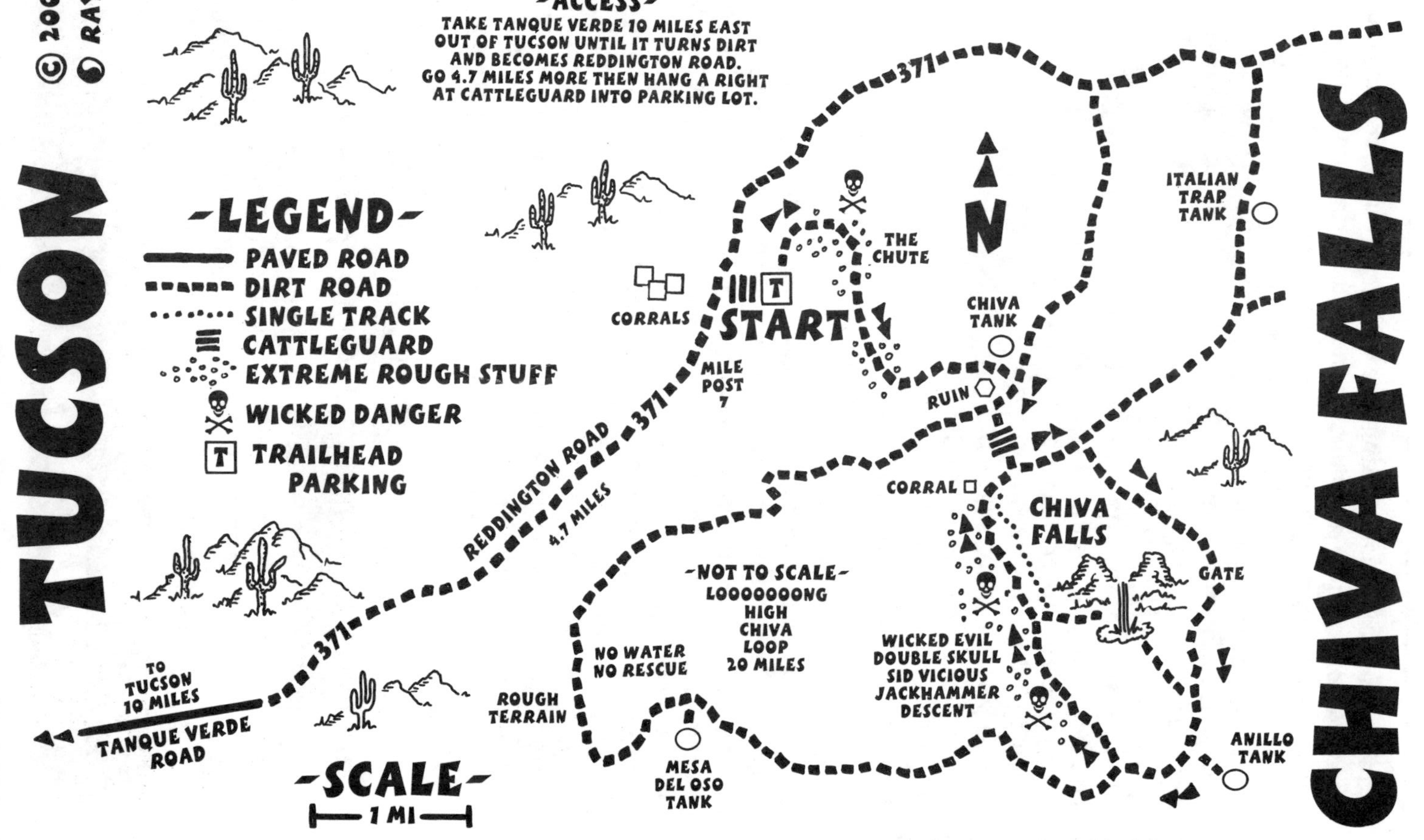

© 2003
RAY
-ACCESS-
TAKE TANQUE VERDE 10 MILES EAST OUT OF TUCSON UNTIL IT TURNS DIRT AND BECOMES REDDINGTON ROAD. GO 4.7 MILES MORE THEN HANG A RIGHT AT CATTLEGUARD INTO PARKING LOT.
TUCSON
-LEGEND-
PAVED ROAD
DIRT ROAD
SINGLE TRACK
CATTLEGUARD
EXTREME ROUGH STUFF
WICKED DANGER
T TRAILHEAD PARKING
371
CORRALS
START
MILE POST 7
THE CHUTE
N
ITALIAN TRAP TANK
CHIVA TANK
RUIN
REDDINGTON ROAD
4.7 MILES
371
CORRAL
CHIVA FALLS
GATE
-NOT TO SCALE-
LOOOOOOONG HIGH CHIVA LOOP 20 MILES
NO WATER NO RESCUE
WICKED EVIL DOUBLE SKULL SID VICIOUS JACKHAMMER DESCENT
371
TO TUCSON 10 MILES
TANQUE VERDE ROAD
ROUGH TERRAIN
MESA DEL OSO TANK
ANILLO TANK
-SCALE-
1 MI
CHIVA FALLS

Tucson CHIVA FALLS
TOUGH 2-TRACK TO A BRIDAL VEIL

DISTANCE: 8.4 MILES
TIME: 3 HOURS
EFFORT: TOUGH
SKILL: EXPERT
PUCK-O-METER: PUCK 9
RAPID JACKHAMMER DESCENTS
FIND ROUTE: MODERATE
SEASON: SEP to MAY

DESCRIPTION: Chiva runs late fall to spring. Perfect spot to dip your buns on a hot day. The falls cascade 60ft.to a pool 3ft. deep and 50 ft. wide set in a verdant stone grotto. The Rincons are overhead south. There is a simple out n' back, a favorite high loop above the falls or a veeery long version. All are rough 2-track with double skull Sid Viscous descents. Carry water and munchies.

OUT AND BACK TO CHIVA

0.0 START (see map) east end of parking lot and head down the ultra rough 2-track.
2.6 RIGHT at "T" junction just past Chiva Tank.
3.4 Veer LEFT over cattleguard.
3.5 RIGHT at junction.
3.7 Wash crossings then a single track heading up.
4.0 LEFT at fork. Continue 0.2 miles to the falls.
8.4 Return to GO all shook up!

HIGH CHIVA LOOP

DESCRIPTION: Best loop in the Rincons. Same start as out n' back, but after cattleguard turn LEFT at next junction. 0.4 miles later a faint 2-track heads uphill to the RIGHT. 1.8 miles later cross Chiva Creek above the falls. Great for exploring, lots of pools and a good spot for lunch. A mile after you leave Chiva Creek make a RIGHT at a junction that takes you down ☠heinous descent☠ to Chiva. It's a 12 mile total loop. **TOUGH OPTION:** If you go LEFT at that same junction you are on the Long High Loop. Make sure you have plenty of food, water and daylight. It's a looong 20 mile loop even for fit expert riders.

BROADWAY

TO DOWNTOWN TUCSON 8 MILES

HARRISON

2 MILES

START

-SCALE-

1/4 MI

PERMIT INFO
TUCSON AREA
STATE TRUST LAND
(520) 628-5480

HOUGHTON

IRVINGTON

ONE WAY

ONE WAY

OVER/UNDER (DUCK OR DIE)

ONE WAY

PIT LOOP

BO'S LOOP

BURRO

LONE

CACTUS

HALF PIPE

LOOP

ONE WAY

ONE WAY

ONE WAY

ONE WAY

N

XMAS TREE LOOP

-LEGEND-

PAVED STREET

SINGLE TRACK

TRAILHEAD/ PARKING

DANGER

(BIG DROP, DEEP WASH, BIG LEAP, ETC.)

ONE WAY

ONE WAY

ONE WAY

FANTASY ISLAND

TO VALENCIA

FROM VALENCIA

TUCSON

Tucson FANTASY ISLAND LOOPS
SINGLE TRACK, SCENERY & A HALF PIPE

DISTANCE: 5 TO 18 MILES
TIME: 2 TO ??? HOURS
EFFORT: EASY, BUT . . .
(GO FASTER, WORK HARDER!)
SKILL: ALL LEVELS
PUCK-O-METER: PUCK 6
(SOME PUCK 10 STUFF TOO!)
FIND ROUTE: SIGNED
(FOLLOW THE ONE WAY LOOPS)
SEASON: SEP TO MAY

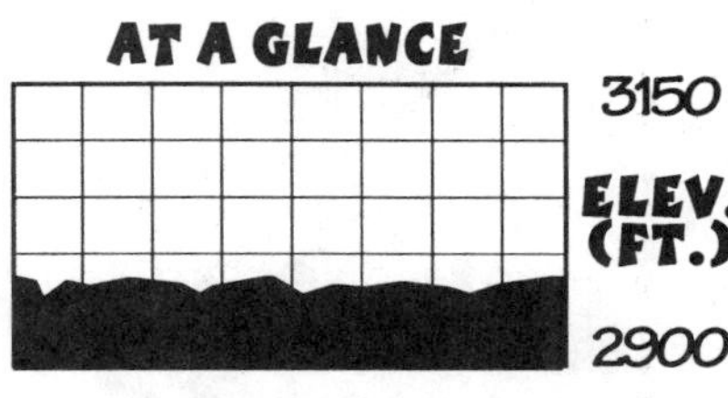

PRIMO TRAIL
WORTH A JOURNEY

DESCRIPTION: Picture pee-wee golf, chutes & ladders, twisting single track, big drops, a do-or-die-duck-your-head under a low bridge and a rock 'n roll half-pipe. There is no destination on this trail. The destination *IS* the trail. The best desert rolling single track you will ever ride. Perfect for all levels. Speed as fast as you dare through the half pipe. Look out for big drops. The trail is a well marked, worn in, winding snake loop that never crosses itself. Ideal for single speeds, no big climbs, tight and twisty, all right turns. You will not get lost. COUNTER-CLOCKWISE ONLY.

This is an ingenious bit of the master trail builders' art making the most of a small pristine plot of giant saguaro Sonoran desert. Fantasy Island Loop is on a less than 3 square mile hunk of State Trust Land. The basic loop has a half-pipe, lots of twisties, switchbacks and some big drops. Out on the extra new bonus loops you're gonna find more of the same with some great do-or-die heart stoppers.

Support cooperation between the State Land Dept. and the Tucson mountain bike community. Permits are $15/year, good on any trust land in AZ. Get them from the state land office, 223 N. Main, Tucson (520-628-5480) or at Broadway Bicycles, Lone Cactus Bicycles or Sabino Bicycles. Worth every penny.

DIRECTIONS: From downtown Tucson go 8 miles east on Broadway to Harrison Road. Turn RIGHT on Harrison then go another 2 miles to Irvington and park at the gate. Crowded weekends and other times.

"Life is a daring adventure or nothing at all."
- mountain bike wisdom

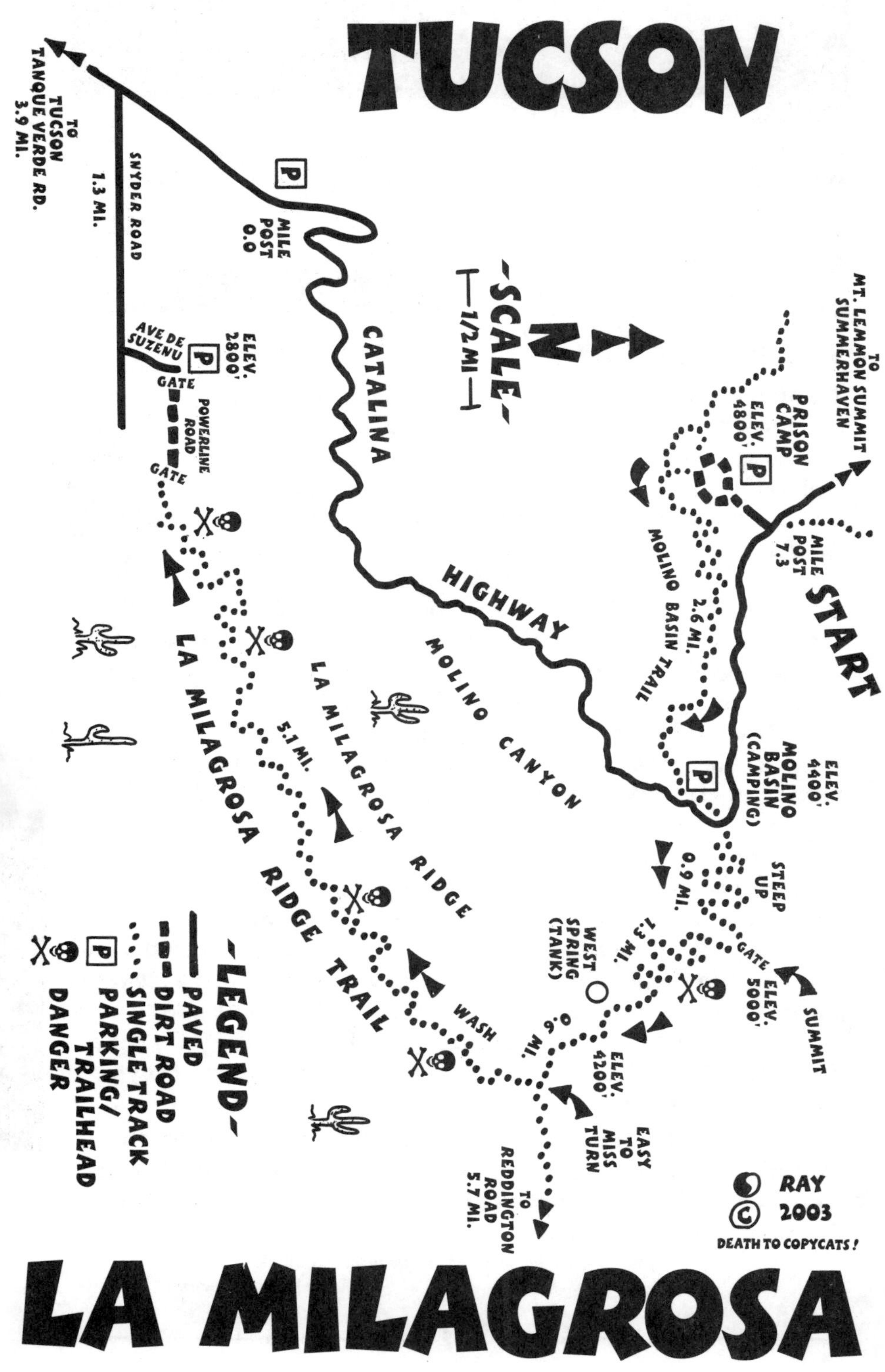

TUCSON

TO MT. LEMMON SUMMIT SUMMERHAVEN

PRISON CAMP

ELEV. 4800'

MILE POST 7.3

START

MOLINO BASIN TRAIL

2.6 MI.

ELEV. 4400'

MOLINO BASIN (CAMPING)

STEEP UP

0.9 MI.

GATE

ELEV. 5000'

SUMMIT

1.3 MI.

WEST SPRING (TANK)

0.6 MI.

ELEV. 4200'

EASY TO MISS TURN

TO REDDINGTON ROAD 5.7 MI.

WASH

MOLINO CANYON

HIGHWAY

CATALINA

-SCALE-

1/2 MI

N

MILE POST 0.0

TO TUCSON TANQUE VERDE RD. 3.9 MI.

1.3 MI.

SNYDER ROAD

AVE DE SUZENU

ELEV. 2800'

GATE

POWERLINE ROAD

GATE

LA MILAGROSA RIDGE

5.1 MI.

LA MILAGROSA RIDGE TRAIL

-LEGEND-

PAVED

DIRT ROAD

SINGLE TRACK

PARKING/ TRAILHEAD

DANGER

RAY

© 2003

DEATH TO COPYCATS!

LA MILAGROSA

Tucson ☠ LA MILAGROSA ☠
FULL COMBAT SINGLE TRACK DESCENT

DISTANCE: 10.5 MILES
TIME: 3 to 4 HOURS
EFFORT: SEMI-TOUGH
SKILL: XXX EVIL EXPERT
PUCK-O-METER: PUCK 10
TWO BLOODBATH-POSSIBLE DESCENTS
FIND ROUTE: MODERATE
SEASON: SEP to MAY

AT A GLANCE

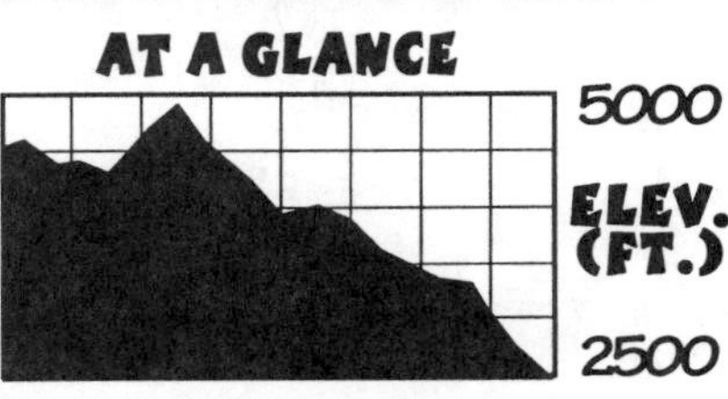

DESCRIPTION: "Built by cows, for cows!" If the sight of your own blood makes you queasy, you best stay safe at home. The number and variety of cacti combined with big drops down narrow chutes almost guarantee some sort of out of body experience. La Milagrosa (The Miracle) Trail is no more than a rut down a saguaro infested ridge on the lower flanks of Tucson rockpile, Mt. Lemmon. My own *satori* came as a heated brawl with a cat's claw whilst dodging boulders. *OW! CURSES!* Then more *CURSES!* Then blood. This might be just your cup of tea. Bring the head and body armor.

MILEAGE LOG

0.0 BEGIN at Prison Honor Camp at milepost 7.3 on Catalina Highway. Molino Basin Trail begins at the end of the parking lot. Fire damage to this trail has been repaired. Nice fast and tough warm up.

2.6 Molino Basin Campground. Cross the road and begin the way steep climb. It's about 60% do-able by most humans or just about a 1/2 hour walk to the top.

3.5 Summit. Dig the view then continue. Muy dangeroso.

4.8 West Spring. Solar powered water tank. Cool.

5.4 Pay attention. Easy-to-miss trail on RIGHT. May or may not be marked with rocks. Heads through brush then a wash as you begin Milagrosa Ridge Trail.

10.5 If you survive, congrats. If not, too bad, so sad.

DIRECTIONS: From downtown, go all the way east out Grant. Go LEFT on Tanque Verde then another LEFT on Catalina Highway. Park near Snyder Road to ride, hitch or shuttle up. I found it to be an easy hitch up to Prison Camp. Yummy-yum apres shred java and snackage at *Le Buzz* next to Safeway at Tanque Verde and Catalina.

TUCSON

MOLINO BASIN

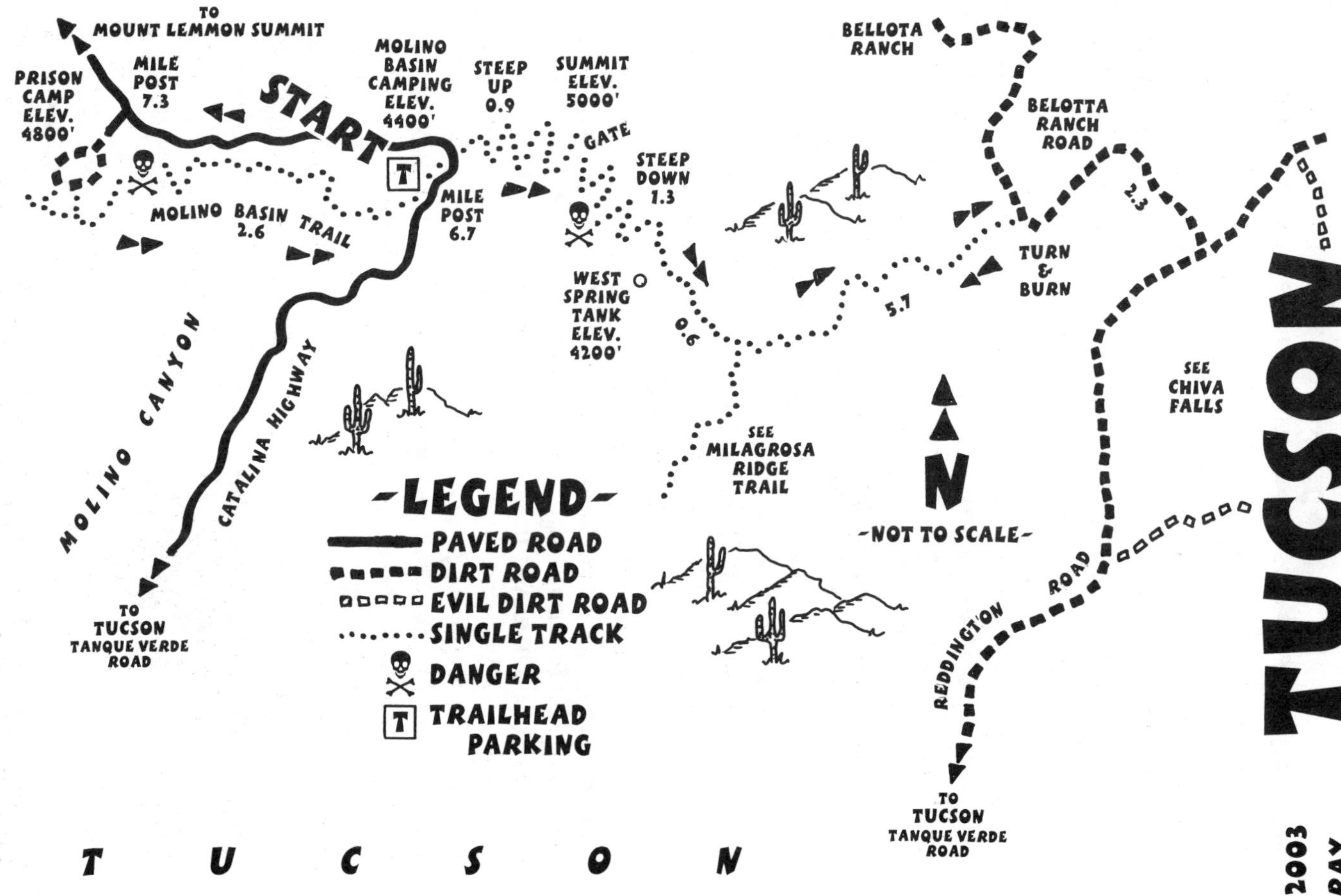

TO MOUNT LEMMON SUMMIT
PRISON CAMP ELEV. 4800'
MILE POST 7.3
START
MOLINO BASIN CAMPING ELEV. 4400'
STEEP UP 0.9
SUMMIT ELEV. 5000'
GATE
STEEP DOWN 1.3
MOLINO BASIN TRAIL 2.6
MILE POST 6.7
WEST SPRING TANK ELEV. 4200'
0.6
BELLOTA RANCH
BELOTTA RANCH ROAD
2.3
TURN & BURN
5.7
MOLINO CANYON
CATALINA HIGHWAY
SEE MILAGROSA RIDGE TRAIL
SEE CHIVA FALLS
N
-NOT TO SCALE-
-LEGEND-
PAVED ROAD
DIRT ROAD
EVIL DIRT ROAD
SINGLE TRACK
DANGER
TRAILHEAD PARKING
TO TUCSON TANQUE VERDE ROAD
REDDINGTON ROAD
TO TUCSON TANQUE VERDE ROAD
T U C S O N
TUCSON

Tucson **MOLINO BASIN**
GREAT SINGLE TRACK OUT AND BACK

DISTANCE: 12.4 MILES
TIME: 3 HOURS
EFFORT: TOUGH
SKILL: ADVANCED
PUCK-O-METER: PUCK 8
STEEP TWISTING DESCENT
FIND ROUTE: EASY
SEASON: OCT to MAY

AT A GLANCE

DESCRIPTION: Starts out as a way steep single track leads up over a pass out of Molino Basin followed by a monster steep technical single track down the other side. Feels like a lifetime, but it's only been 2 miles, under and hour and the best is yet to come. Next, a quick rolling 1-track leads you another 4 miles all the way to Bellota Ranch Road where you turn about and return. Molino trail's fire damage is repaired.

MILEAGE LOG

0.0 START at Molino Basin Campground parking lot at mile 6.7 on Catalina Hiway heading up Mt. Lemmon out of Tucson. The steep technical 1-track climb begins through a row of boulders across the road.

0.9 SUMMIT. Views into Molino Basin and out to the Rincons. HEAD DOWN other side to West Spring.

2.1 WEST SPRING. You came this far, might as well go on for a great 1-track to Bellota Ranch Road.

6.2 BELLOTA RANCH RD. Good spot to turn n' burn OR continue RIGHT 2.3 miles to Reddington Road and meet a support for a 1-way ride. Bellota Ranch meets Reddington on left at mile 7.4 on Reddington.

12.4 Back to GO. if you rode the pass twice, I'm with you. We don't need no stinking cars!

OPTIONS: Employ a shuttle on Reddington Road and make this a moderate 1-way ride OR maybe START at the other end on Reddington for just the easy 1-track. Thank explorer Jim Porter for his pioneer work on Molino Basin.

'It ain't the 'untin' as 'urts 'im.
It's the 'ammer, 'ammer, 'ammer on the 'ard 'igh road."
- Punch, 1856

TUCSON

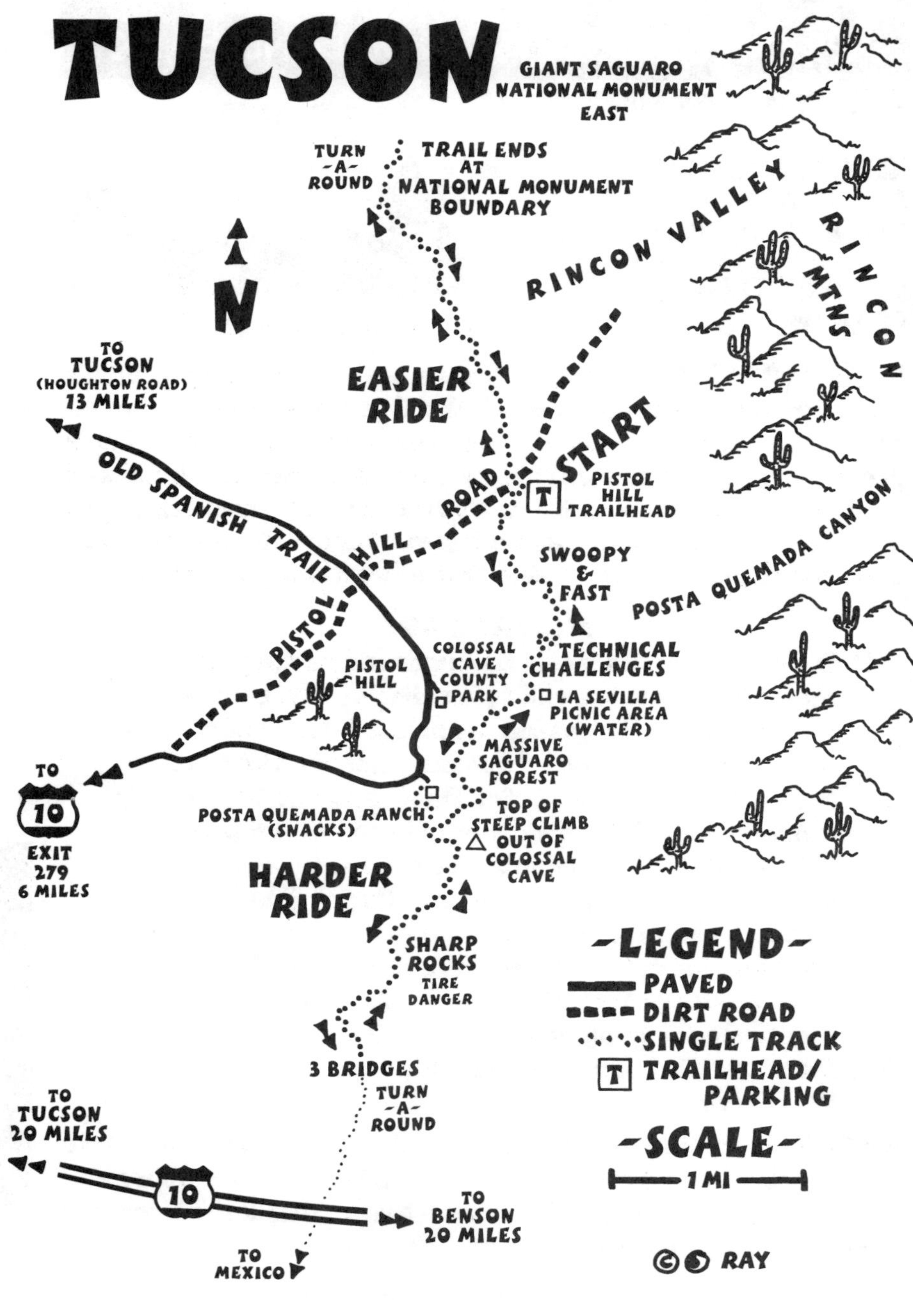

GIANT SAGUARO
NATIONAL MONUMENT
EAST
TURN -A- ROUND
TRAIL ENDS AT NATIONAL MONUMENT BOUNDARY
RINCON VALLEY
RINCON MTNS
N
TO TUCSON (HOUGHTON ROAD) 13 MILES
EASIER RIDE
START
PISTOL HILL TRAILHEAD
OLD SPANISH TRAIL
PISTOL HILL ROAD
SWOOPY & FAST
POSTA QUEMADA CANYON
TECHNICAL CHALLENGES
COLOSSAL CAVE COUNTY PARK
PISTOL HILL
LA SEVILLA PICNIC AREA (WATER)
MASSIVE SAGUARO FOREST
TO 10 EXIT 279 6 MILES
POSTA QUEMADA RANCH (SNACKS)
TOP OF STEEP CLIMB OUT OF COLOSSAL CAVE
HARDER RIDE
SHARP ROCKS
TIRE DANGER
-LEGEND-
PAVED
DIRT ROAD
SINGLE TRACK
TRAILHEAD/ PARKING
3 BRIDGES
TURN -A- ROUND
TO TUCSON 20 MILES
-SCALE-
1 MI
10
TO BENSON 20 MILES
TO MEXICO
©© RAY

PISTOL HILL

Tucson PISTOL HILL
ARIZONA TRAIL: SINGLE TRACK & SAGUARO

DISTANCE: 19 MILES
TIME: 2 TO ??? HOURS
EFFORT: STRONG & SWEET
(ONE BIG CLIMB AT THE END!)
SKILL: STRONG INTERMEDIATE
PUCK-O-METER: PUCK 6
(ONE AREA OF *SHARP* LIMESTONE!)
FIND ROUTE: FAIRLY EASY
SEASON: OCT TO MAY

AT A GLANCE

3500

ELEV. (FT.)

3000

0 **OUT & BACK** 19

PRIMO TRAIL
WORTH A JOURNEY

DESCRIPTION: This single track epic is as good as it gets . . . continuously challenging, but never overwhelming. Start at Pistol Hill Trailhead and roll SOUTH along the base of The Rincon Mountains to La Sevilla picnic area and more water. Pick up the trail in a shady spot on the other side.

Pass Colossal Cave and Posta Quemada Ranch and get ready for the only big climb . . . a steady single-track with killer views and zero shade. After the top, careful as you roll through a couple of miles of really sharp limestone which can slice a tire or your calf with equal aplomb. Bring extra tubes, first aid kit, duct tape for tire patches . . . get it? From there it's a ripping shred all the way to Three Bridges railroad and the turn-&-burn return. Big downhill awaits.

EASIER OPTION: Heading NORTH from trailhead is a easier, mellower, beautacious 7 mile out & back on the Arizona Trail.

DIRECTIONS: Pistol Hill Road is SOUTHEAST of Tucson. From downtown Tucson take Speedway EAST to N. Craycroft and turn RIGHT. Head SOUTH to E. Golf Links and hang a LEFT. Head EAST to Houghton and take a RIGHT. From Houghton, make a LEFT on Old Spanish Trail and CONTINUE SOUTHEAST 13 miles. You'll see unpaved Pistol Hill Road on the LEFT. Drive 2 miles NORTH to the trailhead (No water!). Harder trail starts SOUTH.

"When in doubt, go for it. Either succeed or end the suspense."
- more silly mountain bike wisdom

SWEETWATER SONORAN PRESERVE

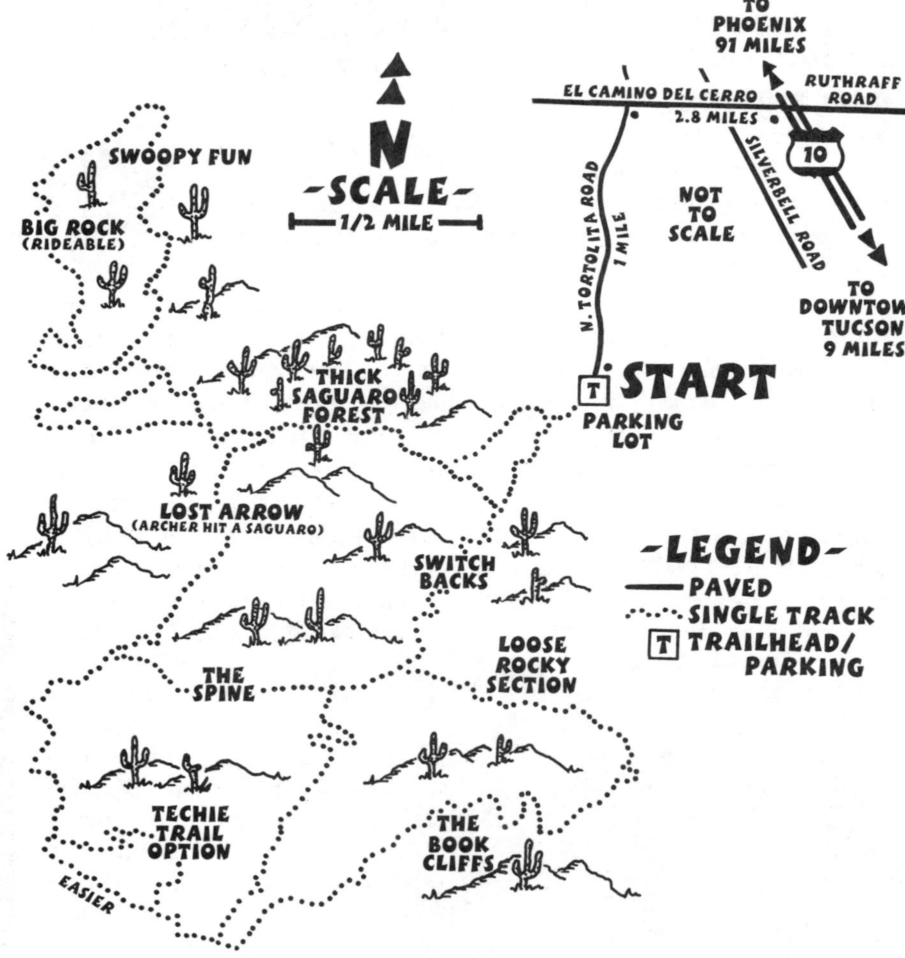

~THANK YOU~
JIM ROSSI & SCOTT MORRIS

TUCSON

©RAY

Tucson SWEETWATER TRAILS
ROLLING SINGLE TRACK & SAGUARO SCENERY

DISTANCE: 8.5 MILES
(NOT ENOUGH? GO BOTH WAYS. 17 MILES!)
TIME: 1 TO 2 HOURS
EFFORT: EASY? GO FASTER.
SKILL: NOVICE/INTERMEDIATE
PUCK-O-METER: PUCK 3
(A FEW ROCKY SPOTS)
FIND ROUTE: EASY
(TUCSON IS ALWAYS IN SIGHT)
SEASON: OCT TO MAY

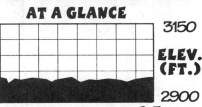

AT A GLANCE

3150
ELEV. (FT.)
2900
0 TOTAL MILES 8.5

PRIMO TRAIL FOR BEGINNERS

DESCRIPTION: Sweetwater is the perfecto ride to thrill a newbie into an endless dissolute life of mountain biking. Gently rolling miles of smooth single track swoop through towering stands of giant saguaro forest with epic views of the Tucson Valley. It has Feng Shui flow with sweeping turns and a few occasional rock gardens to keep even an expert master guru mountain biker spinning away for hours. If the riding is too easy, go faster, go further. These short trails all feed into each other. They are never too steep. There is no wrong way to go. If you get turned around, just head EAST back toward Tucson, always within view.

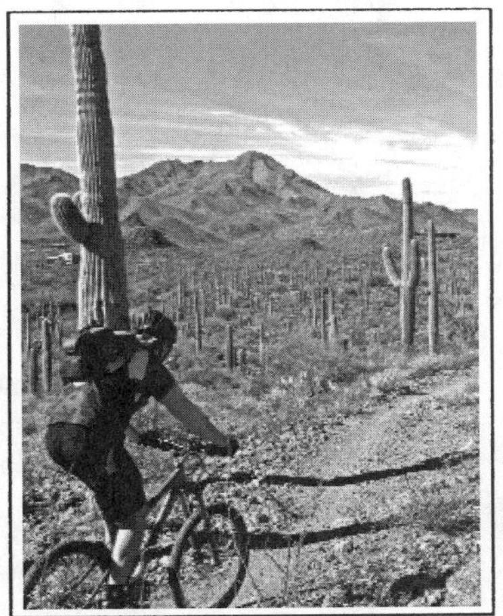
Scott Morris

Mark Flint and Sonoran Desert Mountain Bicyclists started a decade ago with the idea of finding places to ride and making them up as they went along. The 700 acre Sweetwater Preserve is the sweetest reward for their grunt work.

DIRECTIONS: From downtown Tucson take I-10 WEST 9 miles to W. Ruthrauf Road/W. El Camino del Cerro exit and go WEST on W. El Camino del Cerro. After about 2.8 miles you will make a LEFT on Tortolita Road heading SOUTH. The parking lot is at a dead end, about 1 mile. Note: Do not take Tortolita Road from the SOUTH. It does not go through.

"You can observe a lot by watching."
-Yogi Berra

TUCSON MOUNTAINS

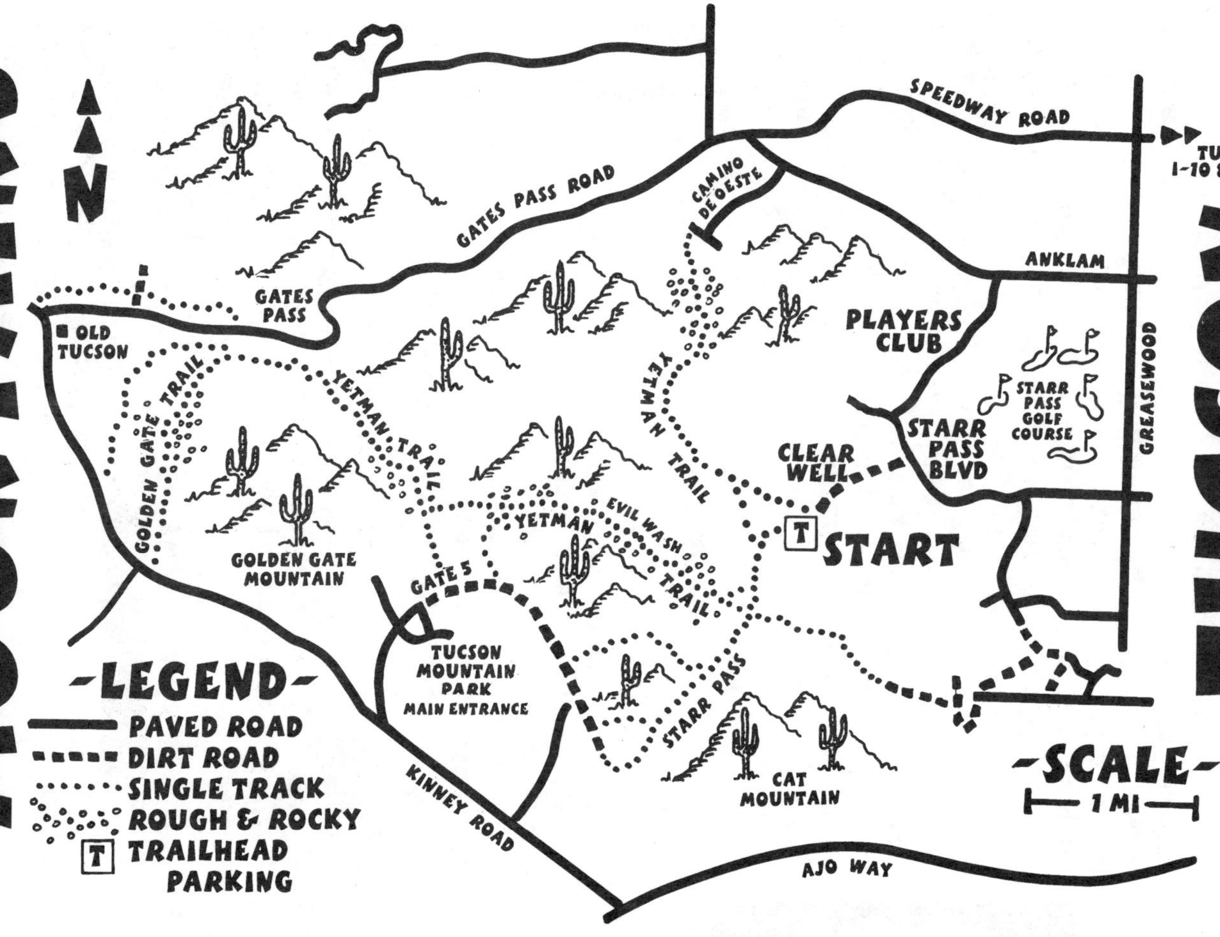

N
GATES PASS ROAD
SPEEDWAY ROAD
TO TUCSON, I-10 & U. OF A.
CAMINO DE OESTE
GATES PASS
OLD TUCSON
ANKLAM
PLAYERS CLUB
GOLDEN GATE TRAIL
YETMAN TRAIL
YETMAN TRAIL
STARR PASS GOLF COURSE
GREASEWOOD
STARR PASS BLVD
CLEAR WELL
EVIL WASH TRAIL
YETMAN
START
GOLDEN GATE MOUNTAIN
GATE 5
TUCSON MOUNTAIN PARK MAIN ENTRANCE
STARR PASS
CAT MOUNTAIN
KINNEY ROAD
AJO WAY
-LEGEND-
PAVED ROAD
DIRT ROAD
SINGLE TRACK
ROUGH & ROCKY
TRAILHEAD PARKING
-SCALE-
1 MI

TUCSON

Tucson TUCSON MOUNTAINS
STARR PASS SINGLE TRACK LOOP

DISTANCE: 7.7 MILE LOOP
TIME: 2 HOURS
EFFORT: MODERATE
SKILL: MODERATE
PUCK-O-METER: PUCK 7
SOME ROUGH STUFF, BUT NOT BAD
FIND ROUTE: MODERATE
SEASON: SEP to JUN

AT A GLANCE

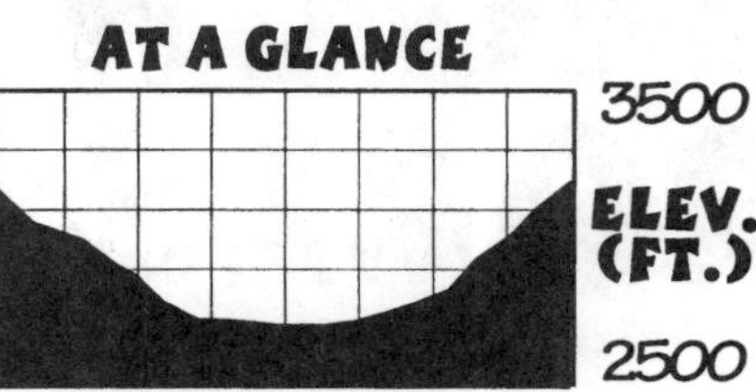

DESCRIPTION: The classic Tucson shred. Fast, intermediate desert single track with a little rough stuff. Giant saguaro forest. Great expansive views. Plenty of wildlife, especially coyote and javelina early mornings. Close to town and easy to find.

MILEAGE LOG

0.0 Park in the lot. Step over the gate. Go 50 yards to the sign marked "Starr Pass". Go LEFT and follow the power lines over Starr Pass.

1.5 Step over gate. Turn RIGHT and continue on 1-track along the park boundary until it becomes a dirt road then look for faintly marked Gate 5 on your right.

3.3 RIGHT on through Gate 5 to Yetman Trail junction. Look around. A left takes you up to Gates Pass.

4.7 RIGHT onto Yetman Trail, so rough it'll knock the plaque off your teeth and save you a trip to the dentist. Yetman leads into a wash . Fist to brain size boulders knock you around pretty good.

6.7 Back to the Starr Pass Trail junction. Go LEFT and follow the power lines back up to where you parked.

7.7 Back to GO. Check out some other great trails in the Tucson Mountains. Good exploring here.

DIRECTIONS: Follow the map. Head west out notorious and aptly named main drag Speedway. If you can't find Speedway, you are indeed lost! Go under the freeway. LEFT on Greasewood. RIGHT on Anklam. LEFT on Players Club at the "STARR PASS" sign. LEFT at "T" intersection then take first RIGHT. Probably still not paved. Park where the road ends. The trail starts to the LEFT up out of the paved parking lot.

"A starry night can quiet the soul."

-Vincent van Go

TUCSON MOUNTAINS ROBLES PASS

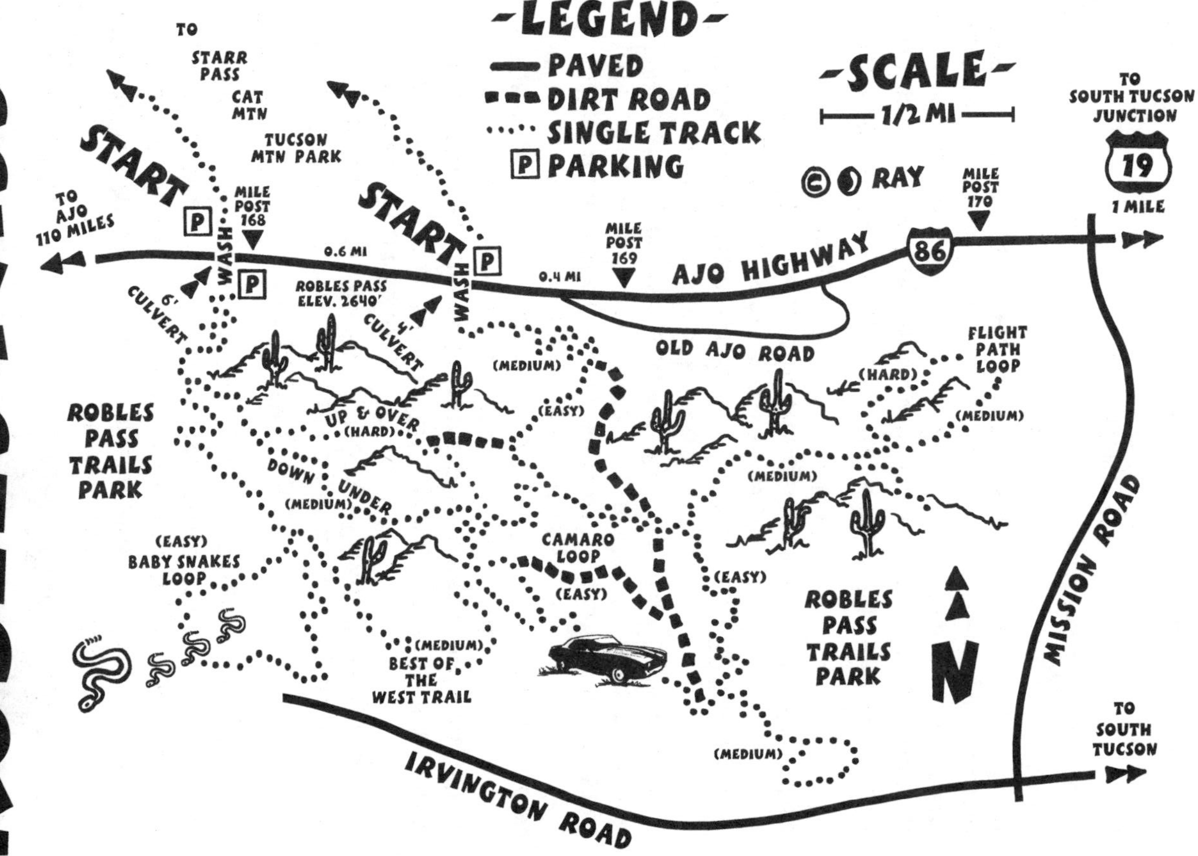

YOU CAN'T GET LOST (ONLY MISPLACED) . . . YOU ARE SURROUNDED BY TUCSON!

Tucson TUCSON MOUNTAINS
ROBLES PASS SINGLETRACK

DISTANCE: 16 MILES TOTAL
TIME: 2 TO 3 HOURS
EFFORT: EASY/MODERATE
SKILL: ROCK SOLID
SOME ROCKY AND OFF CAMBER
PUCK-O-METER: PUCK 5
10+ ON UPPER XXX VOODOO TRAILS
FIND ROUTE: MODERATE
SEASON: SEP to MAY

AT A GLANCE

ELEV. (FT.) 2500–3500; 0 TOTAL MILES 16

DESCRIPTION: Rolling, interconnected singletrack flows through the Sonoran desert on the edge of South Tucson. Epic for beginners, killer workout for experts, perfect for locals. A bit maze-like your first time out, but it's only a few square miles. You're surrounded by Tucson always nearby so you can't really get lost . . . merely misplaced. If it feels like you're pedaling straight up a wall, you headed for the XXX trails. Take stock of your life before proceeding.

DIRECTIONS: Locals prefer to ride in from Starr Pass in Tucson Mountain Park, but that involves a welter of unmarked trails, so if you don't know your way, best to park in one of the small culvert areas on Ajo Highway (see map). The 4' double culvert is 0.4 miles west of the 169 milepost on the north side of the road and has room for about 6 to 8 cars. The culvert is too small to ride, but you can see the trails from there. The 6' culvert is about 100 yards west of the 168 milepost. One side is full of brush and junk, but the other is clear with lots of bike tracks leading to the trails just beyond.

MANY THANKS TO JIM ROSSI, SCOTT MORRIS AND KEN BACHER FOR THEIR HELP.

TUCSON

THUMPER LOOP
DEAD HORSE RANCH STATE PARK

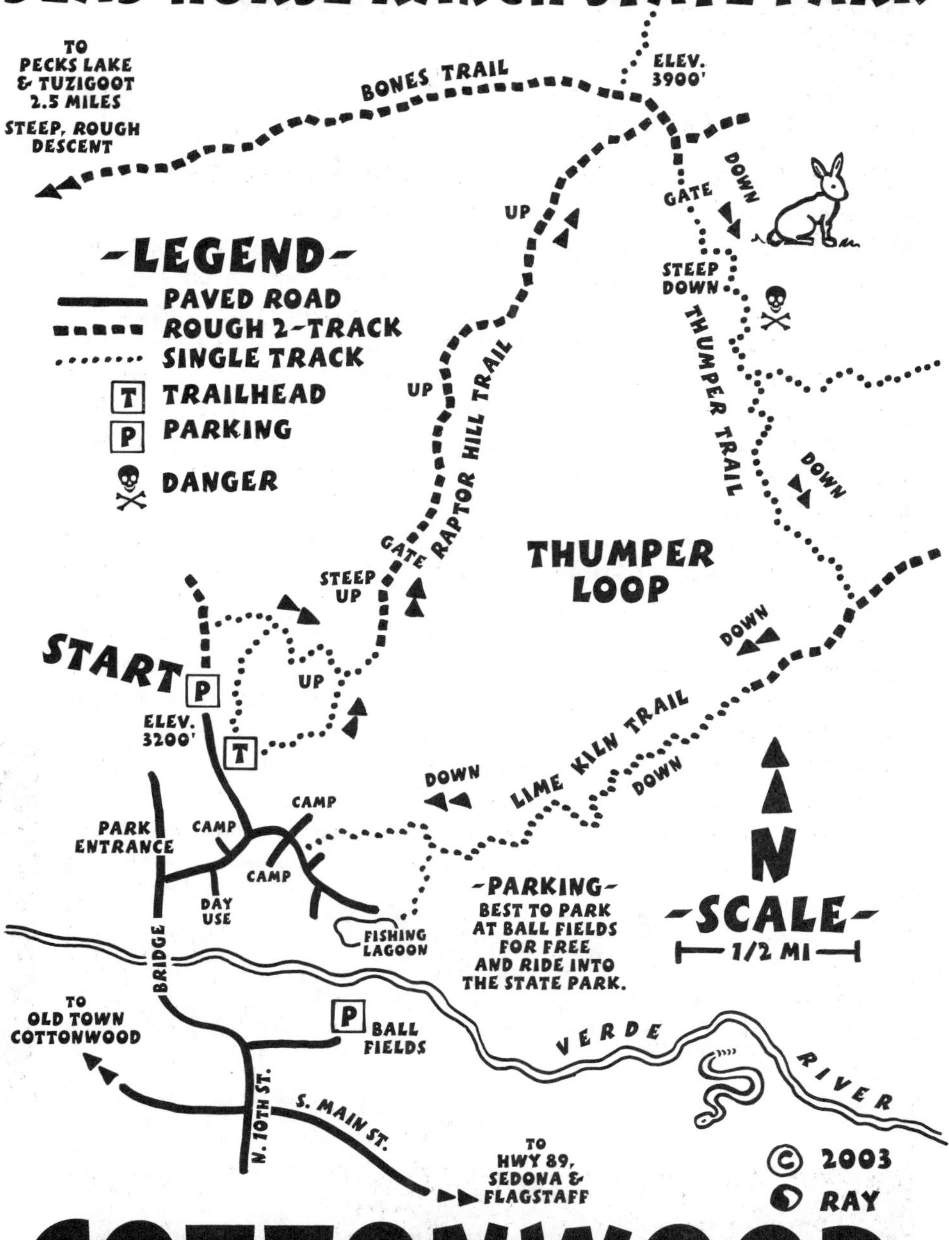

TO PECKS LAKE & TUZIGOOT 2.5 MILES
STEEP, ROUGH DESCENT
BONES TRAIL
ELEV. 3900'
GATE
DOWN
UP
-LEGEND-
PAVED ROAD
ROUGH 2-TRACK
SINGLE TRACK
T TRAILHEAD
P PARKING
DANGER
STEEP DOWN
THUMPER TRAIL
UP
RAPTOR HILL TRAIL
DOWN
GATE
STEEP UP
THUMPER LOOP
START
P
UP
DOWN
ELEV. 3200'
T
LIME KILN TRAIL
DOWN
DOWN
CAMP
PARK ENTRANCE
CAMP
CAMP
DAY USE
-PARKING-
BEST TO PARK AT BALL FIELDS FOR FREE AND RIDE INTO THE STATE PARK.
N
-SCALE-
1/2 MI
FISHING LAGOON
BRIDGE
TO OLD TOWN COTTONWOOD
P BALL FIELDS
VERDE RIVER
N. 10TH ST.
S. MAIN ST.
TO HWY 89, SEDONA & FLAGSTAFF
© 2003 RAY

COTTONWOOD

Cottonwood THUMPER LOOP
FUN SINGLE TRACK LOOP ON THE VERDE

DISTANCE: 8 MILE LOOP
TIME: 0.5 to 1.5 HOURS
EFFORT: SOME SWEAT
SKILL: INTERMEDIATE
PUCK-O-METER: PUCK 7.5
A FEW TECH BITS ON THE DESCENT
FIND ROUTE: EASY
SEASON: OCT to MAY

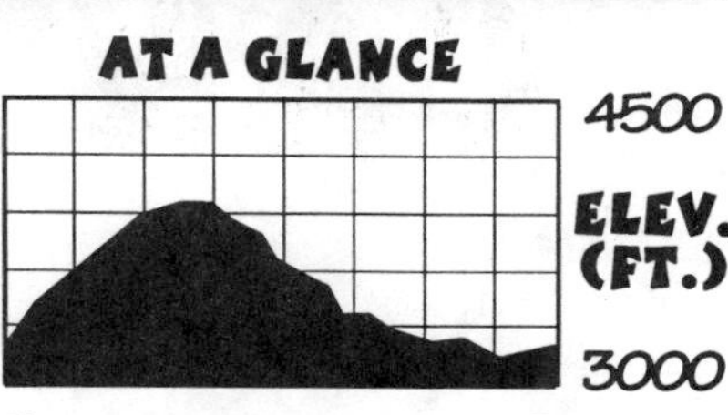

DESCRIPTION: Thumper is a fine short loop anytime, but an especially way jiggy little shred when snow and mud clog Northern AZ trails. Set rockets to burn and dial the assault-mobile ride finder for Dead Horse Ranch.

PRIMO TRAIL
WORTH A JOURNEY

Cottonwood is much too dang hot in summer, but deee-lightful the rest of the year. The exquisite Tuzigoot ruins are only a skip and a hop away. Fishing is great. Campsites are plentiful. Do Thumper either way, but clockwise is best. Climb the 2-track and descend single track. Mo-betta-go-fast fun that way.

The Verde is one of the desert's last free flowing rivers sustaining a lush and large plant and wildlife population. Verde River Greenway is a critical six-mile stretch of The Verde renown for its many natural and cultural resources. Dead Horse Ranch State Park anchors that greenway. You gotta pop for one dead prez to get in.

MILEAGE LOG

0.0 Follow Thumper map to START. After 0.1 mile, take the single track on your RIGHT.
2.8 "T" junction. *Go* RIGHT.
3.0 Right at fork. Singletrack next. *Go* down Thumper.
5.1 Thumper meets Lime Kiln Trail. *Go* Right.
7.2 Pavement. *Go* RIGHT back to trailhead.
8.0 Back to GO. Need more? Ride up Raptor again, *go* LEFT at the top and head down Bones Trail. There is a tough 1- track descent to Pecks Lake and Tuzigoot. Makes a loop to Cottonwood and a 21 mile total day.

"Getting old is when it takes longer to recover than it did to do the damage."
-Andrei Cordrescu

SIX SHOOTER CANYON

TO GLOBE 5 MILES
-LEGEND-
PAVED ROAD
DIRT ROAD
SINGLE TRACK
T TRAILHEAD/ PARKING
DANGER
ELEV. 4000'
SIX SHOOTER CANYON
CHECK DAMS (EROSION CONTROL)
EASY TO MISS TURN
BORROW PIT
CHECK DAMS
RAY'S WRECK OUCH!
SWITCH BACKS STEEP & FAST
N
SCALE
1 MI
ELEV. 7600'
STEEP & FAST
START
T
TO GLOBE SEE SHUTTLE DIRECTIONS
TO PINAL PEAK
PINAL PEAK ELEV. 7848'
GLOBE
SHUTTLE DIRECTIONS TO TRAILHEAD
0.0 START on Broad Street in "Old Town" historic district of downtown Globe. If you plan to ride up, park further on in these directions.
0.6 Go RIGHT over the bridge onto Jess Hayes Road. Corner market here.
1.5 RIGHT onto Ice House Canyon Rd. Sign says "PINAL REC AREA".
3.3 RIGHT onto Kellner Canyon FS55. Sign says "PINAL PEAK 14".
5.5 CONTINUE as road becomes dirt.
6.1 Bear LEFT onto FS651.
11.5 Sign directs you LEFT to "PINAL PEAK". CONTINUE.
15.1 Bear LEFT and CONTINUE on FS651.
16.4 Bear LEFT to "FERNDELL".
16.7 Bear LEFT at sign "SIX SHOOTER CANYON TRAIL #197".
16.8 PARK the shuttle. CHECK the brakes. ADJUST the Attitude. START downhill thru the gate.

GLOBE **SIX SHOOTER CANYON**
SINGLE TRACK MAYHEM & MEXICAN FOOD

DISTANCE: 13 MILES
TIME: 2 to 6 HOURS
EFFORT: NO WHINERS
SKILL: DAREDEVIL
PUCK-O-METER: PUCK 9
STEEP, SWITCHBACK TECH DESCENT
TYPE: SHUTTLE
SEASON: APR TO DEC

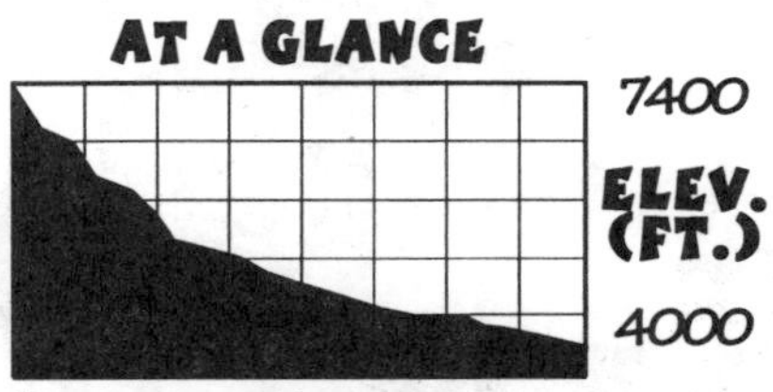

DESCRIPTION: Just 90 miles east of Phoenix, Globe is the last "real" authentic mining town in Arizona . . . a last holdout against the dreaded chi-chi with lots of dangerous old mining junk scattered about, ancient sun-baked brick buildings and hard scrabble people to match. You'll be hard pressed to locate a latte, however *Globe* has more Mexican restaurants per capita than any city in Arizona and they're *ALL good*. This is not to say you won't be able to find a frosty post ride barly pop to wash down the dust. There is a fairly new brew pub in Old Town on Broad Street where you can meet your shuttle driver for the post ride celebration. *Good place to start too.*

Hardcores ride up to start the downhill, but it's 13 miles winding miles on a dirt road and 3000' to the top of the Pinals above Globe. You might prefer a shuttle. Directions are on the map. Bring two cars or con some friendly sofa tater into hauling your butt to the top in exchange for an evening of fine dining, music and brews.

While it's true this ride is mostly downhill, *this* downhill ain't for candy asses. Starts off steep, stays that way for a while and remains way too fast the rest of the way home. Although Six Shooter canyon Trail is not terribly rough, I still managed to have a good crash. At the top, you're in the big trees for the first few miles. Drop down the way hairy fast, off camber single track switchbacks that cut through the pines. Next thing you know you're out of the trees and into the desert above Globe. It's smooth. It's rough. It's steep. It's fast. It's tough. It's all that and it's all single track until the bottom when you get to the rural roads that lead you back to town. It's wicked cool.

"Everything is funny when it's not happening to you."
-Will Rodgers

POINT SUBLIME

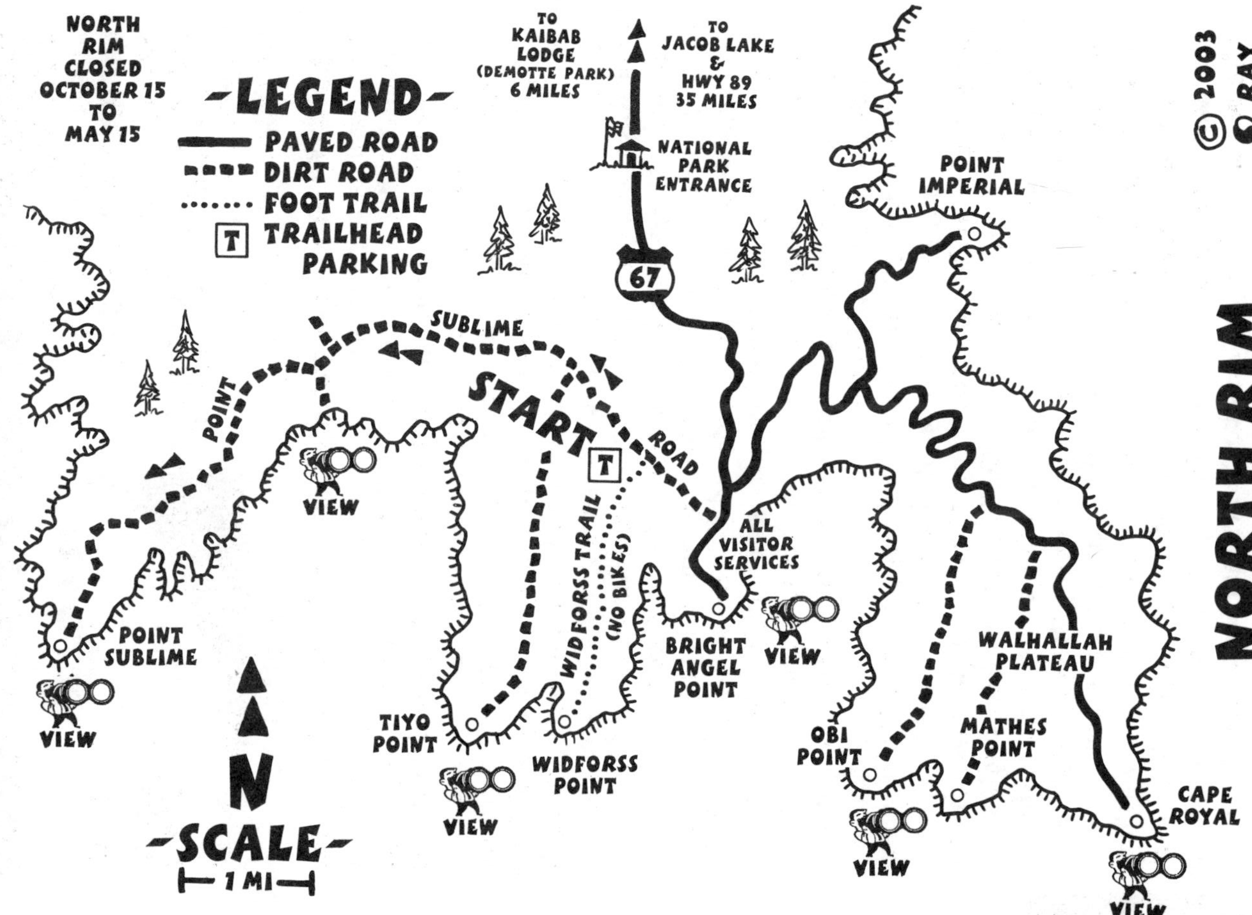

NORTH RIM

GRAND CANYON

Grand Canyon POINT SUBLIME
NORTH RIM TRAIL TO SUBLIME VIEW

DISTANCE: 36 MILES R.T.
TIME: 6 HOURS
EFFORT: VERY LONG RIDE
SKILL: EASY
PUCK-O-METER: PUCK 3
LONG, EASY DIRT ROAD TO VIEW
FIND ROUTE: EASY
SEASON: MAY to OCT

DESCRIPTION: The North Rim sits on a huge thumb of land jutting into The Canyon called The Kaibab Plateau. Sweet smelling old growth pines tower 200 ft. above a silent forest floor. The height and girth of the old growth ponderosas make you feel just a bit wee.

A rough jeep road runs all the way to Point Sublime through sunny meadows and forest. The first 10 miles roll up and down gaining 500 ft. until gradually descending 1,000 ft. to Pt. Sublime. Be sure to check out a great view and photo op about 5 miles before Pt. Sublime. No food or water available along the way. Bring rain gear during the summer monsoon season. Caution, the rescue index on this little travelled road is near zero.

Grand Canyon National Park is struggling to keep up with the burden of over 5 million visitors per year. Plans are afoot at the South Rim for a light rail and closing the park to cars. Included is a bike/foot trail all along the South Rim. Yipee! However, that's 5 years down the road. Meanwhile all dirt roads in the park are closed to bikes except Point Sublime. Camping is limited to the park campground. Reserve way in advance. Free dry camping in nearby Kaibab National Forest is easy. Showers, laundry, food, gas, meals, espresso, trinkets and all that brouhaha are found at North Rim Village inside the national park.

DIRECTIONS: Easy to find. Go 2.7 miles north of Grand Canyon North Rim Lodge and west at the sign "Widfross Trailhead". Go 1 mile to the parking area and start there.

"The life of the land is preserved in the righteousness of the people."
-Hawaii's very cool state motto

RAINBOW RIM

-GETTING THERE-

FIND THE TOWN OF JACOB LAKE AT THE NORTH RIM OF THE GRAND CANYON ON ANY ARIZONA HIGHWAY ROAD MAP. GO SOUTH ON HWY 67 TOWARD THE NATIONAL PARK ENTRANCE FOR 27 MILES TO MILEPOST 605.9 (1 MILE PAST KAIBAB LODGE). TURN RIGHT ON FS 22 AND FOLLOW THE SIGNS 22 MILES TO "VISTA POINTS".

-LEGEND-

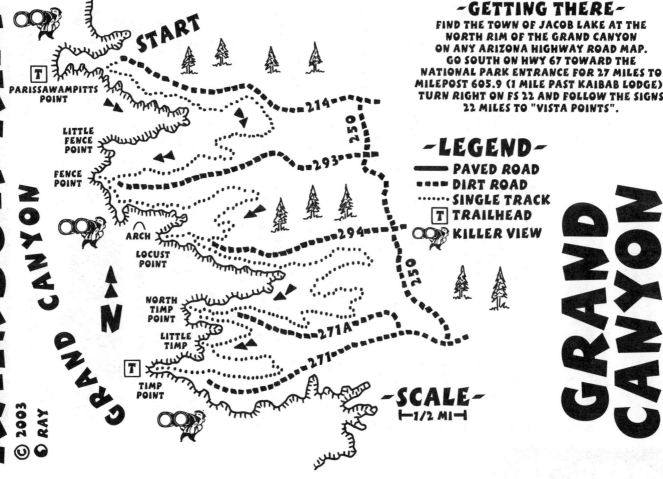

- PAVED ROAD
- DIRT ROAD
- SINGLE TRACK
- TRAILHEAD
- KILLER VIEW

GRAND CANYON (NORTH RIM)

Grand Canyon **RAINBOW RIM TRAIL**
SINGLE TRACK RIGHT ON THE RIM

DISTANCE: 18 MILES 1 WAY
TIME: ALL DAY·LONG
EFFORT: HARD WORK
SKILL: FAIRLY EASY
PUCK-O-METER: PUCK 3
GOOD TRAIL AWAY FROM THE EDGE
FIND ROUTE: EASY
SEASON: MAY 15 to OCT 15

AT A GLANCE

ELEV. (FT.) 8500 / 7500
0 1-WAY MILES 18

DESCRIPTION: YES! At last you can ride your mountain bike along the very rim edge of of the Grand Canyon. Picture the North Rim as a giant thumb sticking out into The Canyon from the Kaibab Plateau. Along an 18 mile stretch of the western edge of that thumb, the Kaibab National Forest has constructed 18 miles of new single track.

Rainbow Rim Trail has been set with a small track machine and lots of hand labor anticipating that, as pine needles fall and native plants grow in, it will mature to a fine single track with a natural look and feel. They built the trail with bikes in mind. *VERY COOL! THANK YOU!*

Along the Rainbow Rim sets a series of five points sticking out into the abyss. The trail connects these as it meanders back up drainages to avoid steep changes in elevation, then back out to the next point. All this makes for constantly changing perspectives and killer views over humongo Tapeats Amphitheater containing whole mountains, canyons, terraces, buttes, spires and castles all in purple, verdant greens and shades of crimson.

The main trailheads are located either end at Parissawampitts Point and Timp Point, but the trail can be accessed at any point along the way. The roads are not great, but they can be negotiated in a 2WD car. You may camp free at any of the points. There is no water or food along the way. Bring rain gear for summer monsoon.

North Rim roads **OPEN MAY 15 AND CLOSE OCT 15** as snow arrives early and stays late in the far northern Arizona high country.

GREEN VALLEY

ELEPHANT HEAD
(SANTA RITA MOUNTAINS)

Green Valley ELEPHANT HEAD
GREAT TRAIL IN THE SANTA RITAS

DISTANCE: 24 MILES
TIME: 3 to 5 HOURS
EFFORT: TOUGH
SKILL: INTERMEDIATE
PUCK-O-METER: PUCK 7.5
FAST DESCENTS ON RETURN TRIP
FIND ROUTE: MODERATE
SEASON: SEP to MAY

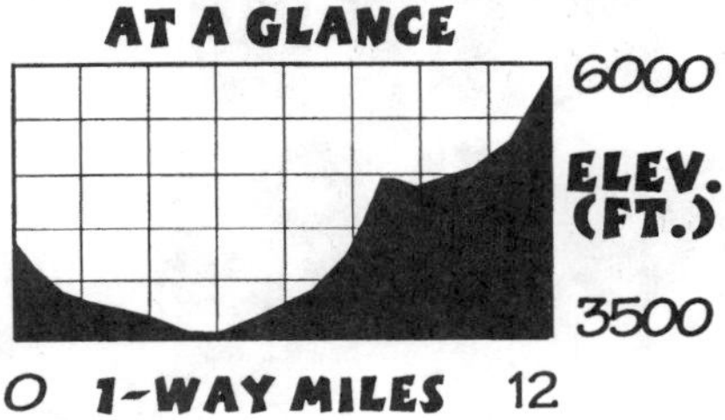

AT A GLANCE

ELEV. (FT.) 3500–6000
0 **1-WAY MILES** 12

DESCRIPTION: Excellent single track and scenery in the Santa Ritas south of Tucson. Color and shadows play across broken granite creating illusions for your viewing pleasure. Save this ride for the cooler months when streams are running and the giant saguaro sonoran desert is lush with life and full of birdsong.

Head SOUTH from Tucson 25 miles on I-19, take the CONTINENTAL EXIT #63 just past Green Valley and head EAST 12 miles on Madera Canyon Road. Proctor Road is well marked. Proctor soon goes all to hell and turns single track through the ocotillo, saguaro and mesquite. Frequent stream crossings in the wet months. Finally there's a humongo climb to the radio towers. The trail is well marked. Bring lots of water and a snack. I got so hungry I nearly ate my shoe. Yum!

MILEAGE LOG

0.0 PARK in the lot. Follow Proctor Rd. gradually downhill. Keep a sharp eye out for bike trail signs.
1.6 Through a wash then a gate. Great single track.
5.0 Another gate, then a dirt road. Go LEFT. Begin climb.
7.8 Short steep single track heads up to the RIGHT off the jeep road before the old mine. Not obvious. Keep your eyes peeled for the trail sign.
8.0 A little pass. Check the view then CONTINUE.
8.7 LEFT on F.S. 183 right after a stream crossing. Head up to the towers.
12.0 Towers. View. The whole enchilada. Enjoy the descent.
24.0 Return to the START.

"To be on one's bike is the ultimate goal of all ambition."
- *mountain bike wisdom*

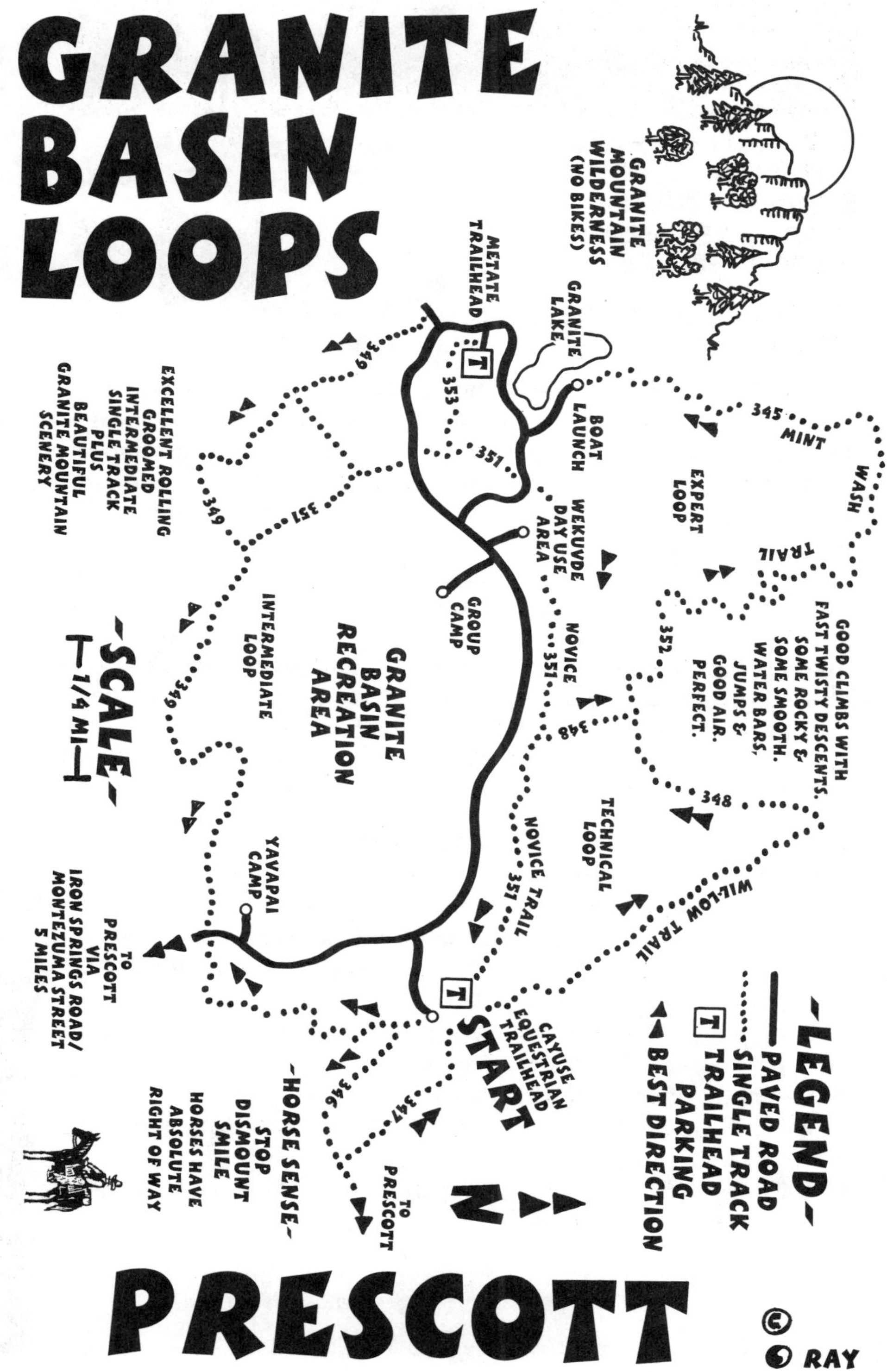

GRANITE BASIN LOOPS

GRANITE MOUNTAIN WILDERNESS (NO BIKES)

WASH
MINT
345
TRAIL
EXPERT LOOP

GOOD CLIMBS WITH FAST TWISTY DESCENTS. SOME ROCKY & SOME SMOOTH. WATER BARS, JUMPS & GOOD AIR. PERFECT.

352
348
WIL-LOW TRAIL
TECHNICAL LOOP

-LEGEND-
PAVED ROAD
SINGLE TRACK
T TRAILHEAD PARKING
BEST DIRECTION

GRANITE LAKE
BOAT LAUNCH
WEKUVDE DAY USE AREA
NOVICE 351
348
NOVICE TRAIL 351
CAYUSE EQUESTRIAN TRAILHEAD
START
N

METATE TRAILHEAD
T
353
351
GROUP CAMP
T

349
351
GRANITE BASIN RECREATION AREA
347
TO PRESCOTT
346
INTERMEDIATE LOOP
349
YAVAPAI CAMP
349

EXCELLENT ROLLING GROOMED INTERMEDIATE SINGLE TRACK PLUS BEAUTIFUL GRANITE MOUNTAIN SCENERY

-SCALE-
1/4 MI

TO PRESCOTT VIA IRON SPRINGS ROAD/ MONTEZUMA STREET 5 MILES

-HORSE SENSE-
STOP
DISMOUNT
SMILE
HORSES HAVE ABSOLUTE RIGHT OF WAY

PRESCOTT

Prescott GRANITE BASIN LOOPS
GREAT LOOPS FOR ALL ABILITY LEVELS

DISTANCE: 12 PLUS MILES OF SINGLE TRACK LOOPS
TIME: 2 TO 3 HOURS OR MUCH MORE IF YOU LIKE
EFFORT: MANY EASY TO DIFFICULT LOOP TRAILS
SKILL: ROOKIE TO ADVANCED
FIND ROUTE: MOST TRAILS ARE SIGNED, BUT THE AREA HAS *MORE* TRAILS THAN SHOWN ON MAP
SEASON: SOME SNOW IN WINTER

DESCRIPTION: A loop for rank beginners and lots more for the rest of us . . . fast, rough, smooth, twisty-turny single track with jumps, rocks, bumps, hops, hard packed soil and a little exposure here and there to add spice. In short, everything, all great. If you rode out, there's a secret mostly downhill single track back to town. See the map.

This is a Prescott National Forest Recreation Area. Lots of folks recreating here. There's a cool little lake. Good for kids. Be courteous and share the trails. Use special caution around horses. Stop, dismount, smile. Especially smile. It won't kill ya to schmooze a little with the horse people and keep the good vibe going.

DIRECTIONS: From downtown Courthouse Square go northwest on Montezuma Street and continue as it becomes Iron Springs Road and heads out of town. After you've gone 4.7 miles turn right on Granite Basin Road and go 3.9 miles to Metate Trailhead. $2 fee to park the The Beast. Too much? Ride part way out and ride free.

LYNX LAKE LOOP

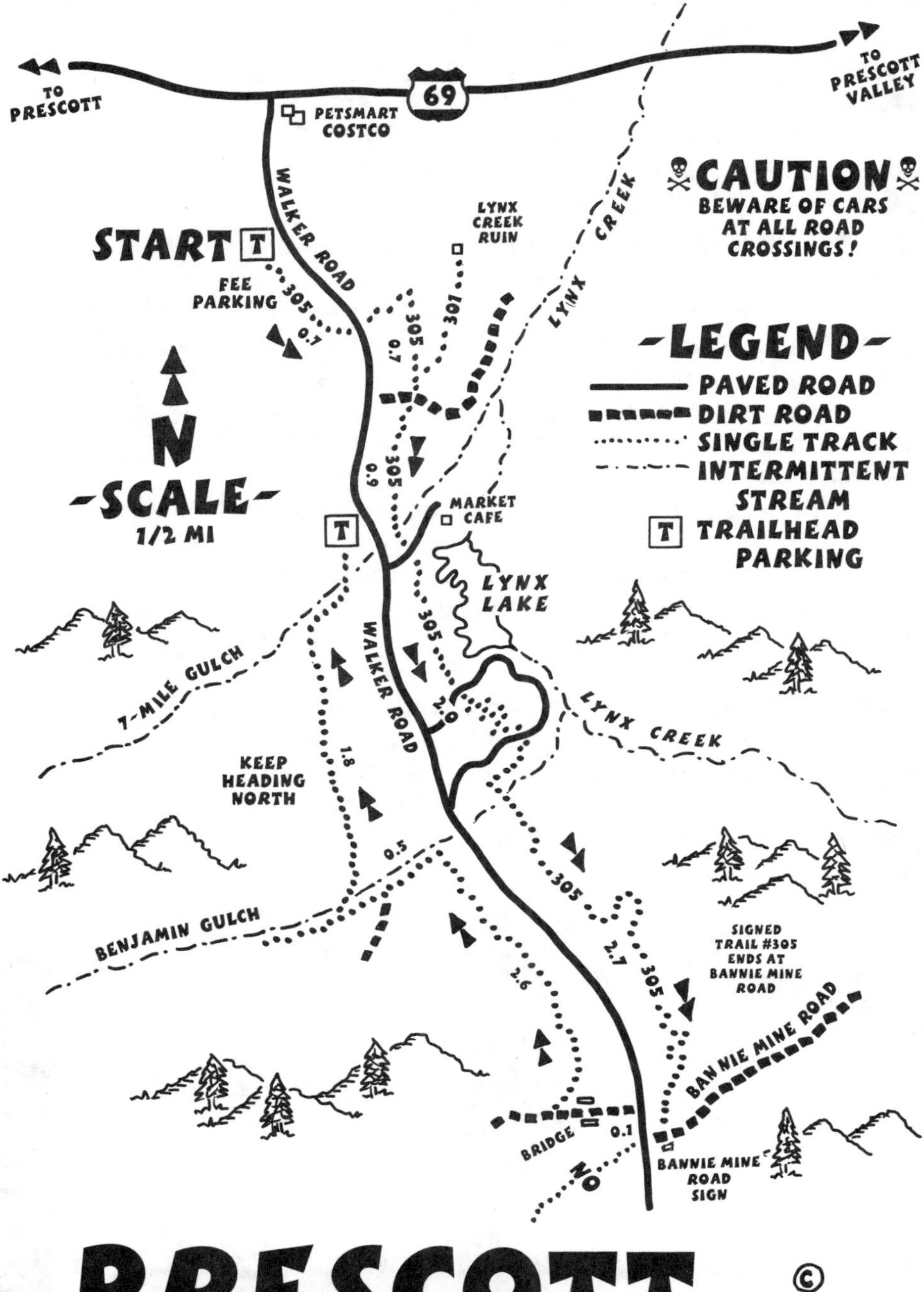

TO PRESCOTT

69

TO PRESCOTT VALLEY

PETSMART COSTCO

WALKER ROAD

LYNX CREEK

☠ CAUTION ☠
BEWARE OF CARS AT ALL ROAD CROSSINGS!

START T

FEE PARKING

305

0.7

LYNX CREEK RUIN

301

-LEGEND-

PAVED ROAD

DIRT ROAD

SINGLE TRACK

INTERMITTENT STREAM

T TRAILHEAD PARKING

N

-SCALE-
1/2 MI

0.9

MARKET CAFE

T

LYNX LAKE

7-MILE GULCH

WALKER ROAD

2.0

LYNX CREEK

KEEP HEADING NORTH

1.8

0.5

BENJAMIN GULCH

SIGNED TRAIL #305 ENDS AT BANNIE MINE ROAD

2.6

2.7

BANNIE MINE ROAD

BRIDGE

0.1

NO

BANNIE MINE ROAD SIGN

PRESCOTT

Prescott LYNX LAKE LOOP
SINGLE TRACK, EAGLES & OSPREY

DISTANCE: 14.5 MILES
TIME: 3 HOURS
EFFORT: MODERATE
SKILL: INTERMEDIATE
PUCK-O-METER: PUCK 3
WATCH FOR CARS AT ROAD CROSSINGS
FIND ROUTE: MODERATE
LAST HALF OF LOOP UNSIGNED
SEASON: MAR to NOV

0 **LOOP MILES** 14.5

PRIMO TRAIL
WORTH A JOURNEY

DESCRIPTION: Superb, uncrowded, rolling single track loop through pine, oak and aligator juniper forest. No big climbs. No rough stuff. Great bird viewing at Lynx Lake. See nesting osprey, bald eagles and heron. Find the market & cafe on the map. Good eats and right next to the trail.

START at the trailhead a half mile in on Walker Road. Trail #305 is well maintained and signed all the way. After about 2.5 miles you go through Lynx Lake Recreation Area. The trail crosses paved roads a few times. Area is busy with cars and campers. Stop at crossings or die. Be warned.

Follow clearly marked Trail #305 all the way SOUTH to Bannie Mine Road. See the map. Cross paved Walker Road and head NORTH to finish the loop. See the map again. The second half of the loop is unmarked, but obvious with a little help from the map. Stay on main trail and keep NORTH.

DIRECTIONS: Walker Road begins next to COSTCO and PETSMART on Highway 69 in Prescott. Park there for free or go a half mile south on Walker Road to the Forest Service trailhead parking lot on the RIGHT. $2 to park there.

PEAVINE TRAIL

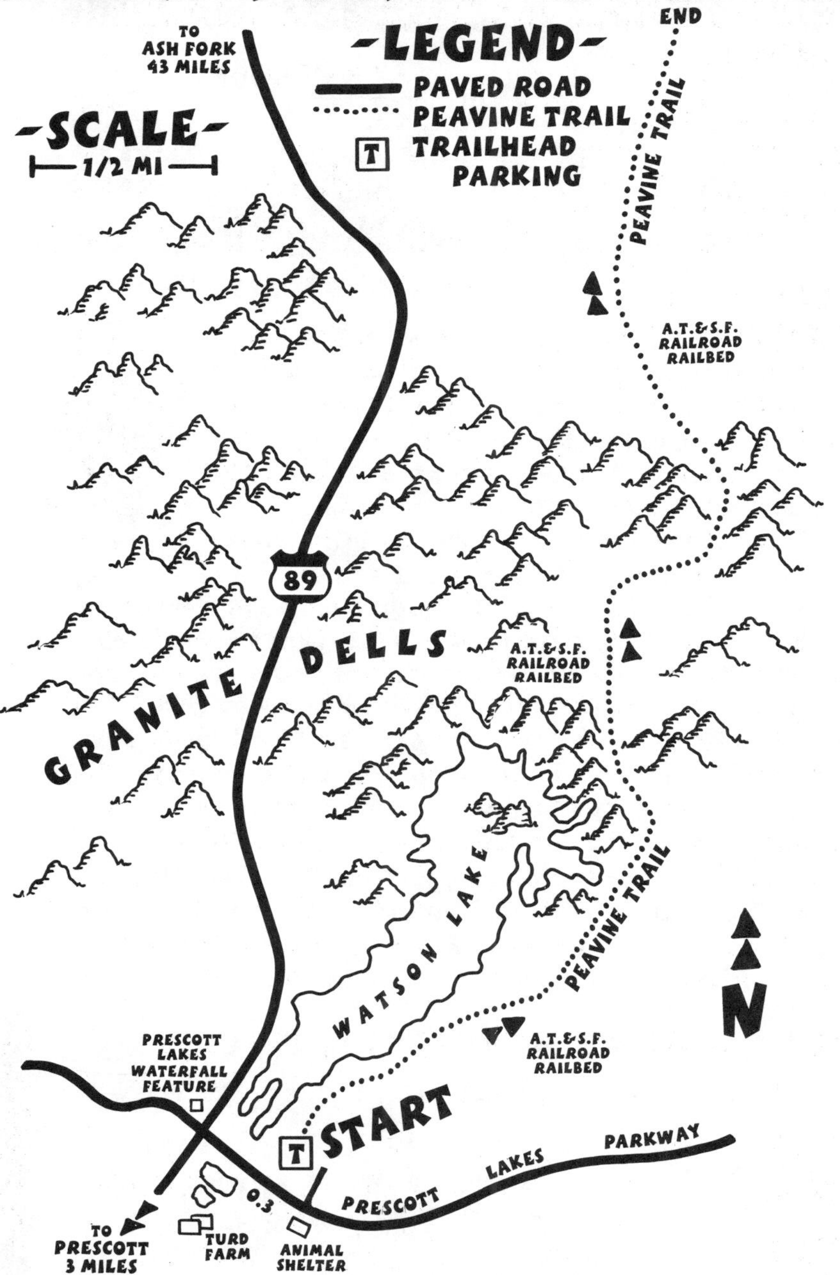

PRESCOTT

© RAY

Prescott PEAVINE TRAIL
EASY ROLL THRU SCENIC GRANITE DELLS

DISTANCE: 9 MILES TOTAL
4.5 MILES EACH WAY OUT AND BACK
TIME: 2 HOURS
EFFORT: EASY
SKILL: NOVICE
FIND ROUTE: EASY
SEASON: MAR to NOV

AT A GLANCE

6000
ELEV. (FT.)
5000
0 **1-WAY MILES** 4.5

DESCRIPTION: "Mighty nature's whims sometimes produce such grotesque and ponderous jumbles of massive rock material that in a place like this, man stands in fascinated awe and respectful admiration." Author unknown.

A golden spike was driven by an Arizona Territorial Governor in 1887 to celebrate the completion of a rail link that connected Prescott to the outside world. Named for its scenic serpentine path, the wandering Peavine Route crossed mighty wooden trestles over deep canyons to connect Prescott with the main east-west line 50 miles to the north. The Granite Dells just north of Prescott presented a hard rock obstacle to this construction. A way was blasted and the bed of that rail line remains today as Peavine Trail.

Peavine is an easy, scenic roll. The tracks are gone thanks the *RAILS TO TRAILS* organization and the way has been made smooth. Perfect for little kids or even someone in a wheel chair. Best of all, it goes right through fabulous Granite Dells next to beautiful Watson Lake frequented by colorful ducks and honking geese. It's 4.5 miles out and 4.5 back, but you can turn-and-burn at any point. In fact, turn around after just a mile and you'll have seen great views of Watson Lake and Granite Dells.

The Granite Dells owe their fantastic form to long term weathering of cracks caused by cooling and stressing of a deeply buried molten mass. The Dells are 1.4 billion years old.

DIRECTIONS: Easy. From Prescott go NORTH 3 miles on HWY 89 toward Ash Fork. Turn RIGHT (EAST) at Prescott Lakes Parkway. The intersection is marked by a huge fake waterfall. The signed parking area is 0.3 miles on the LEFT.

"A train wreck has it's good points. It indicates something is moving."
-*Mark Twain*

SPRUCE MOUNTAIN
TO PRESCOTT (MT. VERNON ST.) 6.0 MI.
-CAUTION-
HORSES AND HIKERS HAVE RIGHT OF WAY
CONTROL YOUR SPEED OF FLIGHT!
N
-SCALE-
1/2 MI
SENATOR HIGHWAY
.9 MI
SPRUCE MOUNTAIN ROAD
DIRT ROAD ASCENT
GROOM CREEK
SHORT CUT TO/FROM TOWN
1 MI
TRAIL 307 START
TRAIL 307 QUICK & STEEP WAY UP
LOOK OUT
VIEW
T
ELEV. 6360'
STEEP UP HURT!
STEEP UP GRUNT CITY!
3.5 MI.
TRAIL 307
ELEV. 7693'
TRAIL 307
TRAIL 307
5.5 MI
YOW! BITCHIN' DESCENT!
SENATOR HIGHWAY
TO CROWN KING
-LEGEND-
PAVED ROAD
DIRT ROAD
SINGLE TRACK
T TRAILHEAD PARKING
PRESCOTT
© RAY

Prescott SPRUCE MOUNTAIN
SINGLE TRACK LOOP & VIEW

DISTANCE: 9 MILES
TIME: 2 HOURS
EFFORT: WHAT GOES UP...
SKILL: ADVANCED
PUCK-O-METER: PUCK 9
MACH 9 DESCENT WITH SOME DEBRIS
FIND ROUTE: E-Z
SEASON: APR to NOV

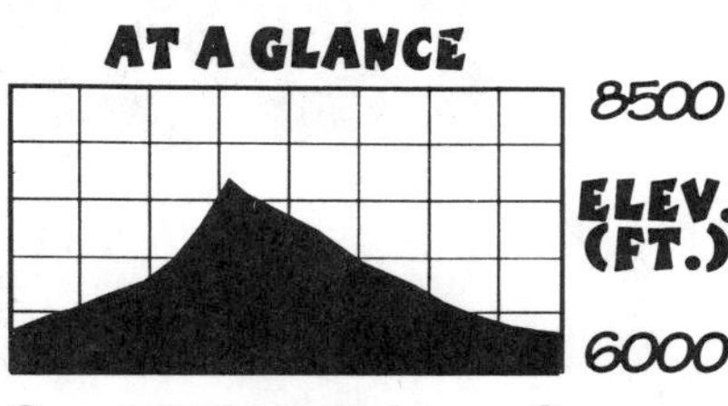

DESCRIPTION: Nine miles of the best . . . killer views, smooth line, banked turns, way steep and deep ravines. Miss a turn, next stop Groom Creek! Weekdays best. Horse people work! AM weekends are worst.

From the parking lot it's easy up for the first miles then a wall near the top. The lookout is 0.1 miles from the top of #307. Find a sittin' rock and scope some eye poppin' views. North see The Frisco Peaks beyond Flagstaff. In front of The Peaks is Mingus Mountain. West is a bird's eye view of Prescott. South set the Bradshaws. Finally, rip airborne express 5.5 miles down the bitchin' single track descent. Spruce Mountain gets snow in winter and may be a little rough after spring snowmelt or summer monsoon rain.

DIRECTIONS: Easy. From Courthouse Square go 0.6 miles east on E.Gurley. RIGHT on S.Mt.Vernon St. (Senator Hiway). Groom Creek is at 6.6 miles and Trail #307 trailhead is on the left a mile past Groom Creek. If road turns dirt, you blew the turn.

MILEAGE LOG

0.0 CLOCKWISE is best so head LEFT up #307.
1.9 TRAIL SPLITS. Brain in neutral. LEFT and UP. Ugh!
3.3 TOP of #307. Look out from lookout then DESCEND with care not to die or waste a horse.
9.0 BACK TO BOTTOM. Wipe that cheezy grin off your gub. Try it again in the other direction. It's an itty bitty gear, tech roll up the twisty single track before streaking the lightning descent. Trail rash special. Watch for horses!

THUMB BUTTE LOOPS
©
RAY
N
-SCALE-
1/2 MI
WHITE ROCK LOOP TRAILS
GROOMED INTERMEDIATE FAST
TO IRON SPRINGS ROAD 2 MILES
STREAM TRAIL FAST OUT & BACK
TRAIL
318
316
317
316A
315
START
WHITE ROCK 318
QUICK LOOP
ELEV. 5700'
WILLOW SPRINGS CENTER
DUGAN CAMP ROAD
CREEK TRAIL
WHITE ROCK
THUMB BUTTE ROAD
TO PRESCOTT VIA GURLEY STREET 3 MILES
47
DEARING PARK ROAD 373C
GRADUAL UP
DOWN
THUMB BUTTE
SCENIC TRAILS
(NO BIKES)
GRADUAL UP
ROAD
BUTTE
THUMB
SHORT LOOP
FUN INTERMEDIATE MOSTLY SMOOTH
-LEGEND-
PAVED ROAD
DIRT ROAD
JEEP ROAD
SINGLE TRACK
TRAILHEAD PARKING
DOWN
BIG JUNIPER TREE
BIG ROCK
START
373A
373A
51
51
51
9401
ROLLING JEEP ROADS
-FEE PARKING-
AVOID THE FEE
PARK IN TOWN
RIDE TO RIDE
ROAD
GRADUAL UP
BUTTE
DOWN
SCARY FAST
51A
WEST SPRUCE TRAIL
264
THUMB
LONG LOOP
407T
LOOKOUT TRAIL
TIGHT TECHNICAL ROCKY
LOOKOUT TRAIL
DOWN
TO PRESCOTT VIA COPPER BASIN ROAD
SIERRA PRIETA OVERLOOK ELEV. 6900'
START
TO PRESCOTT VIA COPPER BASIN ROAD
PRESCOTT

Prescott THUMB BUTTE TRAILS
LOTSA FUN OPTIONS WITHIN LOOP ROAD

DISTANCE: LOOP TRAIL OPTIONS 3 TO 20 MILES
EFFORT: NOTHING TOO TOUGH
SKILL: ALL LEVELS OF ABILITY
FEAR: BEWARE THE CARS ON THUMB BUTTE ROAD
FIND ROUTE: SOME SIGNED, SOME NOT
SEASON: ALL YEAR (SNOW POSSIBLE IN WINTER)

PRIMO TRAIL
WORTH A JOURNEY

DESCRIPTION: You can spot Thumb Butte pointing skyward from almost anywhere in Prescott looking west. This huge, thumb-like granite rockpile marks the town's best closest riding and hiking trails.

My GPS survey ride revealed way too many trails to show on a single map (Looks like a plate of linguini!) , thus only the main trails are shown to provide a basis for your exploration. You are always within Thumb Butte *Loop* Road, so you can't get too lost. You always come out somewhere, but a compass or a GPS might come in handy if you like to feel safe. Thumb Butte itself often makes for an outstanding visual landmark.

At 7000', Thumb Butte Road's high point is the expansive Sierra Prieta Overlook to Copper Basin and beyond to the west. FS51 bisects the loop road with a quiet roll through the forest. There are many, many other 4WD roads and trails within the loop that are great to find for yourself although they have been known to miners and ranchers for over 100 years. Thumb Butte Loop Road is nearly all busy dirt road. Too many cars. You have to be careful so as to not end up as a nice hood ornament on some redneck cowboy's monster Dodge Diesel. Avoid getting the stinkeye from hikers and don't ride the trails immediately surrounding Thumb butte.

DIRECTIONS: From Courthouse Square go west on Gurley St. This runs directly onto Thumb Butte Road. Nowadays it costs some minor bucks to park your car in the lot, so ride the 3 miles from town if paying to use your national forest sticks in your craw bag.

"Learn from the mistakes of others. You won't live long enough to make them all yourself."
-mountain bike proverb

BROWN CANYON LOOP

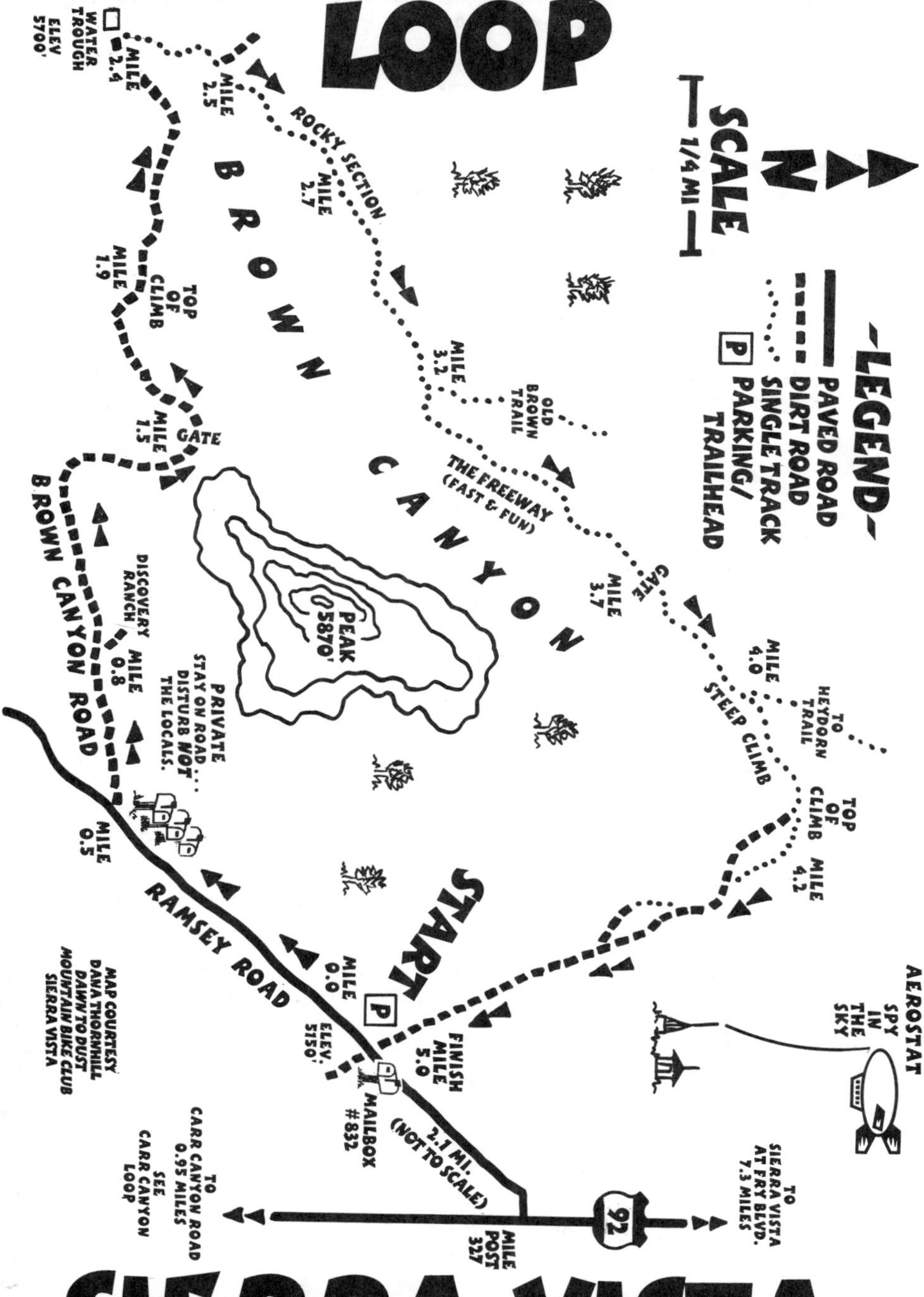

SCALE
1/4 MI
N

-LEGEND-
PAVED ROAD
DIRT ROAD
SINGLE TRACK
P PARKING/ TRAILHEAD

WATER TROUGH
ELEV 5700'
MILE 2.4
MILE 2.5
ROCKY SECTION
MILE 2.7
BROWN CANYON
MILE 1.9
TOP OF CLIMB
MILE 3.2
OLD BROWN TRAIL
GATE
MILE 1.5
THE FREEWAY (FAST & FUN)
BROWN CANYON ROAD
DISCOVERY RANCH
PEAK 5870'
MILE 3.7
GATE
MILE 0.8
PRIVATE STAY ON ROAD... DISTURB NOT THE LOCALS.
MILE 4.0
STEEP CLIMB
TO HEYDORN TRAIL
TOP OF CLIMB
MILE 4.2
MILE 0.5
START
RAMSEY ROAD
MILE 0.0
P
ELEV. 5150'
FINISH MILE 5.0
MAILBOX #832
AEROSTAT SPY IN THE SKY
MAP COURTESY DANA THORNHILL DAWN TO DUST MOUNTAIN BIKE CLUB SIERRA VISTA
2.1 MI. (NOT TO SCALE)
TO CARR CANYON ROAD 0.95 MILES SEE CARR CANYON LOOP
MILE POST 327
92
TO SIERRA VISTA AT FRY BLVD. 7.3 MILES

SIERRA VISTA

Sierra Vista: **BROWN CANYON LOOP**
FUN SINGLE TRACK DESCENT

DISTANCE: 5 MILES
TIME: 1 HOUR
EFFORT: MODERATE
SKILL: JUST A BIT
PUCK-O-METER: PUCK 7.5
HIGH SPEED DESCENT
FIND ROUTE: MODERATE
SEASON: SEP to JUN

AT A GLANCE

6000
ELEV. (FT.)
5000
0 **LOOP MILES** 5

DESCRIPTION: A big fave among the locals. Zoom down to Sierra Vista for a day of muy rapido 1-track action. Brown combines with Carr Canyon Loop. Turn the page to Carr and check it out. Between the two loops and the road connection, you'll milk it for 20 miles with the bulk being single track descent. Brown Loop climbs a gnurly 2-track jeep road and gains about 500' in a couple of miles. Then get airborne for a flying 2.5 mile rip down a whoop-de-doo trail interrupted only by one short grunt climb.

DIRECTIONS: Head south out of Sierra Vista on HWY 92 for about 7 miles to milepost 327. Turn RIGHT onto Ramsey Canyon Road and go 2.1 miles to mailbox #832. Trailhead parking area is just across the road. The first half mile of this loop is paved. As soon as you turn right on dirt Brown Canyon Road, you are going through private property for a quarter mile. Stay on road, follow your nose and mind your own beezwax. Don't disturb the locals and they won't disturb you.

SIERRA VISTA

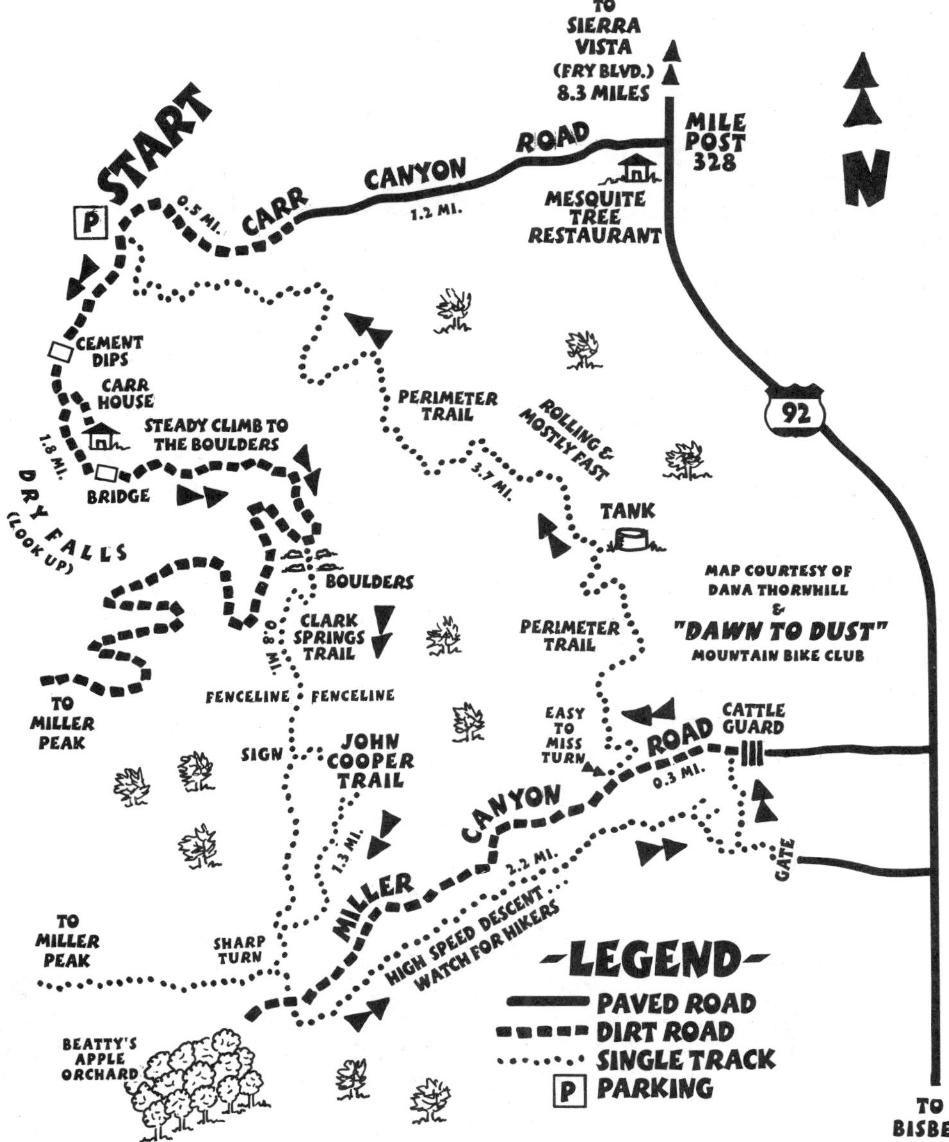
TO SIERRA VISTA (FRY BLVD.) 8.3 MILES
N
MILE POST 328
START
P
0.5 MI.
CARR CANYON ROAD
1.2 MI.
MESQUITE TREE RESTAURANT
CEMENT DIPS
CARR HOUSE
1.8 MI.
STEADY CLIMB TO THE BOULDERS
BRIDGE
DRY FALLS (LOOK UP)
PERIMETER TRAIL
ROLLING & MOSTLY FAST
92
3.7 MI.
TANK
BOULDERS
MAP COURTESY OF DANA THORNHILL & "DAWN TO DUST" MOUNTAIN BIKE CLUB
0.8 MI.
CLARK SPRINGS TRAIL
PERIMETER TRAIL
TO MILLER PEAK
FENCELINE
FENCELINE
EASY TO MISS TURN
CATTLE GUARD
SIGN
JOHN COOPER TRAIL
MILLER CANYON ROAD
0.3 MI.
1.3 MI.
2.2 MI.
GATE
TO MILLER PEAK
SHARP TURN
HIGH SPEED DESCENT WATCH FOR HIKERS
-LEGEND-
PAVED ROAD
DIRT ROAD
SINGLE TRACK
P PARKING
BEATTY'S APPLE ORCHARD
TO BISBEE

CARR CANYON LOOP

Sierra Vista: **CARR CANYON LOOP**
BEST SINGLE TRACK RIDE IN TOWN

DISTANCE: 10 MILES
TIME: 2 to 3 HOURS
EFFORT: FAIRLY TOUGH
SKILL: ADVANCED
PUCK-O-METER: PUCK 7
SPEED AND EXPOSURE TO RISK
FIND ROUTE: MODERATE
SEASON: OCT to JUN

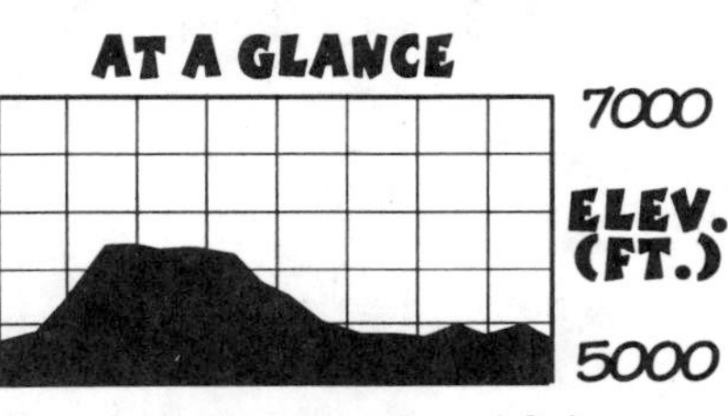

DESCRIPTION: *Gain gravity on a smooth dirt road that climbs up the foothills of the Huachuca Mountains then enjoy your earnings on a long, fast single track descent with lots of dips, twists, drops and a few surprises. Combine with Brown Canyon Loop to make the distance worth the 2-hour-south-of-Tucson drive to Sierra Vista.*

MILEAGE LOG

0.0 *Go south from Sierra Vista on HWY 92 for 8 miles to milepost 328. Go RIGHT on Carr Canyon Road another 1.7 miles. See 'da map. Park and ride uphill.*
1.8 Boulders mark LEFT turn onto 1-track. Fun begins! Lots of exposure to risk here. Good stuff!
2.6 Sign marks John Cooper Trail. Go LEFT.
3.9 Some quick turns. See map. STRAIGHT across Miller Canyon Road and begin speedy single track descent.
6.1 Cattleguard. If you get to a gate, you blew the turn. At the cowguard Head back up Miller Canyon Road.
6.4 Pay attention! *Veeery* sharp oblique RIGHT turn onto Perimeter Trail. More single track rolls up and down across several drainages back to the START.
10.1 Back to GO. Next go visit Kartchner Caverns north of town if you made reservations and have time.

BOOTLEG CANYON
CROSS COUNTRY TRAILS

CALDERA
© RAY
FLAMING HUFFY DEATH TO COPYCATS!
N
BOY SCOUT
LAKE MEAD OVERLOOK
SKYLINE
~SCALE~
1/2 MI
STAY OFF HIKING TRAILS
~DO NOT POACH~
THE TRAIL YOU SAVE COULD BE YOUR FAVORITE!
POWER POLE
ELEV. 3650'
A POSTHUMOUS SHOUT OUT HERE TO TRAIL BUILDER EXTRAORDINAIRE BRENT THOMSON... HE MADE THIS PLACE!
GIRL SCOUT
BOOTLEG CANYON
DOWNHILL STUFF HERE
UPPER LAKE VIEW
WEST LEG
MIDDLE LAKE VIEW
MOTHER
EAST LEG
ELEV. 2800'
START
LOWER LAKE VIEW
I.M.B.A.
REST ROOMS
PAR NONE
TO HOOVER DAM ARIZONA BORDER 10 MILES
-LEGEND-
PAVED
DIRT ROAD
TRAIL
DANGEROSO
PARKING/TRAILHEAD
P.O.W.
BOOTLEG CANYON ROAD
93
ALBERTSONS
STARBUCKS
BOULDER CITY
ELEV. 2450'
93
BUSINESS LOOP
ALL MOUNTAIN CYCLES 702-453-2453
93
BUCHANAN
TO LAS VEGAS 20 MILES
NEVADA HWY

BOULDER CITY
NEVADA

BOOTLEG CANYON
BOULDER CITY, NEVADA
MAD MAX MEETS SIN CITY

BY JIM ROSSI SITTING IN FOR COSMIC RAY

DISTANCE: 5 to 36 miles. X-C loops plus Downhill thrills.
TIME: One Hour to one Lifetime. Good for several days.
EFFORT: Mas fuerte. No wimps or weenies.
SKILL: Expert to Experto Desperato.
PUCK-O-METER: Puck 10+. Some less. Some a bit more.
FIND ROUTE: That's the easy part. Trails are signed.
SEASON: SEP to JUN Way too hot in summer.

PRIMO TRAIL
WORTH A JOURNEY

DESCRIPTION: OK, not in Arizona, but it's just across the river and it's closer to Arizona than to Vegas. Originally a prohibition era smugglers' route delivering hooch to workers building Hoover Dam, Bootleg Canyon is today a Mountain Bike Park . . . a single track masterpiece snaking through the desert mountain-scape above Lake Mead, art deco Hoover Dam and the foreclosed skyline of Lost Wages. Arizona will soon be connected to Nevada by a breath taking, brand new bridge dizzyingly high up over Hoover Dam.

Look before launching! No switchbacks. G-outs drop down and up instead of along steep ravines. Free rides, big air and exposure . . . and not just on downhill runs like Reaper, Kavorkian, Armageddon . . . get the picture? No soft landings.

D-H gravity heads can catch a weekend shuttle to the top. Inquire locally. Trailhead amenities include water, bathrooms and even free hot solar showers. Really.

RATING THE FAVORITE TRAIL*

CROSS COUNTRY

GIRL SCOUT (BEGINNER)	24%
CALDERA (INTERMEDIATE)	16%
SKYLINE (EXPERT)	11%
MOTHER (INTERMEDIATE)	9%
P.O.W. (BEGINNER)	8%
BOY SCOUT (INTERMEDIATE)	6%
LAKE VIEW (INTERMEDIATE)	6%
EAST LEG (INTERMEDIATE)	5%
POWER POLE (EXPERT)	5%
WEST LEG (INTERMEDIATE)	5%
I.M.B.A. (BEGINNER)	4%
PAR NONE (BEGINNER)	2%

DOWNHILL

SNAKEBACK (INTERMEDIATE)	28%
REAPER (EXPERT)	17%
ONA LEE (EXPERT)	17%
ARMAGEDDON (EXPERT)	10%
DIVA (INTERMEDIATE)	10%
POOPCHUTE (EXPERT)	10%
G-STRING (INTERMEDIATE)	8%
KEVORKIAN (EXPERT)	5%
GINGER (☠☠☠EXPERT☠☠☠)	☠%

* RATINGS *NOT* TO BE TRUSTED. THINK. USE THE *BIG* HEAD!

DIRECTIONS: From Arizona take HWY 93 into Boulder City. Head up Bootleg Canyon Road (see the map) and follow signs.

WHITE MTNS

SHOW LOW

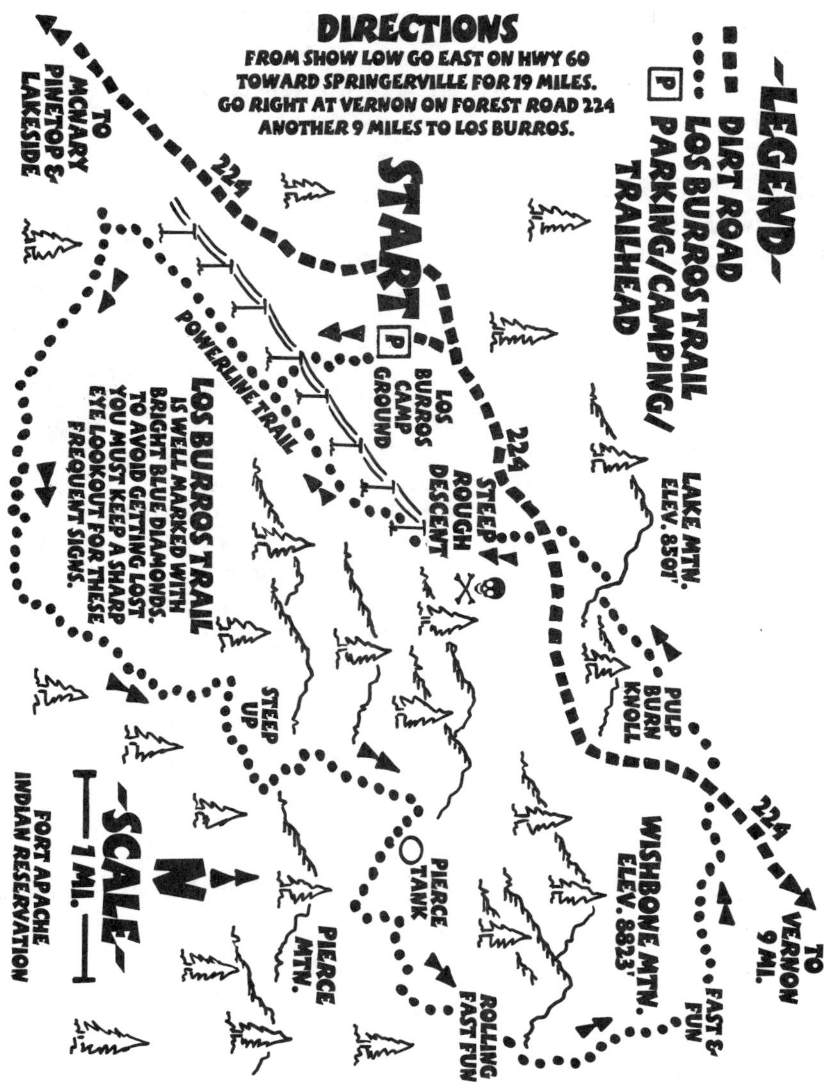
DIRECTIONS
FROM SHOW LOW GO EAST ON HWY 60
TOWARD SPRINGERVILLE FOR 19 MILES.
GO RIGHT AT VERNON ON FOREST ROAD 224
ANOTHER 9 MILES TO LOS BURROS.
-LEGEND-
DIRT ROAD
LOS BURROS TRAIL
P PARKING/CAMPING/ TRAILHEAD
TO MCNARY PINETOP & LAKESIDE
224
START
P
LOS BURROS CAMP GROUND
POWERLINE TRAIL
LOS BURROS TRAIL IS WELL MARKED WITH BRIGHT BLUE DIAMONDS. TO AVOID GETTING LOST YOU MUST KEEP A SHARP EYE LOOKOUT FOR THESE FREQUENT SIGNS.
STEEP ROUGH DESCENT
LAKE MTN. ELEV. 8501'
PULP BURN KNOLL
STEEP UP
PIERCE TANK
PIERCE MTN.
ROLLING FAST FUN
WISHBONE MTN. ELEV. 8823'
FAST & FUN
TO VERNON 9 MI.
N
-SCALE-
1 MI.
FORT APACHE INDIAN RESERVATION

LOS BURROS LOOP

SUCKING MUD
DEATH TO
COPYCATS!

WHITE MTNS: **LOS BURROS LOOP**

SUPER SINGLE TRACK NEAR SHOW LOW

DISTANCE: 13.5 MILES
TIME: 1.5 to 2.5 HOURS
EFFORT: NOT TOO TOUGH
SKILL: INTERMEDIATE
PUCK-O-METER: NO ALARM
FIND ROUTE: MODERATE
SEASON: APR to OCT

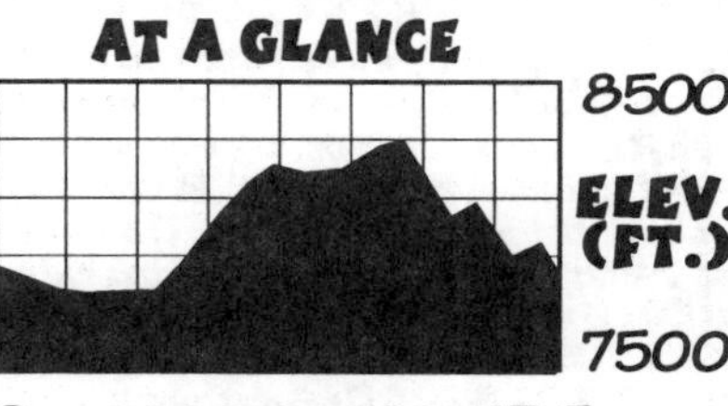

0 **LOOP MILES** 13.5

PRIMO TRAIL — WORTH A JOURNEY

DESCRIPTION: Los Burros Loop DID NOT BURN in the massive fire that threatened Show Low in 2002. Thnak *God!* I reckon this hoot and holler rolling single track loop to be the very best fat tire ride in the White Mountains. That's what all the local dirtheads say and I have to agree. There's one good tough climb and many twisty turny descents through towering old growth pine and aspen forest plus you really get a feeling that you're in an as yet undiscovered part of the state. I had a great time. The White Mountains are the closest thing Arizona has to a rain forest. The winter storm track dips down over eastern Arizona to dump loads of snow and the summer monsoon keeps the forest floor damp and cool, yet mud does not seem to be a problem. The soil is made of mostly soft forest humus rather than that icky clay stuff that sticks to your tires and makes you go postal.

The Los Burros Loop is maintained and well marked. If you go more than 100 yards without seeing a diamond nailed to a tree, you are headed in the wrong direction and should backtrack to the last marker. Lotsa tire tracks to follow too.

DIRECTIONS: From Show Low go 19 miles east on HWY 60 toward Springerville then RIGHT at Vernon onto FS224. Continue 10 miles to Los Burros Camground and trailhead. From Phoenix take HWY 170 via Globe to Pinetop-Lakeside and Show Low. It's about a 3 hour drive.

OPTIONS: Los Burros is part of the White Mountains Trail System, a dozen nearby connected trails. Get a free copy of the superb White Mountains Trail System Guide free from the USFS in Lakeside (520) 368-5111.

G-NARLY G-LOSSARY

OF ARCANE TRAIL JARGON

(THE BURLACIOUS WORDAGE!)

AFEARD: Nothing to fear but feard itself.
AIR: To launch or fly. Sky it. Fly it. Hairy air.
AMPED: Psyched, wired, stoked or even go ballistic.
ANNO: Anodized parts. Purple is sooo over. Rasta anno *still* rocks.
AUGER: Wreck. Crater. Stack. Do a digger.
BACON: Scabby trail jerky. Road rash.
BAIL: Quit. Exit. Weenie out. Go home.

BAD DOG: Pit bull on crack. Hard ride.
BAKED: Used up. Burnt, busted or bent.
BARNEY RIDE: Rubble and rocky debris.
BEAVER BREATHER: Seat with a hole.
BELLY TART: Sour bark up after big eat.
BETTY: Nice. Plush. Fine. Smooth. Easy. A betty ride.
BIFF: Bite. Stack. Crash. Dig. Wipe. Wreck. See auger.
BOING: Bounce. Full boing. Suspension.
BOMBER: Stout. Way burly. Tough.
BONK: Your body is baked. Outa gas.
BUFF: Ripped musculature. Perfecto bike or trail.
BUNNY HOP: Hop like bunny over stuff.
BURR: Burly. Honkin'. Mondo gnurly. Way burr, dude.
BUTT FUR: That what gets ruffed on a butt ruff.
BUTT RUFF: Not rough enough to stand, but too rough to ride seated.
BUZZ: The buzz. Word around the campfire. Buzzed. Wired. Excited.
CAGER: Motorist. Person trapped in a car.
CARVE: Rip, rail, cut or tear a turn.
CHOP: The chop. Washboards. Rough stuff.
CHUB: Chubby. Excited. Engorged elation. To get one.
CLEAN: Clear all obstacles. Nail it.
CLOTHESLINE: Dismounted by rope or wire. Decapitation points.
CLYDESDALE: Big boy mountain biker.
COMMANDO: To go commando. Go off trail . Go without undies. Ouch.
COSMIC: The yin and yang. Balance in all things.
COSMIC RAY: Stream of atomic nuclei from space.
CRATER: Auger. Wreck. Especially to dig using head for shovel.

CURB GRIND: Wreck on rocks. To "roach it" on a curb grind.
CUSTOM: Innovative bike repair. Custom retro.
DAB: To touch down or not clean an obstacle.
DIAL: Fine tune. Precision perfect dynamo hummmm.
DIPPED: Stoked. Happy. Dipped in doo.
DIRT SQUIRT: Mutant offspring. Grommet. Bike child.
DOUBLE TRACK: 2-track. Jeep road.
EFFLUVIA: Bugs, dirt, snot, sputum and spit. The crap on your glasses.
EPIC: Siege shred. Hairball bloodbath. Hard ride.
E-TICKET: Epic scary, hairy, fun ride. Total hairball.
FASHION FELONY: Neon. Skunkbutt togs.
FAT: Large, big, portly, rotund, thick, corpulent, chubby.
FATTY: Twisted up fat one.
FUN: Very elastic term to describe almost anything. Often hateful.
GAK: Cough, hack or hork. Phlegm points.
GHOST RIDE: You bail, bike wrecks alone.
GIBLETS: After market add on bike parts. Bolt-ons.
GRANNY: Small gear reduction. Nice old lady.
GRAVITY SCHOOL: Mè magna cum laude.
HAIRBALL: So scary as to require the amount of hair to weave a wool rug.
HAMMER: To pound. To pedal or ride hard and fast. A hammerfest.
HARSH: Rough. As in, "Dude, don't harsh my shred."

HEADBANGER: Nutcase. Haircut with attitude.
H.O.H.: Hateful old hiker.
HOOKY: *Grippy trail that hooks up like velcro.*
HORK: Toss. Throw. Huck your HO-HOs up or down.
J.R.A.: I wuz just riding along when . . . Warranty fraud.
LAWYER TABS: Hateful tabs on fork tips.
MACHIN': 740 m.p.h. = mach 1. Going very fast.
MONGO: Giganto humongo as in way killer mongo.
MOTO: Worthy shreddage. Nice bike or trail.
MULCH IT: To turf it in the sticks and weeds.

MUTANT: Tweaked out mountain bike maniac.
NIG-NOG: Wig-wag corndog. A ding-dong.
NO WAY: Hans Ray. Yes way.
OBSERVED TRIALS: Risk the nuts doing stupid stuff.
OFF BEAT: Off kilter. Irregular. Half bubble off level.
OILED: Lubricated. Intoxicated.
O.T.B.: *Over the bars.*
P.L.F.: Parachute landing fall. Leg, hip, side roll. *Good luck.*

POGO GEEK: Trials maneuverist.
POSER: Lycra ding-dong. A Fred. Possibly a full on MTV nig nog.
POUND: Hammer with gusto as in pound java or pound the dog.
PSYCHO: Disturbing behavior. Hateful headbanger.
PUCK-O-METER: Fear factor. Pucker factor.
RAD: Wicked cool. The bomb. The freak.
RAGER: A radical ride or rider.
RETRO-GROUCH: Technophobic coot.
RHOID BUFF: Butt contacts rolling rear tire. *OW!*
RIGGED-TO-FLIP: Secured by all manner of wire and tape.
ROACH: Roach it. Wreck. Icky bug.
ROCK GARDEN: Eyeball- rattling, tooth-banging hell.
ROOKIE MARK: Chain grease mark on leg. Points for wrong leg.
RUBBLING: Wreck in rubble. To go jeeping.
SALAD BAR: Turf it in the shrubbery. The shmorgy of shred.
SHOTGUN: Blow-&-go on the fly nose blow.
SHRED: A fine ride or pleasant experience.
SHUCKS: *Expletive denoting bitter disappointment.*
SHWAG: Swag. Loot. Free bike stuff. *Gimme some!*
SHWANK: Swank. As in shwanky shwag.
SKANKY: *Groaty, gooey, messy and gross. As a bike chain.*
SKINNY: Tires ridden by nerds, geeks, dweebs and feebs.
SLICK ROCK: Humongo smooth stones to ride.
SNORKLED: Too busy at work. No time to ride.
SOCK WASH: Laundry. Trail through creek or wet grass.
SPHINCTER PHACTOR: Puck-o-meter scale in degrees of repose (1 to 10).
SPOOGE: Skanky, gooey, groaty, gross grime and guck. Oh wretch.
STINK EYE: *Getting "THE LOOK" from a hiker. See H.O.H.*
STYLIN': Styling. On deck. Possible poser factor.
SUCK AND SLAP: The misbehaving evil chain twins.
TACO: Bent wheel resembling same or potato chip.
TECH WEENIE: Poser nig-nog with the latest cool stuff.
THRASH: To trash, bash or smash. Mutated video music.
TOSS: Throw, spew, hurl and hork. Frequently enchilada style.
TRIALS: Tribulations. *Obstacle course. Skill test.*
TUNED: Dialed, tooned, tweaked, psyched, buzzed and hot wired.
URGE: *Power, drive, energy, desire and surge.*
VELCRO: Hooky or grippy trail surface.
VERT: Big vertical steepness. *To fly or go vertical.*
WEENIE: Whimpering, whining weakling.

WEENIE WALK: *Sketchy or steep as to cause weenies to walk.*
WORKABLE: Do-able section along the road to hell.
YARD SALE: Big wreck scatters your stuff here to there.

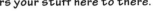

BACKTALK

Greetings earthling! I be Cosmic Ray. Half man, half wit. Been burning the candle at both ends, holding the lighter in my teeth and riding around the planet with young daughter at my side. Dangerous? Not to worry. The *WAY BURLY NEW MIGHTY MOTO LOCALS ONLY* (22nd) *EDITION* is here. Less reading, more riding and 100% guaranteed *NOT* to be the normal homogenized dookie dished up by some dufus corndog armchair mountain biker who's never gone over the bars, wrecked big, gotten lost or scared. Heck, that's every ride!

My little treasure maps are to scale and point north, but still look a bit the primitive doggerel of a demented adolescent. I am a bike mechanic by trade. Be thankful. They used to look the scribble of some crazed, glue sniffing, mutant bike rat. My maps are rough like mountain biking, not an exact science. It's hard dirty fun that often hurts. I've broken bones. I *know* it hurts. Real sport for real people.

Pals Micah, Eric, Ben, Jane, Tom, Paul and myself are still to blame for the art. Printing by Dawn and Jason. D-1 sells it and keeps me reeled in. Special thanks to Jim Rossi, Tom, Mimi, Kay, NOD, Rama, D-2, Tony, Gonzo, Bryce, Ken, Bill, Steve, Chewy, Ursula, Shaggy, Bryce, Ken, Dan, and all my weirdo ultra-gnarly buds who tell me jokes, turn me on to rides and put me up on their couches all over Arizona while I test 'em out. The rides, silly, not the couches! Wait, there's more!

The hardcores need credit . . . them what puts up with my nut case self every day . . . my way groovy friends here and abroad, my together again mom and pop who bought all those first bikes and especially daughter, muse and teen-age Cosmic Grommet Elena Marie. Wild Thing, you make my heart sing!

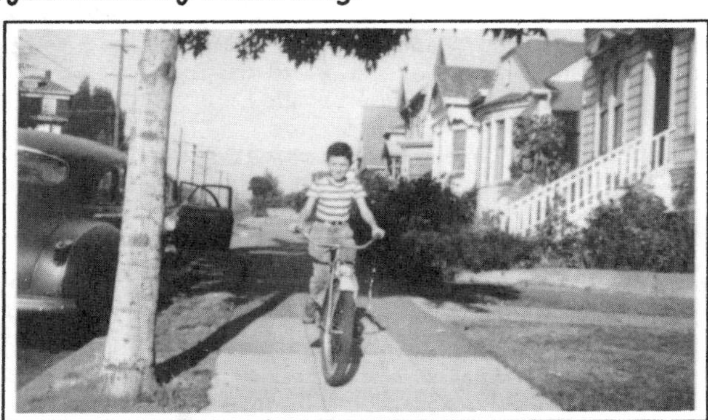

Cosmic Ray and Fat Tire Friend, October 21, 1954

22nd edition *cosmic ray* TM

COSMIC RAY 3960 N. ZURICH ST. FLAGSTAFF, AZ 86004

e-mail: cozray@juno.com fax: (928) 526-8243

ARIZONA MOUNTAIN BIKE YELLOW PAGES

AHWATUKEE

CACTUS BIKES, 4747 E. Elliot Rd. 480 940-7433
CURBSIDE CYCLERY, 4855 E. Warner Rd. 480-598-6778
JAVELINA CYCLES, 4647 E. Chandler Blvd. 480 598-3373
SOUTH MOUNTAIN CYCLES, 3636 E. Ray Rd. 480 706-0858

APACHE JUNCTION

JUNCTION BICYCLES, 10839 E. Apache Trail 480 380-0811

BULLHEAD CITY

TRI STATE BIKES, 1385 Hancock Cr. 928 758-7400
CYCLE THERAPY, 1710 Lakeside Drive 928 763-3553

CASA GRANDE

ROUND TRIP BIKE SHOP, 1148 E. Florence Blvd. 520 836-0799

CAVE CREEK

FLAT TIRE BIKE SHOP, 6149 E. Cave Creek Rd. **480 488-5261**
SOUTHWEST BICYCLES, 29605 N. Cave Creek Rd. **480 342-9200**

CHANDLER

BIKES DIRECT, Gilbert & FWY 202 .... **480 855-8998**
CACTUS BIKES, OCOTILLO, 1960 S. Alma School Rd. 480 782-5483
GLOBAL BIKES, Arizona Av. & Pecos Rd. **480 782-8342**
PERFORMANCE BICYCLES, 5955 W. Ray Rd. **480 705-9001**

COTTONWOOD

ZOOMER'S BIKE & GEAR, 743 N. Main St. **928 202-4941**

FLAGSTAFF

ABSOLUTE BIKES, 18 N. San Francisco St. **928 779-5969**
AZ BIKES, 620 E. Rt. 66 .... **928 773-9881**
BICI MUNDO de Elson, 222 E. Brannon Av. 928 779-3121
BIKESHOPHUB.COM, 120 E. Phoenix. **800 717-2596**
COSMIC CYCLES, 901 N. Beaver St. **928 779-1092**
FLAGSTAFF BIKE & FITNESS, 2404 E. Route 66 .... **928 526-2780**
REVOLUTION BICYCLES, 3 S. Mikes Pike 928 774-3042
SINGLE TRACK BIKES, 575 W. Riordan Ranch Rd. 928 773-1862

FOUNTAIN HILLS

BICYCLE GARAGE AZ, 11857 N. Saguaro Blvd. 480 837-1413
SLIPPERY PIG #2, 15225 N. Fountain Hills Blvd. 480 837-2069

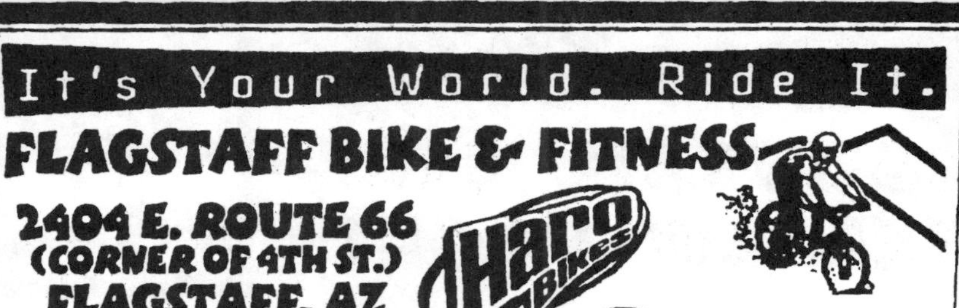

GILBERT

ADVENTURE BICYCLE, 2336 E. Baseline ... 480 649-3394
ARIZONA BIKE SOURCE, 1450 W. Warner Rd. ... **480 988-5055**
CACTUS BIKE SAN TAN VILLAGE, 2244 E. Williams Field Rd. ... 480 814-1323
FOCUS CYCLERY, 3107 S. Gilbert Rd. ... **480 558-0104**
GLOBAL BIKES, Gilbert & Guadalupe ... **480 892-1315**

GLENDALE

AZ CYCLE & MULTISPORT, 6808 N. Dysart Rd. ... 623 935-2721
BIKE DEN, 4312. W. CACTUS ... 602 938-0989
BICYCLE DEPOT OF ARIZONA, 59th Ave & HWY 101 ... 623 362-4100
GORDY'S BICYCLES, 4205 W. Thunderbird ... 602 843-6490
ROAD RUNNER, 6740 W. Deer Valley Rd. ... 623 537-0647
SWISS AMERICAN BIKE CENTER, 16835 N. Park Place ... **602 938-4330**

GOODYEAR

EVERGREEN BIKE, 880 E. Van Buren St. ... 623 932-0060
ESTRELLA MTN CYCLERY, 13380 w. Van Buren ... **623 925-1352**

GREEN VALLEY

BIKE HUB, 284 CALLE DE LAS TIENDAS ... 520 648-1308
GREEN VALLEY BIKE & HIKE, 125 W. Calle de las Tiendas, Suite 133 ... 520 393-7433

HAVASU CITY

CYCLE THERAPY, 2144 N. McCulloch Blvd. ... 928 855-3553
MBK, 76 N. Lake Havasu Ave. ... 928 453-7474

KINGMAN

BICYCLE OUTFITTERS, 3001 Stockton Hill Rd. ... 928 753-7538
BICYCLE WORLD, 1825 Northern Ave ... 928-757-5730

LITCHFIELD PARK

ARIZONA CYCLERY & MULTISPORT, 6808 N. Dysart Rd. 623-935-2721

MESA

A-1 BIKE CENTER, 3638 E. Southern #C109 .... **480 641-0819**

ADVENTURE BICYCLE, 2336 E. Baseline Rd. 480 649-3394

BIKES DIRECT, 1545 S. Power Rd. 480 981-8901

DNA CYCLES, 2031 N. Power Rd. **480 924-2453**

MIKE'S BIKE CHALET, 5253 E Brown Rd **480 807-2944**

PARAGON CYCLING, 1106 N. Gilbert Rd. 480 830-1620

PAT'S CYCLERY, 5052 S. Power Rd. **480 964-3330**

TWO WHEEL JONES, 1917 S. Signal Butte Rd. **480 380-8222**

PARKER

RABBIT BIKE & REPAIR, 1016 S. Joshua Av. 928-669-5639

PAYSON

Hike Bike & Run, 600 E. HWY 260 #3 928-257-1316

PEORIA

BIKER'S EDGE CYCLE & FITNESS, 10545 N. 83rd Ave. 623 486-8565

GOLDEN SPOKE CYCLERY, 7616 W. Thunderbird 623 931-8910

PERFORMANCE BICYCLE, 8402 W. Thunderbird Rd. **623 435-3250**

SOUTHWEST BICYCLES, 8155 W. Bell Rd. **623 412-3150**

PHOENIX

BIKE BARN, 4112 N. 36th St. **602 956-3870**
BIKES DIRECT, TATUM & 101 (DESERT RIDGE) 480 419-8171
BUILD A BIKE, 6036 N. 43rd Ave 623 937-5222
EXHALE BIKES, 2814 W. Bell Rd. **602 548-0567**
LANDIS CYCLERY, 712 W. Indian School Rd. **602 264-5681**
PALO VERDE BICYCLES, 4747 E. Bell Rd. 602 788-0808
REI, 12634 N. Paradise Village Pkwy **602 996-5400**
SLIPPERY PIG BIKE SHOP, 5036 N. Central Ave. 602 263-5143
SUN CYCLERY, 5833 N. 7th St. **602 279-1905**
SUNDAY CYCLES, 3321 E. Bell Rd. 480 440-2142
TRAILHEAD CYCLERY & CAFE, 6825 N. 16th St 602 264-2328
TRY ME BICYCLES, 1514 W. Hatcher 602 943-1785

PRESCOTT

BIKESMITH CYCLE, 723 N. Montezuma St. **928 445-0280**
HIGH GEAR, 237 N. Mount Vernon Ave. **928 445-8417**
IRONCLAD BICYCLES, 710 White Spar Rd. 928 776-1755
SOUTHWEST SOUNDS & CYCLERY 115 1/2 N. Montezuma **928 443-8996**

PRESCOTT VALLEY

BICYCLE SOURCE, 6594 E. 2nd. St. 928 772-2122
BIKE WORKS, 8561 E. Florentine 928 775-4860

QUEEN CREEK

BIKES DIRECT, 20952 S. Ellsworth Loop Rd. 480 888-2577

RYE

ALL BIKES, HWY 87 .... 928 474-2526

SAFFORD

CYCLE PATH, 726 S. 6th Ave. 520 428-4666

SCOTTSDALE

ARIZONA OUTBACK ADVENTURES, 16447 N. 91st St. 480 945-2881
BICYCLE HAUS, 7025 E. 5th Av. 602 994-4287
BICYCLE SHOWCASE, 7229 E. Shea **480 998-2776**
BICYCLE RANCH, 15454 N. Frank Lloyd Wright Blvd 480 614-8300
BIKE EMPORIUM, GRANITE REEF & MCDONALD 480 991-5430
BOB'S BIKE SHOP, 1608 N. Miller Rd. 480 946-9461
DNA CYCLES, 7077 E. Mayo Blvd. #100. .... **480 515-2453**
KORE BIKE INDUSTRIES, 2240 N. Scottsdale Rd. 480 966-5673
LANDIS CYCLERY, 10417 N. Scottsdale Rd. **480 948-9280**
PERFORMANCE BICYCLES, 14747 N. Northsight **480 348-1875**
RAGE BICYCLES, 2724 N. Scottsdale Rd. **480 968-8116**
TRIBE MULTISPORT, 7624 E. Indian School Rd. 480 421-9442
TRIPLE SPORTS, 4032 N. Miller Rd. 480 994-1174

SEDONA

ABSOLUTE BIKES, 6101 HWY 179, Village of Oak Creek **928-284-1242**
FAT TIRE BIKE SHOP, 325 Jordan Road, Uptown Sedona **928-852-0014**
MOUNTAIN BIKE HEAVEN, 1695 Hwy 89A, West Sedona **928-282-1312**
SEDONA BIKE & BEAN, 6020 HWY 179, Village of Oak Creek **928-284-0210**

SHOW LOW

CYCLE MANIA, 100 N. White Mountain Road , #101 .... 928 537-8812

SIERRA VISTA

M & M CYCLING, 1301 E. Fry Blvd. 520 458-1316
SUN & SPOKES, 164 Fry Blvd. **520 458-0685**

SURPRISE

SURPRISE BIKES, 12875 W. Bell Rd. 623 933-8695

TEMPE

DOMENIC'S 2-WHEELERS, 2010 S. Rural Rd. **480 968-8011**
EHRHARDT'S SCHWINN, 111 E. University Dr. 480 967-2137
LANDIS CYCLERY, 2180 E. Southern **480 839-9383**
LANDIS CYCLERY, 1006 E. Warner **480 730-1081**
REI, 1405 W. Southern **480 967-5494**
TEMPE BICYCLE, 405 W. University Dr. **480 446-3033**
TEMPE BICYCLE, 715 S. Rural Rd (in The Cornerstone) **480 966-6896**

- Bikes yield to horses & hikers.
- Ride on right. Pass on left.
- Downhill riders yield to uphill.
- Stay on trail.

ORIENTEERING FOR IDIOTS

SOUTH
NOON

10 AM 11 AM 1 PM 2 PM

EAST WEST

NOON
NORTH

LOOK UP! Arizona mountains and monuments make for great landmarks. Also, if you are working from a map, it's easy to find NORTH. Every day the sun scribes an arc across the southern sky from EAST to WEST moving 15° per hour. At NOON the sun is due SOUTH and your shadow points due NORTH. Take a fix on the sun then look at your watch. Since the sun appears to move around the earth 360° every 24 hours, we know that each hour the sun moves 15° toward the west. If it is 1 PM, the sun has moved 15° off due south toward the west. At 2 PM, 30° and so on. Interpolate a bit and north will be yours. What a co-incidence . . . maps point NORTH. You don't need no stinkin' *GPS*.

TUCSON

AJO BIKES, 1301 E. Ajo Way, #117 .... 520 294-1434
ARIZONA BIKE EXPERTS, 2520 E. 6th St. 520 881-2279
ARIZONA CYCLIST, 4300 N. Cambell 520 615-7570
ARIZONA CYCLIST, 5350 E. Broadway 520 745-8020
BIKES DIRECT, 1880 E. Tangerine Rd. 520 797-1990
BROADWAY BICYCLES, 140 S. Sarnoff 520 296-7819
DESERT CYCLE WORKS, 2410 N. Huachuca 520 791-2453
FAIR WHEEL BIKES, 1110 E. 6thSt. 520 884-9018
ORDINARY BIKE SHOP, 311 E. 7TH St. **520 622-6488**
ORO VALLEY BICYCLE, 12985 N. Oracle Rd. **520 825-2751**
ORO VALLEY BICYCLE, 2840 W. Ina Rd. **520 544-5999**
ORO VALLEY BICYCLE, 4749 E. Sunrise Dr. **520 577-5511**
PERFORMANCE BICYCLES, 3302 E. Speedway **520 327-3232**
PERFORMANCE BICYCLES, 7204 E. Broadway **520 296-4715**
PIMA STREET BICYCLES, 5247 E. Pima St. 520 326-4044
RC CYCLES, 428 N. Fremont 520 624-9673
ROADRUNNER BICYCLES, 6177 E. Broadway 520 790-9394
SABINO CYCLES, 7131 E. Tanque Verde 520 885-3666
SUPERCYCLES, 2563 E. Fort Lowell Rd. 520 327-1441
TREK BICYCLES OF TUCSON, 1740 E. Ft. Lowell Rd. 520 327-2265
TRI-SPORTS.COM, 2555 N. Coyote Dr. 520 884-8743
TUCSON BICYCLES. 4743 E. Sunrise Dr. 520 577-7374

YUMA

Johnny Yuma's Bicycle Inc., 1198 S. 4th Ave. 928 373-0700
MR. B'S, 1870 S. 4th Ave. 928 782-0028
MR B'S, 1701 S. Avenue B 928 343-7802
MR B'S, 11242 Foothills Blvd. 928 342-2957

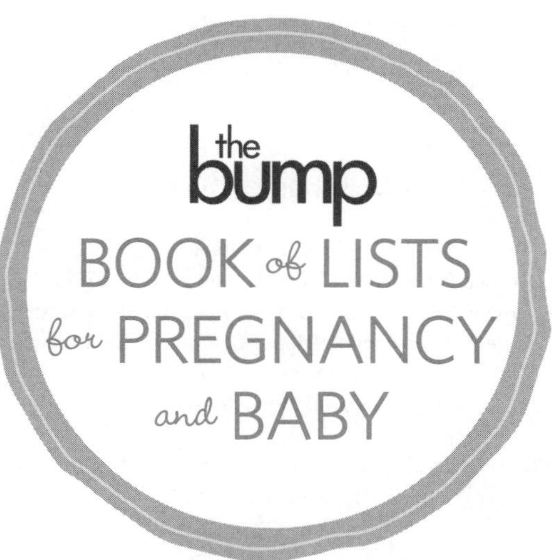

checklists and tips for a *very special* nine months

The ideas, procedures, and suggestions contained in this book are not intended as health care or other professional advice, diagnosis, or a substitute for consulting with your health care professional. Every baby is different and circumstances vary, so you should consult your own physician and use your own common sense. The author and publisher offer no warranties or guarantees, expressed or implied, in the completeness or advisability of the information contained in this book for your particular situation, and disclaim any liability arising from its use.

Published in the United States by Potter Style, an imprint of the Crown Publishing Group, a division of Random House LLC, a Penguin Random House Company, New York.
www.crownpublishing.com
www.potterstyle.com

POTTER STYLE and colophon are registered trademarks of Random House LLC.

Library of Congress Cataloging-in-Publication Data
Roney, Carley.
The bump book of lists for pregnancy and baby : checklists and tips for a very special nine months / Carley Roney and the editors of TheBump.com.
pages cm
1. Pregnancy--Popular works. 2. Pregnant women--Health and hygiene--Popular works. I. Title.
RG525.R6787 2015
618.2--dc23
2014016899

ISBN 978-0-8041-8574-5

Printed in the United States of America

Book design by Renata De Oliveira
Illustrations by Ashley Castro

10 9 8 7 6 5 4 3 2

First Edition

the bump BOOK *of* LISTS *for* PREGNANCY *and* BABY

CARLEY RONEY
& TheBump.com

checklists and tips for a
very special nine months

Potter Style
New York

contents

we love
lists!

Ever since you found out you were pregnant, your mind has probably been racing. You're happy and excited, but there are suddenly so many questions to consider, new things to learn, and new tasks to tackle. That's why we love a list. Everything feels infinitely more doable when you get to check off a box. Chapter by chapter, this book transforms the mind-boggling experience of planning for baby into clear, simple steps. We promise it will make the process much less overwhelming!

YOU SHOULD START AT THE BEGINNING Even if you are at the three-month mark already, skim the sections from conception on—there are tasks and tips you don't want to miss.

YOU DON'T NEED TO CHECK ALL THE BOXES This book should simplify your to-dos, not make you feel like a slacker. In other words, while it's nice to have the whole nursery set up by week 30, if you have not picked out the perfect area rug by the time baby arrives, he will still be completely fine.

YOU WILL LEARN HOW TO TALK LIKE A DOCTOR What is a CVS test? An Apgar score? Rotavirus? You will read about all this and more as you plow through our lists. Don't be surprised if by month nine, you start rattling off facts about cord blood banking and meconium (baby's first poop) and expect everyone else to know what the heck you are talking about.

YOU CAN KEEP NOTES IN THIS BOOK Sure, it's pretty, but go ahead and mark it up anyway. We included a ton of checklists, worksheets, and charts to help you get organized and collect your thoughts. Write your own lists in the margins—we created space for that!

ENJOY! Pregnancy is a time filled with literally hundreds of tasks, but don't forget the fun, indulgent ones. In between tackling to-dos, make time for a prenatal massage, a few date nights, and a prebaby getaway. A wild ride is coming—you need to get some rest. Congrats!

xoxo,
Carley and The Bump team

month-by-month timeline

The countdown is on—you have fewer than forty weeks. The biggest to-do you are going to tackle is obviously growing a baby, which means knowing what to eat, quit, and do, including doctor visits and tests to get. And then there are all the other important tasks—setting up a nursery, getting insurance and finances in order, even just buying new clothes for yourself!

before you get pregnant

- [x] Start tracking your cycle, so you know when you are fertile (page 16).
- [x] Visit your regular doctor or ob-gyn for a preconception checkup (page 17).
- [ ] See the dentist. (You may not be able to have X-rays or certain dental work once you are pregnant. Pregnancy can also make you more vulnerable to gum disease and other problems.)
- [ ] Get German measles and chicken pox immunizations. (They are not recommended during pregnancy.)
- [ ] Talk to relatives about family medical history, including birth defects, miscarriages, and genetic disorders. (If there are any concerns, you may want to have genetic counseling and testing before trying to conceive. Your doctor will ask you about this at your first visit.)
- [x] Start taking prenatal vitamins. (Yes, you do this before you're pregnant. That's because the folic acid they contain helps prevent birth defects when taken in early pregnancy and before.)
- [ ] Apply for a private disability policy if you are self-employed. (This insurance policy can help you receive payment during time you do not work after birth.)

month 1: weeks 1–4*

- [x] Take an official pregnancy test.
- [x] Calculate your (approximate) due date (page 20).
- [x] Find an obstetrician (page 22).
- [x] Schedule your first prenatal checkup as soon as possible.
- [ ] Prepare your health history (page 24).

* *We start counting pregnancy from the first day of your last menstrual period*

- ○ Quit all those pregnancy no-nos (page 26).
- ○ Create a pregnancy nutrition plan (page 28).
- ✓ Start taking a prenatal vitamin (if you haven't already; page 29).

month 2: weeks 5–8

- ✓ Go on your first prenatal visit (page 36).
- ○ Schedule first trimester tests (page 38).
- ○ Figure out how pregnancy and baby will affect your finances (page 40).

month 3: weeks 9–13

- ○ Start buying maternity clothes (page 50).
- ○ Revamp your beauty routine (page 52).
- ○ Plan a babymoon for the second trimester (page 53).
- ○ Chorionic villus sampling (CVS) test (weeks 10-12; page 39)
- ○ Noninvasive prenatal testing (NIPT) (around week 10; page 39)
- ○ Multiple marker screening/nuchal translucency screening (NTS; weeks 10-14; page 39)
- ○ Decide how to tell friends and family you are pregnant (page 56).
- ○ Month 3 prenatal visit (page 59)

month 4: weeks 14–17

- ○ Schedule second trimester tests (page 62).
- ○ Tell your boss about the pregnancy (page 64).
- ○ Start planning your maternity leave and postpartum work schedule (page 65).
- ○ Decide whether you and your partner will both return to work after baby (page 66).
- ○ Month 4 prenatal visit (page 67)

month 5: weeks 18–22

- ○ Amniocentesis and triple screen (weeks 15-18; page 62)
- ○ Midpregnancy ultrasound (page 62)
- ○ Find out baby's gender, if you want to know (page 70).

continues

month-by-month timeline

continued

- ◯ Work on choosing baby's name (page 72).
- ◯ Brainstorm nursery design ideas (page 76).
- ◯ Start your baby registry (page 78).
- ◯ Book childbirth and parenting classes (page 80).
- ◯ Start interviewing pediatricians (page 82).
- ◯ Look into child care options (pages 84).
- ◯ Pass baby shower guest list to host (page 90).
- ◯ Month 5 prenatal visit (page 91)

month 6: weeks 23–27

- ◯ Start babyproofing your home (page 94).
- ◯ Plan your postbaby finances (page 98).
- ◯ If banking cord blood, figure out where and order kit (page 101).
- ◯ Decide whether or not you will circumcise, if it is a boy (page 102).
- ◯ Start counting baby's kicks (page 104).
- ◯ Month 6 prenatal visit (page 105)

month 7: weeks 28–31

- ◯ Schedule third trimester tests, if you can (page 108).
- ◯ If using a doula, start interviews (page 109).
- ◯ Tour your hospital's maternity ward (page 110).
- ◯ Start writing your birth plan (pages 112).
- ◯ Arrange for postbaby help (page 115).
- ◯ Brush up on breastfeeding (page 116).
- ◯ Update or write will, and decide guardianship.
- ◯ Buy life insurance.
- ◯ Update 401(k) and retirement account beneficiaries.
- ◯ Start childbirth class.
- ◯ Your host sends out shower invites.
- ◯ Month 7 prenatal visits (two this month; page 120)

month 8: weeks 32–35

- ○ Prepare baby announcements ahead of time (page 124).
- ○ Make sure you have all baby essentials (page 126).
- ○ Have your baby shower.
- ○ Send thank-you notes for gifts (start one week after shower).
- ○ Finish the nursery (including painting).
- ○ Prepare all baby first-aid and emergency items (page 128).
- ○ Finish your maternity leave paperwork (page 129).
- ○ Pack your hospital bag (page 132).
- ○ Month 8 prenatal visits (two this month; page 136)

month 9: week 36 to delivery

- ○ Install the car seat and get it inspected.
- ○ Find out what screening tests your hospital routinely gives newborns (page 157).
- ○ Speak with your doctor about any additional tests you may need.
- ○ Group B strep test (weeks 35–37; page 108)
- ○ Biophysical profile (if your doctor orders one; page 108)
- ○ Cook and freeze meals for postdelivery.
- ○ Month 9 prenatal visits (weekly until delivery; page 144)
- ○ Birth (cute how we put that there like a little to-do, right?)

newborn: month 1

- ○ 1-month pediatrician visit (weeks 2–4; page 177)

newborn: month 2

- ○ Baby's old enough to be accepted at some day cares (week 6).
- ○ Meet with manager to discuss work hours and return to projects.
- ○ 2-month pediatrician visit (page 178)

baby: month 4

- ○ 4-month pediatrician visit (page 188)

See Planning Baby's Checkups (page 162) and Tracking Baby's Vaccines (165) for the rest!

conception!

let's take a moment to brush up on the basics of exactly how we get pregnant. Even though we all tried to pay attention in health class, some of the finer points probably have faded from memory (or were barely explained in the first place!).

For example, did you know that there is a very small window (usually 24 to 36 hours) in which you ovulate? This is when the egg travels from your ovary (remember, only one ovary will drop an egg each month) down to your fallopian tube. Your most fertile window usually begins five days before ovulation.

Don't worry if you aren't entirely sure when you ovulate. Sperm can live in the body for 72 hours, and in some cases for up to five days—and each ejaculation contains thirty million to three hundred million of them (you only need one to get you pregnant)—so your chances are still good for pregnancy if you come close (earlier is better!).

it's not too late!

If you are already pregnant, use this section to catch up on all the things you have not done yet.

preparing to get pregnant

Even before you start to try for a baby, you will want to wrap your head around some important fertility facts.

IT MAY NOT HAPPEN QUICKLY

It takes healthy couples under the age of 35 an average of six months of unprotected sex to become pregnant.

AGE PLAYS A ROLE

For couples over the age of 35 it takes an average of one year of unprotected sex to become pregnant.

DON'T HAVE YOUR HEART SET ON A SPECIFIC GENDER

There is plenty of anecdotal information suggesting that you can implement lifestyle changes in order to go for a girl or boy. But none are proven to work.

IT'S SIMPLY NOT A PREDICTABLE PROCESS

Doctors cannot always explain why some couples conceive faster than others. It is a puzzle of genetics, age, maternal and paternal health, as well as environmental factors. That is why babies—and pregnancies—are such miracles!

take charge of your health

Prepare your body for pregnancy by taking care of these to-dos.

GET A CHECKUP

Schedule a preconception checkup for yourself and your partner. Address any health or lifestyle issues that might interfere with your ability to conceive, such as polycystic ovary syndrome (PCOS) or uterine fibroids, or that might complicate a pregnancy, such as obesity or diabetes.

CLEAN OUT YOUR CABINETS

Rid your home of ingredients that could affect fertility or harm your baby-to-be. For example, antibacterial soap, plastic bottles, canned goods, laundry detergents, and shower curtains may have ingredients that can disrupt hormonal function. (Toss out anything with triclosan, Teflon, or BPA—bisphenol A.) Ask your doctor if any medicines or supplements you or your partner regularly take could affect your pregnancy.

GIVE YOUR DIET A MAKEOVER

Eat a variety of whole grains, fruits, and vegetables each day, and reduce your intake of trans fat and processed foods. Eat meals rich in iron and calcium. Consider starting a prenatal vitamin now. You will need at least 400 mcg of folic acid per day to help prevent birth defects—even before conception.

GET TO A HEALTHY WEIGHT

Being overweight might make conception more difficult. Plus, losing weight may reduce baby's risk of certain health problems, including being overweight himself or developing high cholesterol, high blood pressure, and insulin resistance later in life. Being overweight could also increase your risk of developing gestational diabetes or preeclampsia, having a stillbirth, or needing a c-section. Being significantly underweight can negatively affect fertility, too.

GET WITH THE (FITNESS) PROGRAM

If you are a couch potato, this is a great time to start working out. Choose exercises that you can continue throughout your pregnancy, like yoga or power walking, because being physically active will help with many pregnancy symptoms, such as backache, leg cramps, and breathlessness.

LIMIT THE LATTES

If you consume more than 200 mg of caffeine—that's about one to two 8-ounce cups—per day, ease up. Heavy caffeine consumption has been associated with fertility problems.

LOSE THE LUBE!

Chemicals in sexual lubricants can kill sperm.

TIP: find your fertile days

Use the Fertility Chart at TheBump.com/tools

knowing when you are fertile

Knowing when you ovulate can only increase your chances of conception. Look for specific clues to when you should be doing the deed.

CHARTING YOUR CYCLE

Ovulation typically happens about fourteen days before a woman's expected period. Start tracking your menstrual cycle, and once you know its typical length, you can predict when you are most fertile each month.

BASAL BODY TEMPERATURE

Doctors suggest measuring your basal body temperature (you can pick up one of these special thermometers at the drugstore). Keep the thermometer next to the bed and take your temp before you sit up in the morning. (Your temperature is less stable at other times each day, so earlier is better.) When you notice a slight spike, even by a few tenths of a degree, you have probably ovulated.

CERVICAL MUCUS

When you ovulate, your cervical mucus is abundant, clear, slippery, and stretchy (kind of like egg whites). The mucus will increase gradually over about nine days before ovulation.

HORMONAL SURGE

If you use an at-home ovulation prediction kit (they are available over the counter), you will notice that your LH (luteinizing hormone) surges around the time that you expect to ovulate. It is best to do the deed on the days just prior, during, and right after the surge.

JUST FEELING DIFFERENT

Sometimes it is as simple as feeling crampy, cranky, or generally sensing that something has shifted. Other symptoms of ovulation can be increased sex drive, bloating, a heightened sense of smell or taste, pain on just one side of the pelvis, and breast tenderness.

having a preconception checkup

A preconception checkup is a smart move, particularly if this is a first baby or there are any underlying health concerns, such as polycystic ovary syndrome or obesity. You will want to see an obstetrician, or—if you are concerned about your fertility—a reproductive endocrinologist. These are some questions you need to ask:

Am I at risk for any problems?

Are there any health issues I should take care of before trying to conceive?

Is my weight okay?

Do you recommend genetic testing?

Are all my immunizations up to date?

Are all my medications safe? If not, what can I do or take instead?

baby's size

almost microscopic!

WEEKS 3–4

poppy seed

sometime this month, a fertilized egg makes its way down your fallopian tube and, once fertilized, begins the long journey into your uterus (baby's home for the next nine months). From week 1 to week 4, you probably don't even know you are pregnant yet. It can take up to six weeks before you even see a positive reading on an at-home pregnancy test (a blood test can tell you sooner).

how baby is growing

Right from the get-go, baby's major organs, like the brain and spinal cord, start to develop.

how you are feeling

Since your body is working hard, you are about to get very, very sleepy. More intense pregnancy symptoms will not kick in until later, but you may have some other telltale signs: sore boobs, bloating, or a good old-fashioned case of the cranky pants.

CALCULATING YOUR DUE DATE

There's no way to be sure exactly when baby will arrive. Here's how you can get an idea: Find the first day of your **last menstrual period (LMP)** on this chart, then look at the **estimated date of delivery (EDD)** directly next to it.

LMP **JANUARY**	EDD **OCT/NOV**	LMP **FEBRUARY**	EDD **NOV/DEC**	LMP **MARCH**	EDD **DEC/JAN**	LMP **APRIL**	EDD **JAN/FEB**	LMP **MAY**	EDD **FEB/MAR**	LMP **JUNE**	EDD **MAR/APR**
1	8	1	8	1	6	1	6	1	5	1	7
2	9	2	9	2	7	2	7	2	6	2	8
3	10	3	10	3	8	3	8	3	7	3	9
4	11	4	11	4	9	4	9	4	8	4	10
5	12	5	12	5	10	5	10	5	9	5	11
6	13	6	13	6	11	6	11	6	10	6	12
7	14	7	14	7	12	7	12	7	11	7	13
8	15	8	15	8	13	8	13	8	12	8	14
9	16	9	16	9	14	9	14	9	13	9	15
10	17	10	17	10	15	10	15	10	14	10	16
11	18	11	18	11	16	11	16	11	15	11	17
12	19	12	19	12	17	12	17	12	16	12	18
13	20	13	20	13	18	13	18	13	17	13	19
14	21	14	21	14	19	14	19	14	18	14	20
15	22	15	22	15	20	15	20	15	19	15	21
16	23	16	23	16	21	16	21	16	20	16	22
17	24	17	24	17	22	17	22	17	21	17	23
18	25	18	25	18	23	18	23	18	22	18	24
19	26	19	26	19	24	19	24	19	23	19	25
20	27	20	27	20	25	20	25	20	24	20	26
21	28	21	28	21	26	21	26	21	25	21	27
22	29	22	29	22	27	22	27	22	26	22	28
23	30	23	30	23	28	23	28	23	27	23	29
24	31	24	1	24	29	24	29	24	28	24	30
25	1	25	2	25	30	25	30	25	29	25	31
26	2	26	3	26	31	26	31	26	1	26	1
27	3	27	4	27	1	27	1	27	2	27	2
28	4	28	5	28	2	28	2	28	3	28	3
29	5			29	3	29	3	29	4	29	4
30	6			30	4	30	4	30	5	30	5
31	7			31	5			31	6		

LMP **JULY**	EDD **APR/MAY**	LMP **AUGUST**	EDD **MAY/JUNE**	LMP **SEPTEMBER**	EDD **JUNE/JULY**	LMP **OCTOBER**	EDD **JULY/AUG**	LMP **NOVEMBER**	EDD **AUG/SEP**	LMP **DECEMBER**	EDD **SEP/OCT**
1	6	1	7	1	7	1	7	1	7	1	6
2	7	2	8	2	8	2	8	2	8	2	7
3	8	3	9	3	9	3	9	3	9	3	8
4	9	4	10	4	10	4	10	4	10	4	9
5	10	5	11	5	11	5	11	5	11	5	10
6	11	6	12	6	12	6	12	6	12	6	11
7	12	7	13	7	13	7	13	7	13	7	12
8	13	8	14	8	14	8	14	8	14	8	13
9	14	9	15	9	15	9	15	9	15	9	14
10	15	10	16	10	16	10	16	10	16	10	15
11	16	11	17	11	17	11	17	11	17	11	16
12	17	12	18	12	18	12	18	12	18	12	17
13	18	13	19	13	19	13	19	13	19	13	18
14	19	14	20	14	20	14	20	14	20	14	19
15	20	15	21	15	21	15	21	15	21	15	20
16	21	16	22	16	22	16	22	16	22	16	21
17	22	17	23	17	23	17	23	17	23	17	22
18	23	18	24	18	24	18	24	18	24	18	23
19	24	19	25	19	25	19	25	19	25	19	24
20	25	20	26	20	26	20	26	20	26	20	25
21	26	21	27	21	27	21	27	21	27	21	26
22	27	22	28	22	28	22	28	22	28	22	27
23	28	23	29	23	29	23	29	23	29	23	28
24	29	24	30	24	30	24	30	24	30	24	29
25	30	25	31	25	1	25	31	25	31	25	30
26	1	26	1	26	2	26	1	26	1	26	1
27	2	27	2	27	3	27	2	27	2	27	2
28	3	28	3	28	4	28	3	28	3	28	3
29	4	29	4	29	5	29	4	29	4	29	4
30	5	30	5	30	6	30	5	30	5	30	5
31	6	31	6			31	6			31	6

my baby is due: 

planning your prenatal visits

Over the course of your pregnancy, you might start to feel like you live at your doctor or midwife's office. Scheduled visits will vary depending on your physician and how everything is going, but these guidelines should give you an idea of how often you will see your practitioner:

WEEKS 4–28
Every four weeks

WEEKS 28–35
Every two to three weeks

WEEK 36 TO DELIVERY
One visit per week

how pregnant you are

When you find out what week you are in, you may be shocked. That's because doctors count pregnancy as starting the first day of your last period (yes, before you were actually pregnant). So if you are four weeks pregnant, you only conceived about two weeks ago.

choosing an ob

If your gynecologist or family doctor is not an obstetrician, it is time to interview a few and find a good fit. Asking the right questions will help you make an informed decision. After your interview, think about whether the doctor really listened to your concerns and seemed comfortable with your views on pregnancy, childbirth, and medical care. If the answer is no, keep looking.

How many babies do you deliver per year?

If it's a group practice, what are my chances of having my primary OB deliver my baby?

Who will be there if my primary OB is not available in an emergency or when I am in labor?

What is your cesarean rate?

Do you perform episiotomies regularly?

What is your attitude about patients having a birth plan?

How do you feel about labor pain medication? Immunizations? Doulas? Inductions?

What are your after-hours policies? Are you available between visits, or is there a nurse who can provide answers?

What experience do you have with high-risk pregnancies?

considering a midwife?

A midwife is trained to give medical care to a woman having a normal pregnancy and may also emphasize emotional and social needs. Midwives are also trained to help moms wishing for natural births with as few interventions as possible. However, a midwife may not be an option if you have certain pregnancy risk factors, including those that require a c-section.

preparing your health history

Knowing about a genetic problem or a pregnancy disorder that runs in your family can inform you and your doctor that you might need to be monitored extra-closely once you get pregnant, or it might make you decide to get special genetic testing to ensure baby is doing okay. Before you head to the doctor, know the answers to these questions:

Has either of our moms had a history of preeclampsia, any premature babies, or babies with malformations?

Were any babies in my extended family ever born premature or with a birth defect?

Has anyone in my family had genetic disorders like cystic fibrosis, Tay-Sachs disease, or sickle-cell anemia?

What is my ethnicity? (Certain conditions run in specific cultural lineages. For example, Tay-Sachs disease is more common in Ashkenazi Jewish backgrounds and sickle-cell anemia is more common in African Americans than in some other populations.)

How old am I? (Obviously you know the answer. Your doctor will want to know, too, since the chance of certain genetic issues, like Down syndrome, increases with maternal age.)

BRING YOUR PARTNER

It's okay to go to obstetrician appointments solo, but your partner should definitely come along to the first one, where you will likely be asked a ton of questions. His family's history can affect your baby as much as yours does.

CONSIDER GENETIC TESTING

Armed with your health histories, your doctor can explain the different genetic tests available to you and your partner, so you can decide together what tests you might want to get.

Here are the questions you can expect:

Will you be age 35 or older on your due date?

Do any of these conditions run in your families?

- ○ Thalassemia (a blood disorder that leads to anemia)
- ○ Neural tube defect
- ○ Congenital heart defect
- ○ Down syndrome
- ○ Tay-Sachs disease
- ○ Canavan disease (a neurological disorder)
- ○ Muscular dystrophy
- ○ Huntington's disease
- ○ Cystic fibrosis
- ○ Familial dysautonomia (a disorder that affects the nervous system)
- ○ Sickle-cell anemia or trait
- ○ Hemophilia or other blood disorders
- ○ Mental retardation
- ○ Fragile X syndrome
- ○ Other inherited genetic or chromosomal disorders

Do you have a maternal metabolic disorder (e.g., type 1 diabetes, phenylketonuria [PKU])?

Have you or the baby's father had a child with birth defects not listed above?

Have you had recurrent pregnancy loss or a stillbirth?

Have you taken any medications, supplements, vitamins, herbs, alcohol, or drugs since your last menstrual period? If yes, what and how much?

adoption and egg and sperm donors

If you or your partner is adopted, or you used a donor egg or sperm, you may not have all the information other couples do about your family's medical history. That is okay, though. Share what you know with the doctor and listen carefully in order to make an informed decision about genetic testing.

knowing what to quit now

When your body is busy with the delicate work of building a human being, certain toxins and activities can mess with the program and cause serious problems. Take this list seriously.

AVOID THESE NOW:

DRINKING Alcohol can cause fetal alcohol syndrome (FAS) during pregnancy. FAS can lead to a host of disabilities, including mental retardation. Sure, you can take a sip or two of champagne at that New Year's party, but otherwise, it's imperative to hold off until baby is here.

SMOKING The list of concerns is even greater with tobacco intake. Premature birth, low birth weight, and even stillbirth have been associated with a mom's use of cigarettes. Secondhand smoke can be a silent culprit as well. So, ask your partner to quit, too.

COLD CUTS Say good-bye to turkey and Swiss on rye. Deli and lunch meats can contain a minuscule bacterium called *Listeria monocytogenes*, which causes the food-borne illness listeriosis. The illness can lead to meningitis, preterm labor, miscarriage, and even stillbirth.

RAW FISH AND MEAT Sushi, raw or uncooked eggs, and raw meat can also cause food poisoning. Now that you are pregnant, eat only fish, meat, and poultry that has been fully cooked.

UNPASTEURIZED FOODS Skip the cheese, raw milk, or farmers market juice if the label does not say it has been pasteurized. It could contain harmful bacteria.

SOME MEDICATIONS Bring a list of your medications to your doctor or midwife and see if they are safe to take during pregnancy. While many are considered unsafe (or untested) for pregnancy, there are some situations in which doctors believe the risk to an unborn baby is minimal compared with the benefits to mom's health. Two examples are when a mother has diabetes or suffers from clinical depression.

CLEANING THE LITTER BOX While Frisky is cute and cuddly, his poop could contain a parasite called toxoplasma. It can cross the placenta and infect an unborn baby. If you do change the litter box, wear thick rubber gloves and a mask.

CAFFEINE (This one seems so unfair!) You may be dead tired, but too much caffeine has been linked to an increased risk for premature birth and miscarriage. Limit your daily intake of caffeine to 200 mg or less (one or two 8-ounce cups of coffee). And watch out for the stimulant in forms other than coffee, too. Chocolate, tea, energy drinks, and many desserts contain it, so count those in your daily caffeine total.

BURNING THE MIDNIGHT OIL Now is a great time to get on a better sleep schedule. Skip the late nights and turn in at an earlier hour when you can. Catching more z's also lowers your body's stress levels, which can only benefit you and your new passenger.

knowing what to eat

Now that you are pregnant, it is even more important that you (and baby!) get the right nutrients. You will need an extra 300 calories a day to help baby grow. And more than ever, you need to eat plenty of brain-cell-building fats as well as foods with calcium, iron, and folic acid. Log your daily intake and make sure you are on the right track.

EACH DAY YOU NEED:

GRAINS (6–8 OUNCES) Brown rice, wild rice, whole-grain bread and cereal, whole wheat pasta, pitas and tortillas, wheat germ

DAIRY OR OTHER CALCIUM-RICH FOODS (3 CUPS) Low-fat milk, pasteurized low-fat cheese, yogurt, collard greens, edamame, sesame seeds, calcium-fortified juices (just watch the sugar), tofu

VEGETABLES (2½ TO 3 CUPS) Winter squash, spinach, kale, lettuce, broccoli, bell peppers, carrots, sweet potato, green beans, zucchini, corn, broccoli, cauliflower

FRUITS (2 CUPS) Oranges, grapefruit, kiwis, strawberries, blackberries, raspberries, mangoes, peaches, cantaloupes, honeydew melons, apricots, apples, pears, bananas, cherries, blueberries

PROTEIN (5½ TO 6½ OUNCES) Poultry, beef, lamb, low-mercury seafood, DHA-enriched eggs, pasteurized low-fat cheese, yogurt, nuts, peanut butter, tofu, edamame, beans, soy pasta

FLUIDS (AT LEAST EIGHT 8-OUNCE SERVINGS) Water, juice (again, watch the sugar), decaf tea

picking a prenatal vitamin

Start taking a prenatal vitamin immediately, if you haven't already. These specially designed multivitamins contain specific ingredients to promote a healthy pregnancy. The number-one most important ingredient is folic acid, a nutrient that is known to prevent neural tube defects like spina bifida in babies.

CHECK THE LABEL. YOURS SHOULD HAVE:

- ○ **FOLIC ACID, AT LEAST 400 MCG** For preventing birth defects
- ○ **CALCIUM, 1,300 MG** For healthy bones and teeth (for you and baby); you may need a calcium supplement to reach this total
- ○ **IRON, 30 MG** To fuel your increased blood flow and prevent iron-deficiency anemia (translation: so you won't feel so tired)
- ○ **VITAMIN A, 770 MCG** For vision and cell growth
- ○ **VITAMIN B-12, 6 MCG** To help keep those nerves and red blood cells healthy
- ○ **VITAMIN B-6, 29 MG** For synthesizing serotonin, an important brain builder
- ○ **VITAMIN C, 85 MG** To help with iron absorption
- ○ **VITAMIN D, 400–800 IU** To help your body absorb calcium (for strong bones!)
- ○ **VITAMIN E, 15 MG** Important for fetal growth
- ○ **RIBOFLAVIN, 2 MG** For growth and energy
- ○ **COPPER, 1–2 MG** For iron absorption
- ○ **THIAMINE, 1.4 MG** For nerve and muscle function
- ○ **ZINC, 15 MG** For staving off colds and the flu
- ○ **DHA/OMEGA-3, 300 MG** For brain development (sometimes it comes in a separate pill)

top 10 healthy 300-calorie snacks

Eating snacks throughout the day will help boost your energy level—and keep you from overeating at mealtimes. Try these (roughly) 300-calorie ideas.

1. **one third cup hummus** served with one cup assorted raw veggies, like carrots or celery, and one half of a 6-inch whole wheat pita
2. **eight-ounce smoothie** made of 8 ounces 1-percent milk or soy milk and 1 cup mixed berries, and 1 tablespoon flax or chia seeds
3. **medium baked potato** topped with a half-cup black beans, 2 tablespoons 2-percent Greek yogurt (in place of sour cream), 2 tablespoons salsa, and chives
4. **one banana and 2 tablespoons peanut butter** Use all-natural PB to be extra-healthy; you can sub in an apple instead.
5. **one cup low-fat cottage cheese** with 1 cup fresh fruit and 2 tablespoons chopped nuts
6. **a quarter-cup dried nuts and a quarter-cup dried fruits** This snack is full of healthy fats and proteins.
7. **six cups air-popped popcorn** with a quarter-cup Parmesan cheese
8. **one cup whole-grain cereal** Pour on soy or skim milk and add 1 tablespoon nuts and a half-cup chopped fruit.
9. **two handfuls baked tortilla chips** and a half-cup salsa for dipping
10. **two slices of whole wheat toast** with a quarter of an avocado spread onto them

curbing your cravings

The whole pickle-and-ice-cream thing seems so cliché, but pregnancy cravings are real. It's not good to give in to every one you have, though. If you are jonesing for junk, try these healthy alternatives.

INSTEAD OF ICE CREAM

Try sorbet; Popsicles; low-fat frozen yogurt

INSTEAD OF DOUGHNUTS AND PASTRIES

Try whole-grain toast with jam or decaf tea with a touch of honey

INSTEAD OF COOKIES, CAKE, AND PIE

Try angel food cake; graham crackers and peanut butter; low-fat banana, zucchini, or pumpkin bread; oatmeal with brown sugar and cinnamon; low-fat pudding

INSTEAD OF CANDY

Try trail mix

INSTEAD OF CHOCOLATE

Try low-fat chocolate milk or low-sugar hot cocoa

INSTEAD OF CHIPS

Try popcorn (air-popped or light microwave); pretzels; whole-grain cereal

TIP: crazy cravings not to ignore

If you start craving things that are not food, such as dirt, charcoal, clay, or laundry starch, this is a disorder called pica, which some experts think may be related to iron deficiency or other dietary needs. Call your doctor ASAP! (And, obviously, don't eat anything that's not food.)

feeling first pregnancy symptoms

Your body is working hard to create the right situation for baby to grow and thrive. This means it is producing more hormones, and there are bound to be side effects.

Don't worry, though, if you are not feeling these. Some women get the pregnancy nasties and some don't. Not having early pregnancy symptoms is not a sign of a problem. (You are just lucky!)

SPOTTING

Light bleeding, called "implantation bleeding," may occur five to ten days after conception; it's a sign that the embryo has implanted itself in the uterine wall (home for the next nine months!). If you notice anything more than light spotting, or are at all concerned about spotting, talk with your doctor.

SORE BOOBS

Breasts may get tender as early as five or six weeks as a surge in progesterone signals the body to prepare for breastfeeding and blood flow to your chest increases. Your breasts may start getting bigger then, too.

DARKER AREOLAS

Darkening of the area around the nipples, also a result of hormonal surges, can appear as early as a week or two after conception. Some believe that the darkening happens to help your newborn find the food.

FREQUENT URINATION

Two to three weeks after conception, your body produces the hormone human chorionic gonadotropin (HCG), which leads to more frequent urination.

FATIGUE (WE ARE TALKING TOTAL EXHAUSTION)
Imagine the amount of extra energy your body needs to create the framework for a human being. That's why you are probably more exhausted than you have ever been. Nap and rest as often as you can.

MORNING SICKNESS
The one-two punch of (all day) nausea and vomiting strikes for most sufferers around week 6. There's no clear answer why an estimated 50 to 90 percent of pregnant women get morning sickness, but it is likely hormones again. See page 42 for our tips.

SENSITIVITY TO SMELLS
There's no science to back up that this symptom even exists, but there are enough pregnant women who swear they have newly increased powers of smell to make us believers. From your coworker's perfume to the trash can on the other side of the house that needs to be emptied, smells may suddenly become much stronger (and maybe unbearable) to you. Scientists speculate that it's due to the estrogen spike, and almost certainly linked to morning sickness.

BLOATING
The boost in progesterone and estrogen causes many women to swell up early in pregnancy.

month TWO (weeks 5–8)

baby's size

WEEK 5
apple seed

WEEK 6
sweet pea

WEEK 7
blueberry

WEEK 8
raspberry

at this stage, pregnancy still feels pretty surreal. You don't look like you are expecting, and you are probably keeping your news under wraps—to most people at least. But having a baby is constantly on your mind, so you are ready to start planning ahead. Reveal your pregnancy whenever you feel comfortable, but most new moms wait until they hear the fetal heartbeat, which can happen as early as six to nine weeks (at your first prenatal visit). Some wait until they hit the second trimester mark.

how baby is growing

Here we go! Baby's circulatory, digestive, and nervous systems are developing. Her hands, feet, legs, and arms are starting to form. By the end of this month, baby's brain will be producing one hundred brain cells a minute and she will sprout a nose, mouth, and eyes.

how you are feeling

This month, all those annoying pregnancy symptoms will kick in, if they haven't already. You are probably running to the bathroom (either to pee or throw up!), having some mood swings, and feeling bloated and oh-so-tired. All totally normal.

having your first prenatal visit

Your first visit to the doctor is typically around week 8. Waiting those first few weeks between your positive test result at home and this first visit can feel like forever. Here is what to expect when you finally get there.

DUE DATE

The obstetrician will give you an estimated due date. There are a couple of ways to figure this out. If you know the date of your last period, you can count ahead 280 days, or 40 weeks (use the chart on page 20). The size of the baby on the ultrasound can also help determine the due date.

EXAM

You will have a thorough physical, including a urine test, pap smear, pelvic exam, breast exam, and blood work—even if you recently had your yearly gynecological checkup.

ULTRASOUND

You may need to get an ultrasound to confirm everything looks as it should and to see how far along you are. (In case you are wondering: *Ultrasound* is the name of the procedure; the *sonogram* is the picture that is created.) Don't think you are going to get to count fingers and toes—it's too early to really see anything yet. It's not until about week 20 when your technician will be able to determine the sex. However, you may be able to see the heartbeat—a flicker on the screen!

GENETIC TESTING COUNSELING

Your OB will discuss genetic testing and what warning signs to look for. It's routine—don't be alarmed.

HEALTH QUESTIONS

Expect to give your OB or midwife a full medical history. You will answer lots of questions about your partner's family history, so bring him if you can!

Questions you will want to ask the doctor:

How much weight is ideal for me to gain?

Am I at risk for any complications or conditions?

What are the screenings that I need? When and why should I get them?

What should I (and shouldn't I) be eating?

Is my normal workout routine okay? What should I change?

Is it safe to have sex during my pregnancy?

Is it safe to travel while I am pregnant? Until how many weeks?

Are there over-the-counter medications I can take? What should I avoid?

What about my prescription medications—are they safe? If not, what can I take or do instead?

Is there a prenatal vitamin brand you recommend?

Are there local prenatal classes you recommend?

Are there symptoms I can expect before my next visit and what can I do about them?

Will I see you every visit, or do you rotate with other doctors in your practice? What about delivery—will you definitely be there, or might it be someone else?

How do I know what is covered by insurance? Does your office have a person who specializes in insurance claims?

getting the lowdown on first trimester tests

All those pee cups and needle pokes can start blurring together. This list should help: the most common tests in early pregnancy.

URINE TEST

Each time you see the doctor or midwife, you will give a urine sample to be screened for glucose and protein. If your glucose is high, it could be a sign of gestational diabetes. Elevated protein may mean a more serious issue like preeclampsia—a high-blood-pressure condition that puts you at risk for complications.

ULTRASOUND

Around week 8 to week 10, an ultrasound can detect a fetal heartbeat and confirm that the pregnancy is uterine (as opposed to ectopic or tubular). At this point, baby will look like a small lima bean—just how much detail you can see will depend on how sophisticated your doctor's machine is. Have the technician point out the yolk sac, gestational sac, and fetal pole (the first evidence of an embryo). You may even be able to see a quick flutter—that's the heartbeat. If you have an uncomplicated pregnancy, you may only have one more ultrasound (the midpregnancy one), but if your doctor needs to check on baby because of gestational diabetes or another condition, you may have many more.

INITIAL BLOOD WORK

Your obstetrician will take blood for a long list of screenings. She will determine your blood type and measure your levels of HCG—the hormone indicates whether baby is developing well. She will look for signs of anemia or infection, and you will be screened for hepatitis B, syphilis, and other STDs, HIV, and immunity to German measles.

PAP SMEAR

In addition to blood work, your first visit will include a pap smear to check for infections and abnormal cervical cells.

NONINVASIVE PRENATAL TESTING (NIPT)

Known by brand names MaterniT21 or Harmony, this is a blood test taken around week 10 to determine a fetus's risk for chromosomal disorders, including Down syndrome (trisomy 21), Patau syndrome (trisomy 13), Edwards syndrome (trisomy 18), and sex chromosome disorders, such as Turner's syndrome. It can help you decide if you would like further tests, such as amniocentesis or chorionic villus sampling. It's typically offered to women over age 35 and those at increased risk of carrying a baby with an abnormality due to family history.

CHORIONIC VILLUS SAMPLING (CVS)

This optional test can detect genetic disorders such as Tay-Sachs disease and sickle-cell anemia, and rule out chromosomal disorders like Down syndrome. CVS is done between week 10 and week 12, and involves analyzing genetic material from a small piece of the placenta. It also determines baby's gender with total accuracy, so if you get it, you will know whether it is a boy or girl earlier than most pregnant women do.

MULTIPLE MARKER SCREENING/NUCHAL TRANSLUCENCY SCREENING (NTS)

A special ultrasound, performed between week 10 and week 14, screens for Down syndrome and other chromosomal disorders, as well as congenital heart defects. While NTS does not provide definitive results, it can determine your risk factor and help you decide whether to pursue further testing. A blood test, performed at the same appointment as the NTS, screens for HCG and PAPP-A, two pregnancy hormones. Abnormally high or low levels could indicate a problem.

predicting your health care costs

The bill for the birth of your baby can vary vastly depending on your insurance, health care provider, and hospital. Make sure you are well versed in the following factors that can affect your costs before you make your prenatal care and birth plans.

UNDERSTAND YOUR INSURANCE PLAN

One insurance plan can be so different from the next. Call your plan's pregnancy hotline and ask a ton of questions. Find out the deductible, co-pay, and out-of-pocket maximums to estimate what your costs will be. Don't have insurance? You *can* enroll after you find out you are pregnant.

CHOOSE IN-NETWORK PROVIDERS

Choose an ob-gyn and a hospital or birthing center that is "in-network" to avoid large out-of-pocket costs. This means the insurance company has prenegotiated a fixed cost for the service of birthing a baby, so you will have no surprises when you receive your bill. Be forewarned that they also have decided exactly what they will and won't pay for—you should know the details in advance. Hoping for a private hospital room? Chances are, it isn't covered.

KNOW THAT AN ALTERNATIVE WILL COST YOU

If you can't bear to part with your ob-gyn, even though she is not on your plan, ask if she charges her own fees for delivery. Consult her office about what you will likely pay for nine months of prenatal care (including labor and delivery, tests, and newborn and postnatal appointments).

AVOID EXTRA TESTS

Insurance companies dictate exactly what they feel is essential in prenatal care for a low-risk pregnancy. Your obstetrician might offer up other options—

TIP: stay up to date

Get the latest scoop on health insurance and how it affects pregnancy at TheBump.com/healthinsurance.

additional sonograms, for example. Be clear about what is covered. If you are high-risk, the rules often change and the plan may cover more maternity tests.

DON'T STAY TOO LONG AT THE HOSPITAL

Check the length of hospital stay that is covered and only stay that long. It may seem extremely short to be there only for 24 to 48 hours after a vaginal birth or 48 to 72 hours after a cesarean birth, but being home is good for you and baby anyway.

SHOP AROUND

If you are not tied to a hospital because of a relationship with your ob-gyn, and you will be responsible for the cost, look for one that offers good rates for delivery and postnatal care (yes, you can ask). If you anticipate an uncomplicated birth, consider using a birthing center—this is a more home-like place to give birth, often under a midwife's care—instead of a hospital. The costs are often about half of what a hospital birth would carry.

TAKE GENERIC MEDICATIONS

Work with your doctor to explore if there are generic alternatives to drugs prescribed during prenatal or postnatal care. You may also be able to take over-the-counter prenatal vitamins instead of prescription ones.

BE CAREFUL ABOUT A SCHEDULED C-SECTION

There might be an expense related to having a c-section "by choice." Call your provider to make sure your procedure is covered based on your reason for having it.

NOTIFY YOUR CARRIER OF BABY'S BIRTH ASAP

Many plans require that a new baby be added to a family's insurance policy within thirty days of birth—or even sooner—in order for their expenses to be covered.

top 10 morning sickness solutions

Nausea, the most notorious pregnancy symptom, typically shows up around week 6 and can hang out until the beginning of the second trimester. Here is how to ease the queasiness.

1. **graze.** Eating five to seven small meals a day can keep your blood sugar stable, which can prevent excess nausea. Stock up on cheese sticks, yogurt cups, whole-grain crackers, and packable fruits and veggies, so you never get that empty-stomach-meets-I-want-to-puke feeling.
2. **avoid triggers.** Pay attention to when you are feeling sick. If riding in the backseat of the car or smelling strong perfume makes you want to throw up, then switch to the front, or avoid that coworker who seems to bathe in cologne.
3. **go for ginger.** Ginger is a natural belly soother. Try it in tea, which can be sipped slowly, so as not to irritate your stomach, and can be calming, too. Ginger ale and ginger candies are also popular remedies.
4. **keep candy on hand.** Licking a lollipop, sucking on a lozenge, or chewing a piece of gum can distract you from feeling sick, and also prevent you from puking. Try pregnancy lollipops made with spearmint, ginger, lavender, and other homeopathic ingredients to help with morning sickness.
5. **brush your teeth.** Especially if you have been getting sick a lot, cleaning your pearly whites is not only an obvious choice, but also can help prevent nausea. (Plus, being pregnant makes you more likely to develop gum disease. So, brushing: win, win, win.)

6. **skip fatty foods.** Those greasy fries will just make you feel sicker. Instead, get your fill of healthy carbs like pasta, rice, and whole-grain bread. They will help keep you satisfied all day and stave off nausea caused by low blood sugar.

7. **get outside.** Some moms-to-be swear just stepping out into the fresh air helps them feel better. Take a walk or spend some time sitting under your favorite shady tree. Hey, it's good for your mental state, too.

8. **save your drink until after your meal.** You might think sipping a smoothie while eating your lunch is a pregnancy "do," but it will probably give you a bad case of the bloat and lead to undue queasiness. Eat your meal now and drink up later to keep from filling your stomach with too much at once—that could set things off.

9. **say no to sudden moves.** Getting up quickly from a seated or lying-down position can cause you to become woozy and bring on nausea. Take it slow. Your body, and belly, will thank you.

10. **try these other tummy tamers:** Peanut butter, apple cider vinegar (add a tablespoon to a glass of water with honey), peppermint, lemon, and Gatorade (not together, of course!). Suck on ice, or sip a cold beverage: Even a quick shift in temperature—like drinking a hot beverage and then an icy one—can keep sickness at bay.

creating an exercise plan

Now that you have gotten over the shock of knowing you are pregnant, you will need a workout that will ease some of the aches and pains of pregnancy without giving you new ones. Aim for at least 30 minutes a day of moderate exercise.

A SAMPLE SCHEDULE

Make it a goal to exercise six days a week. (And feel free to take an extra day off here and there.)

MONDAY

- ◯ Core work
- ◯ Pelvic floor exercises (think squats, lunges, and leg lifts)

TUESDAY

- ◯ 20 to 30 minutes of cardio activity

WEDNESDAY

- ◯ Upper body strength training
- ◯ Lower body strength training. (Tip: Use full water bottles as barbells. Invest in an exercise ball, which can do double duty as a birthing ball later.)

THURSDAY

- ◯ 20 to 30 minutes of cardio activity

FRIDAY

- ◯ Core work
- ◯ Pelvic floor exercises
- ◯ Upper body strength training
- ◯ Lower body strength training

SATURDAY

- ◯ Core work
- ◯ Pelvic floor exercises

CHOOSING YOUR WORKOUT

Most exercises are safe to continue now that you're pregnant. Be careful not to overheat, overexert, lie on your back for long periods of time, or do anything where you risk falling or injury. (That includes some yoga poses—your balance is not the same once you have a bump!) These are some examples:

SAFE	NOT SAFE
Walking	**Running to the point of exhaustion**
Jogging or spinning	**Kickboxing**
Swimming	**Scuba diving**
Prenatal yoga	**Bikram (hot) yoga**

WARNING!

It's important not to overdo it. Listen to your body. Call your doctor if you experience muscle weakness, vaginal bleeding, calf pain or swelling, dizziness, headache, overheating, pain in your pubic bone area, shortness of breath, cramps, chest pain, severe nausea, or leakage of amniotic fluid.

capturing your growing bump

As your body changes, take plenty of photos to document your journey.

Take a picture of your growing bump every month.

Try the same pose (stand to the side to really show that belly!) in the same place in your home.

Wear something slightly formfitting that will stretch as you grow.

Get creative and hold a colorful sign or pose next to a chalkboard that says what week or month you are in.

For fun, add a seasonal item, like a Santa hat during the holidays, to show how time passes, or pose with meaningful things, like the first onesie you buy for baby.

After birth, take a picture with your brand-new baby.

date: ______________ weight: _________

FIRST PRENATAL VISIT

tests i had:

____

____

____

____

symptoms/issues we discussed:

____

____

____

____

i saw/heard:

____

____

____

____

doctor's orders:

____

____

____

____

my next appointment is:

____

____

____

____

baby's size

WEEK 9
olive

WEEK 10
prune

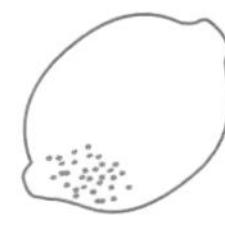

WEEK 11
lime

WEEK 12
plum

WEEK 13
peach

if pregnancy were a marathon (and trust us, it is), you are about to complete the first leg. While you still may be dealing with some unpleasant pregnancy symptoms, by the end of the month they should start to lessen. Your body is beginning to change—so you will need to revamp your wardrobe (even if you are not ready for maternity clothes yet). This month's big milestone: You will probably hear your baby's heartbeat! That means it's almost time to start screaming from the rooftops that you are expecting!

how baby is growing

Baby is no longer an embryo. As a fetus, he continues to grow like crazy, developing cartilage and the beginnings of bones, hair, teeth, and nails. Major organs are fully functional, and hands and feet look less webbed. He can even swallow and kick and has reflexes.

how you are feeling

Moody! Those hormones just keep raging. You may be experiencing morning (or all-day) sickness. Do trial and error to see what makes you feel better. Frequent peeing, fatigue, nasal congestion, and headaches are also common in month three.

TIP: get a belly band

This slide-on panel of fabric covers an unzipped zipper, making your regular jeans into maternity jeans for the first few months.

knowing what to wear

When it comes to your wardrobe, the good news is you can keep wearing some things that you already have in your closet, like leggings, wrap dresses, and almost anything stretchy. Then, you will just need a few basics to hold you until about month four. After that, head to the maternity store for some clear mom-to-be wardrobe staples.

YOU HAVE

- ◯ **JEANS** Forget those skinny jeans and go for your loosest pair (like those low-slung boyfriend jeans) for the first few months.
- ◯ **BLAZER** Button up a jacket with a bit of stretchy Lycra (not a stiff one) to hide your growing belly, or keep it open to let your bump breathe.
- ◯ **TANK TOP** Believe it or not, this skimpy staple probably has loads of stretch and you will be able to wear it until d-day. Bonus if it has side ruching.
- ◯ **T-SHIRT** A larger-size shirt from your own closet will work for the first few months.
- ◯ **CARDIGAN** A basic button-up keeps you prepared for random hot-flashes and cold spells.
- ◯ **YOGA PANTS OR LEGGINGS** Choose a dark hue (it's more slimming) and a thicker pair that can take you through the seasons.
- ◯ **LITTLE BLACK DRESS** A style that is not fitted and has stretch is ideal.
- ◯ **BLACK PANTS** A pair with a side zip is easy to leave open unnoticeably.

YOU NEED

- ◯ **MATERNITY JEANS** Getting a pair (with a stretch panel) that flatters is worth the investment. You will wear them almost every day and can dress them up or down.
- ◯ **MATERNITY TANK TOP** Hide your unbuttoned pants with extra-long styles.
- ◯ **MATERNITY T-SHIRT** Flaunt your great cleavage with a V-neck.
- ◯ **MATERNITY CARDIGAN** Pick a neutral hue, like black, so you can wear it with many different outfits and dress it up or down.
- ◯ **MATERNITY SKIRT** Show off your legs (maybe your thinnest assets!) with a short hemline.
- ◯ **BIG BLACK DRESS** Toward the end of pregnancy, a maternity style will be the only one that will not ride up in front. This is the piece you will want to wear to your shower, work, and other special events.
- ◯ **UNDER-BELLY BLACK PANTS** These don't show seams when you wear fitted tanks and tees.
- ◯ **MATERNITY BLACK PANTS** A wide panel keeps your belly covered—and prevents the pants from sagging.

giving your beauty routine a makeover

You may have a pretty set beauty routine, but pregnancy will force you to make some adjustments, whether it's because your skin is changing or you're using ingredients that could be harmful. Here are some cautions and solutions to common pregnancy beauty problems.

BE KINDER TO YOUR SKIN

You might find that hormones wreak havoc on your skin. It may get super-dry. When this happens, exfoliate, moisturize, and use a mild facial cleanser. If you suddenly have oily, pimply skin, switch to oil-free products, use blotting papers, and change your facial cleanser to one that is for oily skin types (avoid ones with salicylic acid, benzoyl peroxide, or retinoids because they could be harmful to your fetus).

GO EASIER ON THE COVER-UP

Irritated skin? Foundation can make it worse. Instead, use a light, oil-free tinted moisturizer or BB cream (moisturizer, sunscreen, and light foundation in one).

STEER CLEAR OF THE SUN

Pregnancy hormones make you much more susceptible to sunburns and dark spots triggered by exposure to UV rays. Use SPF 30 or higher on your face every day and avoid spending too much time in the sun.

ALERT YOUR COLORIST

Avoid coloring your hair during your first trimester (we know, that one hurts!) since no one knows whether or not it is safe for you or baby. Later in pregnancy, you might want to choose highlights, which don't come as close to your scalp as other dyes. Or try an all-natural dye made with henna.

TIP: avoid these!

Do not use acne products such as Accutane, tetracycline, topical salicylic acid, and benzoyl peroxide (as we mentioned above) because they could be harmful to baby. If you are unsure about anything else you use, check with your OB. Also, skip nail polishes with dibutyl phthalate (DBP), formaldehyde, and toluene. These chemicals can be harmful to a fetus.

planning your babymoon

We know it's early—you have not even announced your pregnancy to everyone. But think ahead and book a trip for your second trimester—this should be the most comfortable time to travel. By then, the nausea of the first trimester is hopefully a distant memory and you are not quite as uncomfortable as you will be at the end of pregnancy.

KEEP YOUR OBSTETRICIAN IN THE LOOP

The most important thing is safety, so speak with your doctor before booking your trip. This is especially vital if you are carrying multiples or are considered "high risk." Don't be too disappointed if your OB wants to keep you close to home.

KNOW THE MEDICAL FACILITIES

When researching locations, find out if there are quality medical facilities in the area (just in case). Write down the contact info for nearby hospitals to keep on hand as you travel, along with your OB's number back home.

CHECK RESTRICTIONS

If you are flying, verify with the airline that they will let you on the plane! Most physicians say it's safe to fly up to week 36, but airlines have varying restrictions, including different policies for domestic and international travel. Cruise lines have varying restrictions, too, and may not have a doctor on board.

KEEP YOUR BLOOD PUMPING

No matter how you are traveling, get up and move around every hour or two to aid circulation, and try not to cross your legs—both of these things will lessen the risk of blood clots. Keeping your tootsies elevated will also help prevent swelling and leg cramps.

TIP: wear your seatbelt low

Position the seatbelt with the shoulder portion over your collarbone and the lap portion under your abdomen as low as possible on the hips. You will save yourself and your belly from hitting the dashboard in the event of an accident.

predicting baby's gender unscientifically (quiz!)

During your midpregnancy ultrasound, which usually happens between week 18 and week 22, your practitioner should be able to tell you whether you are having a boy or a girl (if you want to find out). Some moms-to-be find out even earlier with amniocentesis and CVS tests—first and second trimester procedures that look for birth defects. Until you know for sure, and if you want an unscientific (okay, mythical) approach, take this quiz (it's based on a host of old wives' tales):

1. **Hold a chain, with a pendant or ring on it, above your belly. What does it do?**
   - ◯ **a.** It swings from one side to another.
   - ◯ **b.** It swings around in a circle.
2. **Ask someone to hand you a key. Which end did you grab first?**
   - ◯ **a.** The thick, round end
   - ◯ **b.** The skinny, jagged end
3. **Take off your shirt and check out your chest. Which boob is bigger?**
   - ◯ **a.** The right one
   - ◯ **b.** The left one
4. **This one is a little gross. Pee in a cup. Then add the pee to a cup of Drano. What color is the mixture?**
   - ◯ **a.** Blue
   - ◯ **b.** Green, yellow, or white
5. **Are you craving sour foods (pickles) or sweet (ice cream)?**
   - ◯ **a.** Pickles
   - ◯ **b.** Ice cream

6. **Are you carrying baby high or low?**

◯ a. High

◯ b. Low

7. **When the doctor measures baby's heart rate, how fast is it?**

◯ a. 140 beats per minute or slower

◯ b. Faster than 140

8. **How is your skin looking these days?**

◯ a. Clear and glowing

◯ b. Oily and pimply

9. **Have you had a lot of morning sickness?**

◯ a. No

◯ b. Yes

10. **Note your age and the year you conceived baby. (For example, 28 and 2015.) Are the numbers odd or even?**

◯ a. One is odd and one is even.

◯ b. Both are even or odd numbers.

MOSTLY A'S: **Boy oh boy!**

MOSTLY B'S: **You go, girl!**

sharing the news

Many moms-to-be reveal their pregnancy news once they reach the end of the first trimester. Start thinking of how you will spread the word now! Here is how other moms-to-be have done it.

> *"We picked up a onesie that says, 'I'm what happened in Vegas.' We wrapped it up and gave it to both sets of parents as a 'late Christmas gift that just came in.' It was cute, vulgar, and well received by all!"* **—tinebean20**

> *"We announced our pregnancy on Facebook with our dog sitting next to a chalkboard, and it said, 'I am going to be a big brother in February!' A lot of people noticed it and thought it was cute."* **—Jaki35**

> *"We announced at Christmastime. We wrapped up little booties that read 'Baby's First Christmas' and gave them to our mothers."* **—Becki982**

> *"We had a photo taken with balloons and confetti falling from a box with blue and pink question marks."* **—bannerners**

> *"We got our three-year-old son a baby doll to practice with and took pictures!"* **—Briasarillas**

> *"I made my mom a scrapbook. The first page was the picture of her holding me in the hospital bed, and there were pictures of her and me over the years. The last page said 'Grandma' and had a picture of my positive pregnancy test."* **—kelliellie94**

"We took the sonogram, scanned it, and made copies, and presented them in a picture frame to each of our parents. I took a video of them opening the gifts, too." **—finallyPG**

"I made an Easter basket for my sister-in-law and in one of those little plastic eggs, I put a slip of paper saying, 'You're going to be an aunt!'" **—RugbyBride**

"We posted a photo on social media of my feet and my husband's with an empty pair of baby shoes. Everyone got the hint!" **—LisaLulu**

"Our baby was due on April 15th. So we said 'Taxes aren't the only thing due April 15th . . .' People got it pretty quickly." **—cassianddavid**

prepping for tests

Right now, you may be getting tests and ultrasounds, and while you want to know everything is okay with baby, you might be completely stressed out until you find out whether or not it is. Here's how to handle the whole testing process.

GENETIC TESTING

Some parents-to-be choose extensive genetic testing. Some do none at all. Genetic testing helps evaluate baby's risk of having genetic problems. But if baby has a birth defect or genetic disorder, know that it can't be "healed." Some parents-to-be choose to test because they want peace of mind that baby is healthy. Others want to have advanced warning of certain issues so medical specialists can be there at birth. Still others might want to end the pregnancy, depending on baby's risk factor. Before you test, talk with your partner about how you expect things to go—you don't need to have all the answers now (especially because it's most likely that everything is completely fine). Your doctor or specialist can walk you through any future decisions.

ULTRASOUNDS

Many moms-to-be only have two ultrasounds: one at their first appointment, to confirm their pregnancy, and the midpregnancy ultrasound coming up in month five. But your doctor could schedule extra ones in between to make sure baby is growing properly or to confirm your due date.

URINE TEST

As we mentioned earlier, your urine is checked to be sure you're not at risk for preeclampsia (too much protein in your urine could be the first sign of the disorder) or gestational diabetes (your urine will contain excess sugar). They'll also check that you're not dehydrated and don't have a bacterial infection like a UTI (urinary tract infection). If your doctor finds any red flags, you may have to have follow-up testing.

month 3

date: ______________ **weight:** ________

PRENATAL VISIT

tests i had:

symptoms/issues we discussed:

i saw/heard:

doctor's orders:

my next appointment is:

month FOUR (weeks 14–17)

baby's size

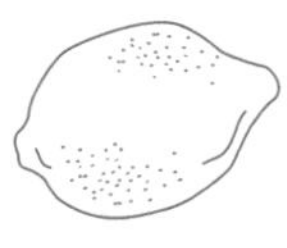

WEEK 14
lemon

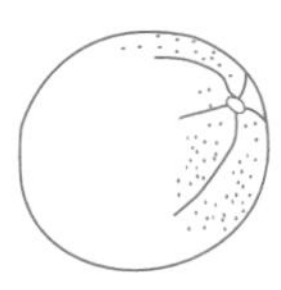

WEEK 15
navel orange

WEEK 16
avocado

WEEK 17
onion

welcome to the "honeymoon period" of pregnancy. The second trimester is known for being the most energetic phase of pregnancy, which makes it the perfect time to prep for the future. Things like going on maternity leave and returning to work as a new mom might seem far away now, but they will be relevant before you know it. Take time for fun projects, too. Daydream about your baby's name and spend some quality time together on a trip. And now that your risk for miscarriage has gone way down, enjoy sharing the good news!

how baby is growing

Baby is getting much more active, kicking and wiggling up a storm. The joints in her limbs, fingers, and toes are working now and she can hear your voice. She might even get the hiccups or suck her thumb! While she puts on fat, she is also growing hair, eyelashes, and vocal cords. The umbilical cord is now stronger and thicker.

how you are feeling

Hooray! Sometime this month, your most debilitating pregnancy symptoms should take a break. Morning sickness wanes, headaches ease up, and you can look forward to a boost in energy.

getting the lowdown on second trimester tests

You will have several tests in the second third of pregnancy to check on baby's growth and development, to verify your own health, and perhaps to scan for potential problems.

MIDPREGNANCY ULTRASOUND

Sometimes referred to as the anatomy scan, this test is a more detailed ultrasound than you had during the first trimester. It's performed between week 18 and week 22. Your baby will be measured from crown to rump and around the waist and head to confirm proper growth; the kidneys, bladder, stomach, brain, spine, sex organs, and four chambers of the heart will be checked for normal development and any potential problems. The ultrasound technician will also check amniotic fluid levels, placenta location, and fetal heart rate. And, if you want to know, you will probably be able to find out baby's gender!

TRIPLE/QUAD SCREEN TEST

This test assesses the probability of genetic disorders and chromosomal disorders like Down syndrome. It's a blood screening that is performed between week 15 and week 20. You might choose to do this if you want a more accurate evaluation of your baby's risk of neural tube defects than the first trimester screen offers.

AMNIOCENTESIS

An amniocentesis is a test for genetic disorders (normally performed between week 15 and week 20). Your doctor may recommend you have an amnio if you get an abnormal triple or quad test result, if your noninvasive prenatal testing raised a red flag, or if you have other genetic concerns about baby. In an amniocentesis your doctor will use an ultrasound to guide a needle into a safe place in the amniotic sac and collect a sample of amniotic fluid. The procedure normally takes 45 minutes. Amniocentesis can detect chromosome abnormalities, neural tube defects, and genetic disorders. In general, amniocentesis is a safe procedure, but it does pose some risks. Speak to your doctor to decide whether it is the right choice for you.

GLUCOSE CHALLENGE SCREENING TEST

This blood screening is administered between week 24 and week 28. Your doctor will gauge how effectively your body processes sugar, to see if you are at risk for gestational diabetes mellitus. To do that, you will be asked to drink a sample of Glucola (a sweetened drink that contains 50 g of glucose), then an hour later, your blood will be drawn and its glucose levels will be tested. If there are signs you are not processing the glucose normally, your doctor will likely order additional glucose testing called the Glucose Tolerance Test.

telling your boss you are pregnant

Your pregnancy can be a nerve-racking conversation to broach with your boss. Most women wait until the second trimester to break the news to their employer. When you choose to do it may depend on your relationship with your boss and when you start to show.

BE THE MESSENGER

Better to break the news yourself than let someone else (or your growing belly!) do it for you.

PICK THE RIGHT TIME

Try to break the news after you've completed an assignment—this will show that being pregnant hasn't impacted your productivity, and that you plan to work hard for the remainder of your pregnancy.

BE PREPARED

Before you meet, have a rough plan of how your duties will get done during your leave. Your boss is much more likely to react positively to the news if he or she knows you intend to have the situation covered. Together, you can iron out the full details over the next few months.

asking your employer about maternity leave

Now that word is out, it's time to talk to human resources. Bring these questions and take notes. Every company's different, and state laws differ, too.

What types of paid and unpaid leave are available?

While I am on maternity leave, is my job protected?

Will I be able to go on short-term disability?

How can I help get my department prepared for my leave?

Who will do my job while I am gone?

How will I transition back postbaby?

deciding whether one of you should stay at home

There are pros and cons to staying home, and ultimately there is no right answer—it's what works best for your family. Ask yourselves these questions:

How will it impact your budget? On one hand, you will need to consider the loss of a salary. On the other, you will have to factor in the cost of child care.

If either of you stays home, will that person be comfortable with doing the housework? (It's not just the baby care, but often the person at home does all the household chores, too.)

Does either of you have parents or other family members or friends nearby who can help you care for baby?

If you're at home, will you have ample opportunities for adult interaction and social connections?

Will you be able to stay intellectually stimulated without work?

Will you want to return to work later? How will your career progress be affected?

Do most of your friends with children stay at home or work? How would you feel about choosing a different route?

Do both of you support the decision either way?

date: ______________ weight: __________

PRENATAL VISIT

tests i had:

symptoms/issues we discussed:

i saw/heard:

doctor's orders:

my next appointment is:

baby's size

WEEK 18

sweet potato

WEEK 19

mango

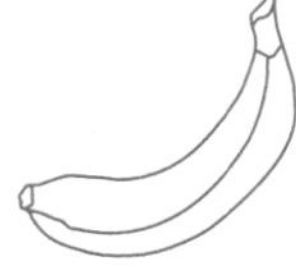

WEEK 20

banana

WEEK 21

papaya

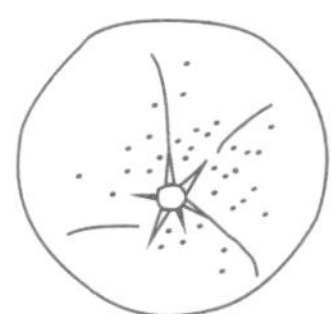

WEEK 22

grapefruit

by now, you are really showing.

Thank you, maternity jeans! That growing belly is a constant reminder that life is changing fast. This month, keep taking advantage of your energy and manageable girth, and get projects done, such as registering for gifts and shopping for baby's nursery. It's time to look for child care and to take classes to prep for baby. Oh, and start to think ahead to your shower!

how baby is growing

Baby continues to be very active, hiccupping, rolling, kicking, punching, and yawning! You might feel his every move now, but not when he is asleep (for 12 to 14 hours a day). The nerve cells that will trigger his five senses are developing in his brain, but—fun fact—he already has fully formed taste buds.

how you are feeling

You are constantly hungry—sometimes get-out-of-the-way-or-I-will-eat-your-face-off ravenous! Your heart and lungs are still working overtime, making you short of breath. You might also be experiencing swollen ankles and feet or backaches (sorry!). If you are lucky, you are relishing an increased libido (turns out there is an upside to all that extra blood flowing down there).

finding out baby's gender

If you want to know whether it's a boy or girl, you will likely find out at the midpregnancy ultrasound, which happens around now. Torn about whether or not to know the gender in advance? Weigh the following:

REASONS TO FIND OUT THE SEX

It will be easier to prep the nursery and purchase clothing, if you are partial to gender-specific colors and styles.

You can pick out baby's name in advance, and start calling him or her by it, if you like.

You can mentally prepare for either a boy or girl—a nice thought, if you have your heart set on one gender or do not like surprises.

Anyone and everyone will want to know, and you will be armed with a definitive answer.

REASONS TO KEEP IT A SURPRISE

Parents who wait until the birth swear the anticipation is worth it.

You will easily resist the urge to buy frilly dresses and hockey jerseys, and instead you'll pick out gender-neutral baby gear that can be reused for a second child, no matter the sex.

Are you a procrastinator? Then you have an excuse to keep a short list of baby names and decide for sure once you meet baby.

You have always wanted to hear that first cry and then the words, "It's a ________!"

announcing the gender

Revealing the news is always exciting. Here are a few fun ideas:

HAVE A PARTY

Open a giant package while all your guests look on. Inside will be pink helium balloons if it's a girl. Blue balloons if it's a boy. Or pop a balloon with pink or blue confetti inside.

HAVE GUESTS GUESS BABY'S GENDER

At the end of the party, announce what it is. Everyone who guessed correctly gets a trinket to take home with her.

HIRE YOUR FAVORITE BAKER

Have her create a blue or pink cake, topped with white (or chocolate!) frosting. Gather friends and family to slice the cake and discover whether it's a boy or girl. Other sweet ideas include cookies with pink or blue batter in the middle, and custom fortune cookies with messages inside that reveal the gender.

LOVE PHOTOSHOPPING YOUR PHOTOS?

Do it to baby's ultrasound pic! Add a pink bow or a blue tie to baby's sonogram, frame it, and gift it to his or her future grandparents.

HAVE PHOTOS TAKEN OF YOUR BELLY

Use either pink or blue booties or baby blocks that spell out "girl" or "boy," and post them on social media.

HAVE GIFTS DELIVERED TO THE GRANDPARENTS-TO-BE

On the tag, write, "Baby is a . . ." Inside, alternate layers of pink and blue tissue, nested boxes, confetti—and whatever else you can find to keep them guessing! At the bottom, a boy's outfit or a girl's outfit will be waiting for them to find.

TIP: make it a party

If you want to find out baby's gender along with your family and friends, ask the ultrasound technician to write it down and place it in a sealed envelope. Then, plan a gender reveal party, where you find out and reveal the news all at once!

getting baby name ideas

BRAINSTORM

It all starts with an idea, so . . . ready, set, go! Don't think—just grab your partner and jot down every semisweet name that comes to mind (the kid you sat next to in eighth grade math class, grandma, your favorite author, something you saw on a restaurant sign . . . whatever inspires you).

BE NOSY

Watch credits to TV shows and movies. Pay special attention to road signs. You can also check newspaper captions for fun options, or even eavesdrop in line at the baby gear store. (Just don't to be too creepy about it.)

BUY A BOOK

Scan the shelves of your local bookstore, and you'll find a bazillion baby-name books.

SCOUR THE WEB

Want to honor your Italian (or Japanese or Romanian) roots? Browse names by origin on the baby-naming tool on TheBump.com. Be sure to check the Social Security Administration site, too—they post an annual list of the most popular names in the United States.

FAST-FORWARD

Some names, like Scout, may sound super-cute when you're referring to a toddler. But what about when she is applying for a job? Remember the kid will grow up, and imagine her as an adult with the name.

COMMUNICATE

It's not just a name. This could be a big deal between you and your spouse. Family relationships, hidden fears, religious conflicts, and childhood regrets can come into play. Don't be surprised if you both get extra-sensitive at some point. Just listen to each other and talk it out.

NARROW DOWN

First off, give each other the power to veto. It's important that you both like the name. If you still haven't had a "that's the one!" moment, find a fair way to shorten the list, like each writing down your top three and only keeping the ones that overlap.

GO WITH YOUR GUT

In the end, this is a choice for you and your partner. Forget any obligations (like the twelve Margarets on your mom's side), any rude comments ("I knew an Ethan in school. He was a real jerk."), and any other pressures. Take your time and find a name that fits your new family to a T. Don't worry, you will.

baby name mistakes

Don't make any of these four naming goofs.

WEIRD INITIALS

Make sure you spell out the initials before you name baby. Henry Anthony Miller sounds great. But HAM? Not so much. And poor Alice Sonia Simpson!

EMBARRASSING NICKNAMES

Be it Mark the Shark or Anna Banana, you can't have total control over what other kids will end up calling your child on the playground. But it's always good to consider the possibilities. You may love the name James, yet hate the nickname Jimbo.

COMPLICATED SPELLINGS

We know you want to be original, but think hard before giving baby a common name with an original spelling. (Think Abagayle or Krys.) Unless you have a really good reason to choose to be different, you may just be making things harder for your kid.

STRANGE MEANINGS

Research baby name meanings before you pick a name. Did you know that Barbara means "stranger"? Mara means "bitter" or "sorrow," Cassandra means "entangler of men," and Cameron means "crooked nose."

NAMES WE LOVE

Jot down your favorite names. Cross off any that you or your partner have vetoed and narrow it down to the finalists!

boy names	*girl names*

decoding your pregnancy dreams

Blame it on all the time you're spending thinking about the nursery, registering, and buying maternity clothes, but your brain stays in baby mode even while you are sleeping now, which leads to some pretty crazy dreams. We have decoded a few of the most popular.

HAVING AN AFFAIR

Cheating dreams are common during pregnancy. You are getting all the attention while your partner is getting "cheated" out of the spotlight. Or maybe your partner gets to do things that you can't do anymore, so you feel "cheated." This dream is a reminder of the couple's sacrifices when making room for baby.

NOT BEING PREPARED

You dream you are back in school and you have not studied for a huge exam, or you go into labor early. This simply means you are anxious about becoming a parent, and that is totally normal!

MEETING YOUR FAVORITE CELEB

Maybe there is a message you relate to in one of the singer's lyrics, or maybe there is a quality of that celebrity that you would like in your life. You don't need to read too much into this dream. Just enjoy it.

BABY IS BORN VERY ADVANCED

It's common for moms-to-be to dream about their babies born with a full head of hair, all their teeth, or already walking or talking. This dream can be connected to your impatience about meeting your baby and getting to know her. Relax, mama. She is going to be here before you know it!

decorating the nursery

Decorating the nursery is an exciting prospect for some—and a dreaded chore for others. If you love themes and paint colors, don't deliberate too long. This work needs to be done about a month before baby is due. If you are not so design inclined, just get the basics organized and you may be inspired postbaby.

PAINT AND WALLPAPER EARLY
Have this done at least eight weeks before your due date and leave windows open for aeration until it completely dries. Painting and wallpapering may release potentially harmful fumes—even some low-VOC paint can carry small amounts of toxins—but having someone else tackle these tasks and finishing them early should eliminate any risk to baby.

NOTICE WHERE LIGHT ENTERS THE ROOM
Don't put the crib somewhere that receives direct sunlight in the morning or is under a streetlight all night.

CHECK THE CRIB SLATS
None should be more than 2⅜ inches apart, and all the bolts and screws should be tight. Make sure there are no gaps between the mattress and crib, and look out for any small parts or plastic coverings.

KEEP COMFORTERS AND PILLOWS OUT OF THE CRIB
They could suffocate baby. If a pretty blanket came with the crib set, hang it on the wall or lay it on the rocking chair.

MAKE SURE THERE IS PLENTY OF ROOM
You will want to replace the crib with a bed once baby is ready.

USE WOOD OR CORK FLOOR OR AREA RUGS, IF YOU CAN
They're easier to clean than wall-to-wall carpeting and don't harbor as much allergy-inducing dust.

SECURE RUGS TO THE FLOOR WITH DOUBLE-SIDED TAPE
Wouldn't want to slip while baby is in your arms!

FIGURE OUT HOW MUCH STORAGE SPACE YOU WILL NEED
And then put in more! Almost without fail, parents underestimate the amount of gear they'll acquire.

CREATE SOMEWHERE FOR YOU TO SIT, AND MAKE IT COMFY
You will spend lots of time nursing, rocking, and reading in that chair.

KEEP ALL DIAPER SUPPLIES CLOSE TO THE CHANGING TABLE
You won't want to have to move far from baby to reach anything.

PLACE FURNITURE AWAY FROM THE WINDOWS, AND USE WINDOW GUARDS
Also, put blind or curtain cords up out of reach, or purchase window treatments without cords.

ANCHOR ALL HEAVY FURNITURE TO THE WALL
This ensures it won't fall over if a growing baby pulls on it.

registry checklist

Time to start "gearing up" for baby! Following the massive list the baby store offers will just overwhelm you. Here's a checklist of what you will really need.

nursery

- ◯ Crib, cradle, or bassinet
- ◯ Crib mattress
- ◯ 2–3 washable crib mattress pads
- ◯ 2–3 fitted crib sheets
- ◯ 4–6 soft, light receiving blankets
- ◯ 1–2 heavier blankets (for colder climates)
- ◯ Rocker or armchair
- ◯ Sound machine or dock to play music
- ◯ Crib mobile with black-and-white images (remove when baby can get on hands and knees)
- ◯ Baby monitor
- ◯ Night-light
- ◯ Dresser
- ◯ Toy basket
- ◯ Swing or bouncy chair

WARNING!

Crib bumpers aren't safe for baby. Skip them!

changing gear

- ◯ Changing table or changing pad for low dresser or bureau, with safety strap or railing
- ◯ Changing table pad
- ◯ 2–3 changing table pad covers
- ◯ Diaper cream
- ◯ 10–12 soft washcloths (for changing wipes) or unscented baby wipes
- ◯ Diaper wipe warmer (really—a cold, wet cloth seems harsh!)
- ◯ 6–8 dozen cloth diapers and 6–8 diaper covers, or 2–3 large boxes of disposable newborn-size diapers
- ◯ Diaper pail or trash can

bath

- ◯ Baby bathtub
- ◯ Baby soap/shampoo
- ◯ 2–4 soft towels or hooded baby towels
- ◯ Baby hairbrush
- ◯ 2–4 soft washcloths (use a different color or pattern than your diaper washcloths!)

feeding

- ◯ 2–3 nursing bras (breasts swell following birth, so start with one size larger than your maternity bra; wait until size settles down—about two weeks after birth—to purchase additional bras)
- ◯ Nursing pads
- ◯ Nipple cream
- ◯ Nursing pillow
- ◯ Breast pump (even if you only plan to nurse, a pump will allow you to leave milk for baby if you want or need to separate)
- ◯ Milk storage bags
- ◯ 6–8 burp cloths (or cloth diapers)
- ◯ 10–16 BPA-free, 4-ounce bottles and nipples (bottle-fed babies can go through about 10 per day)
- ◯ Bottle warmer (cuts down on nighttime trips to and from the kitchen)
- ◯ Bottle brush
- ◯ Dishwasher basket for small items
- ◯ 4–8 bibs
- ◯ High chair
- ◯ 2–4 pacifiers

medicine cabinet

- ◯ Baby nail clippers
- ◯ Cotton balls (don't use swabs to clean baby's nose or ears)
- ◯ Baby thermometer
- ◯ Bulb syringe/nasal aspirator
- ◯ Medicine dropper
- ◯ Petroleum jelly and sterile gauze (for circumcision care)
- ◯ Infant acetaminophen (Tylenol)
- ◯ Antibiotic cream
- ◯ Saline nasal drops
- ◯ Baby gas drops
- ◯ Hand soap (for you)

travel

- ◯ Infant or convertible car seat
- ◯ Stroller (reclining to almost flat for infants)
- ◯ Diaper bag
- ◯ Changing pad
- ◯ Baby carrier/sling

taking classes to prep for baby

Here are the most common childbirth and parenting classes to take now. Which ones are on your list?

CHILDBIRTH CLASSES

LAMAZE Lamaze is by far the most popular childbirth method. You will learn simple, natural strategies like rhythmic breathing, hydrotherapy, massage, position changes, and walking during delivery. Your labor partner will also learn how to encourage and support you.

BRADLEY Natural childbirth is the goal of this method—about 90 percent of class participants deliver without meds. The Bradley Method focuses on self-awareness and trusting the body, and emphasizes relaxation (rather than distraction) for dealing with the pain and stress of labor.

ALEXANDER This method, which teaches posture and movement techniques to ease muscle tension, is actually a general practice adapted for expecting women. The Alexander Technique aims to restore your original poise and posture, which will improve balance, coordination, back pain, breathing, and digestion as your body adjusts to pregnancy.

HYPNOBIRTHING No, not like that guy you saw in Vegas. HypnoBirthing relies on the power of suggestion to help you relax and let your muscles work as they were intended. Affirmations and visualizations are used to guide thoughts and breathing and naturally decrease stress and fear.

PARENTING CLASSES

BREASTFEEDING A lactation consultant will go over how to get the baby to latch properly, how often you should be nursing, how to use a breast pump, and more. It seems like it will all come naturally, but being prepared can be really helpful.

INFANT CPR No one wants to think about bad things, but the reality with newborns and infants is that accidents can happen. It's important to know what to do if your baby stops breathing or needs emergency care quickly. Go to AmericanRedCross.org for what to seek in a workshop and how to find one.

NEWBORN CARE Do you know what a swaddle is? How about meconium? What do you do when the umbilical cord stump finally falls off? When do you give baby her first bath? Not sure? Then you will want to take a newborn care class. Often, this class includes a breastfeeding workshop.

before you enroll

No matter what style of class you choose, check the instructor's certification and credentials in advance. Look for a class with three to ten students. A huge class may provide fewer opportunities for you to ask questions and make it tougher to retain the information.

interviewing a pediatrician

This is a relationship you are likely to have until your child is a teen, so it makes sense to put time into it. You want a doctor who will make you (and your future child!) feel at ease, who communicates well, and who will support your parenting style. Go prepared with these questions:

Do you take my insurance?

How long have you been practicing?

Do you have any sub-specialties?

What are your office hours?

Do you have same-day sick visits? When should well appointments be scheduled?

What if my baby is sick when the office is closed?

Do you have separate waiting rooms for well and sick patients?

How long is your average wait time?

Do you answer questions through email? If I leave a message, how long does it normally take to return the call?

Will you meet baby at the hospital or the first well appointment?

How do you feel about . . .
Pacifiers?
Circumcision?
Alternative medicine?
Antibiotics?
Immunizations?
Breastfeeding?

choosing child care

Here are some pros to weigh when deciding whether day care or a nanny is right for you and your family—both child care arrangements have their advantages.

REASONS TO CHOOSE DAY CARE

It is less expensive.

Baby will be surrounded by other children in a stimulating environment.

There are more safety and procedural regulations involved at day care centers.

Having multiple caregivers means you will never get stranded without care if one person is sick.

REASONS TO CHOOSE A NANNY

A high level of personal attention is given to baby.

Nannies tend to be more flexible when you need to work early or late.

Baby can nap and play at home.

Nannies may be more equipped to help with special needs.

interviewing a day care provider

Going the day care route? You will want to ask these important questions.

How many babies are there per caregiver?

What education and experience do caregivers have?

Are all of your caregivers background checked? Infant and child CPR certified?

How do you handle security? Are the doors locked?

What is your policy on illness? When is it not okay for baby to come?

How often and with what products are toys cleaned?

interviewing a nanny

Your nanny will essentially be a member of your family for the foreseeable future. These questions establish basic appropriateness—is she the right fit from a practical point of view? You also want to spend time with the potential nanny to get to know her and help determine if you will get along and have the same views on how to raise baby.

Can you provide me two references?

What is your citizenship status?

What hours are you available?

What do you charge?

How do you feel about working overtime? What would you charge?

Do you drive? What is your record like? Do you have a reliable car?

Are you open to doing chores, cooking, or laundry?

What other commitments do you have—other job, school, family, activities?

How long do you plan to be a nanny?

Tell me about your child care experience. Have you taken care of infants?

Are you certified in infant CPR and first aid? Do you have any other training?

Explain any issues or concerns you have and ask about her level of comfort and experience.

preparing for your baby shower

You have heard rumblings that there will be a shower thrown in your honor. You are in charge of keeping yourself and baby healthy, and enjoying the bash. Let whoever is planning the party take care of the worrying. There are some things, though, that you should know about showers.

DON'T EXPECT A SHOWER

No one is obligated to throw you a party, so don't be bummed if there is not an offer. And no, you can't throw your own shower. (You can always plan a "welcome baby" party yourself, after baby arrives, to celebrate.)

TIME IT RIGHT

Best time for a baby shower? Between week 28 and week 35. It's nice for your guests to see you with a growing bump and you will (hopefully) still have energy to spare. Plus, there will be at least a few weeks' cushion from the due date—your water breaking during cake and coffee might make a great story, but not so much a great party.

PLAN AHEAD

Give the host your desired guest list, along with the addresses. Complete your baby registry before the invites are dropped in the mail—at least six weeks ahead of the party.

BE A GOOD SPORT

Baby shower games can sometimes be silly or embarrassing. Tell your hosts ahead of time if there's anything you are totally against (like having them guess the measurement of your belly—not fun!), and if something comes up that you might not normally do but is completely harmless (like tasting baby food to guess the flavor), try to have fun with it.

TAKE IT EASY

Moms-to-be are often surprised that opening all those gifts can be exhausting! Drink lots of water, eat healthy snacks, and do not be afraid to say, "I need a break!"

SEND THANK-YOUS

After the event, start writing them and get them in the mail as soon as possible. Handwrite notes with a thoughtful message to really show guests your appreciation. You will feel so much better having all the notes completed before baby arrives. (It goes without saying that you will be a little busy after that!)

don't want a shower?

Whether it's because of your religion or because you don't like being the center of attention, there are plenty of good reasons to decline a shower. Just be clear to friends or family members that you appreciate that they want to celebrate baby, but you are firm on this. If they really want to throw a party, suggest a "sip and see" party—where guests can meet baby and bring a small gift after he arrives.

BABY SHOWER GUEST LIST

While you are not hosting your shower, you should give your party thrower a good idea of exactly who you would like to attend your bash.

friends	*family*

date: ______________ weight: ________

PRENATAL VISIT

tests i had:

symptoms/issues we discussed:

i saw/heard:

doctor's orders:

my next appointment is:

month SIX (weeks 23–27)

baby's size

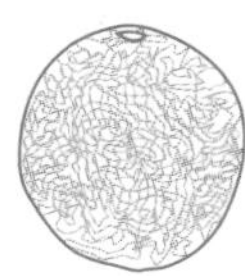

WEEK 23
cantaloupe

WEEK 24
cauliflower

WEEK 25
lettuce

WEEK 26
rutabaga

WEEK 27
eggplant

things really get kicking this month. And we don't just mean baby! As you close in on the third trimester, it's time to consider what life with your little one will be like. That means making big decisions, including some that affect your finances. It's a good time to think more about babyproofing your home, too.

how baby is growing

Baby is really starting to look like a newborn now. Her face is fully formed and she's taken on a pink glow (from all those tiny capillaries under her skin). She might even have hair on her head. She gets smarter every day, practicing breathing and soaking up your antibodies to prepare her immune system for life outside the womb. She hears your heartbeat and voice and can even sense louder sounds like music, a dog barking, or the vacuum cleaner.

how you are feeling

At this stage, it's nearly impossible to sleep well. Braxton Hicks contractions have probably entered your vocabulary (named for the doctor who discovered them). These false contractions aid in preparing your body for the marathon of labor, but cause some minor discomfort now. Stay hydrated and kick up your feet when you have the chance.

babyproofing for a newborn

The best time to get your house ready for baby is long before he or she actually arrives. Prep your place with our ultimate safety checklist. (Later on, you will need Babyproofing for a Crawler, page 184.)

GENERAL SAFETY

- ◯ Install a UL-certified carbon monoxide detector on every story of your house if you use gas or oil appliances or have an attached garage. Check the batteries of any detectors you already have.
- ◯ Do the same routine with smoke detectors.
- ◯ Purchase a fire extinguisher, and learn how to use it (and know where it is!).
- ◯ Stock your medicine cabinet or first-aid kit (page 128).
- ◯ Post emergency numbers next to every phone.
- ◯ Install a temperature guard on your water heater at a maximum of 120° Fahrenheit (about 49° Celsius).
- ◯ Get any flaking or peeling paint sealed or removed by a professional, especially if your home was built before 1978. (Dust from lead paint, which was banned from residential use in that year, can be harmful if ingested.)

EVERY ROOM

- ○ Put nonslip pads under all rugs (you don't want to trip in the middle of the night!).
- ○ Get rid of any blinds or curtains with looped cords, or install safety tassels and cord stops to tuck away the cords.
- ○ Place baby wipes and supplies within your reach from the changing table, but out of baby's reach.
- ○ Put a thick rug or carpet below the changing table.
- ○ Position the crib away from windows, heaters, lamps, wall decorations, and cords.

CAR

- ○ Install an approved rear-facing car seat in the middle of the backseat, if possible.
- ○ If the sun is strong in your area, put hanging shades on the back windows to block the rays.

top 10 things to do before pregnancy gets rough

While you still have the energy, enjoy these indulgences and satisfying activities.

1. **go for a long walk or hike.** By the end of your pregnancy, it will be a struggle to walk for long periods of time and hiking will be off-limits. You don't have to climb Everest, but pick a trail you love, or climb your favorite hill with your partner or a good friend. Drink lots of water on the way.
2. **take a prenatal yoga class.** Even if you are not a huge fitness buff, you just might find this class relaxing and empowering. Plus, you may be able to use the breathing techniques during labor.
3. **host a dinner party.** You are not going to want to spend a long time on your feet in the coming months, so if you love to cook and host events, now is your time to get the Betty Crocker out of your system.
4. **finish decorating the nursery.** Believe us, you are not going to want to be hanging curtains and wall art at week 40.
5. **clean out your closet.** Do yourself a huge favor and make a few Goodwill bags or sell some old clothes to consignment shops before your due date. It will free up much-needed drawer and closet real estate, and (in the case of consignment) you might even get some extra cash out of it.

6. **treat yourself to a prenatal massage.** When else will you have an excuse to get a specialized spa treatment just for you? Look into adding on some fun extras like an aromatherapy footbath (good for swollen feet and ankles) or a mini pregnancy facial (great for skin that is being ravaged by hormones).

7. **make a few baby gear splurges.** Spending an afternoon shopping for baby is super-fun now, but it will not be once cankles take over. Remember the things you must have before baby arrives: car seat, crib, crib sheets, and clothes. (See Registry Checklist on pages 78–79.)

8. **talk tactics.** Epidural? No epidural? Start talking to your girlfriends and to moms in The Bump community about their birth experiences. Hearing stories about HypnoBirthing or anesthesia-free pushing will help you get ideas for your own birth plan, which you will map out on page 112.

9. **have a girls' night out.** Order a fun, virgin cocktail, dance to your favorite tunes, and enjoy some time with your best girlfriends!

10. **flaunt your bump in a swimsuit.** Get yourself to the beach, pool, or spa and flaunt that beautiful belly. If you are too swamped for a full babymoon, go away for a quick weekend or plan a staycation (a tent for two in the living room, maybe?).

budgeting for baby

In the first year, you may spend $30,000 on baby (!). Now is a good time to start thinking about what your finances will look like for the next twenty-four months (never mind the next twenty-four years this little offspring will be looking to you for help!).

Remember that budgeting is not just about paying for diapers and baby gear. Make realistic budget predictions. Consider whether you will need to move to a bigger place once baby arrives, what type of child care you can pay for (or want), and whether your soon-to-be new family can survive on one salary should you or your partner decide to stop working. Then, try to actually live on your new budget—before baby is here.

Estimate how much you will fork over for each to come up with a rough answer to your question. And remember: The amount you plan to spend does not always match up with the amount you actually spend.

BUDGET WORKSHEET

To help you get started, here is a list of major purchases and investments people often forget.

NEW EXPENSES	$ ESTIMATE
◯ **Diapers** *(You will go through 10–12 diapers per day in the beginning.)*	
◯ **Clothes**	
◯ **Child care**	
◯ **Life insurance**	
◯ **Medical insurance**	
◯ **Disability insurance**	
◯ **Medical bills** *(uncovered and co-pays)*	
◯ **College/education contribution** *(Even if it's just a small amount at first.)*	
◯ **Lost income for maternity/paternity leave**	
TOTAL:	

notes:

planning for the future

This isn't exactly the fun stuff, but it is important. Keep files of the paperwork you have prepped in order to get ready for baby. All of this affects your finances.

HEALTH INSURANCE

Go over your policy carefully so you have a full understanding of what it pays for and what it doesn't. Also, check what money in your flexible spending account can be used for—breast pumps and loads of other necessities may be covered under your plan.

DISABILITY INSURANCE

If you don't already have disability insurance, you cannot get it once you are pregnant. But your partner can. Now is the time to make sure your partner has both short- and long-term coverage. This may pay for part of your or his salary if you take time off work after baby arrives.

LIFE INSURANCE

We know this isn't exactly fun to think about, but you will feel better knowing you have taken care of it. Should anything happen to you or your partner, this ensures your child's financial security.

MATERNITY LEAVE

Bone up on your employer's policies. Also, think about whether you will take unpaid leave once your paid leave is over, so you can start budgeting (and saving) well in advance.

ESTATE PLANNING

If you have a 401(k) or retirement account, update the beneficiaries if necessary. The same goes for your will, a must-have once you become a parent. Name a guardian for baby—you know, just in case.

banking cord blood

Stem cells from baby's umbilical cord can be used to combat some rare forms of cancer and other conditions. So it makes sense to bank baby's blood. Your choices are to do it privately or publicly. Here's what to consider when making the decision.

PRIVATE CORD BLOOD BANKING

IT'S YOURS NO MATTER WHAT Privately banking baby's cord blood means you can use it whenever your child might need it, and it's a perfect match for him. One kid's cells also can be used for all siblings.

IT GIVES YOU PEACE OF MIND IF YOU HAVE CONCERNS It may be a good idea if a certain illness runs in your family, which could make you more likely to need it.

IT'S COSTLY AND NOT USUALLY COVERED BY INSURANCE Clients first pay about $1,500 to privately bank the blood and a membership fee for its storage per year (usually $125) for up to ten years.

PUBLIC CORD BLOOD BANKING

IT'S ABSOLUTELY FREE Donating to a public bank doesn't cost a thing, so it may seem like a no-brainer. However, it might not be available in all areas.

ONCE YOU DO IT, THE CORD BLOOD IS GONE If you ever need cord blood, chances are extremely low you will get your donated sample back. But public banks often work to get a matching sample from another donor to parents who have donated if needed.

YOU PROBABLY WILL NEVER NEED IT At the moment, stats of having a condition that cord blood can treat range anywhere from 1 in 2,700 (according to The American College of Obstetrics and Gynecologists) to 1 in 220,000 cases (according to the American Academy of Pediatrics). But by donating, you're likely to help someone who does need the blood.

making the circumcision decision

Having a boy? A growing number of parents are questioning what was once considered a routine newborn surgery. Decide what is right for your baby.

PROS OF CIRCUMCISION

THERE ARE MEDICAL BENEFITS Studies suggest that circumcision actually lessens the risk of being transmitted HIV and HPV (human papillomavirus), and that the surgery can prevent penile and cervical cancer.

IT MAY AFFECT PERSONAL HYGIENE It's debatable, but some believe it's easier to keep the penis clean without the foreskin.

IT COULD KEEP UT'S AT BAY Uncircumcised males are ten times more likely to get a urinary tract infection during their first year (when infections are most dangerous for babies).

IT'S A MATTER OF PERSONAL PREFERENCE Some believe that if daddy is circumcised, Junior should look the same.

IT'S TRADITION Some religious see circumcision as a rite of passage and a significant spiritual ritual.

CONS OF CIRCUMCISION

IT'S UNNECESSARY The American Academy of Pediatrics' stance is that the medical benefits don't necessarily mandate surgery.

THE SURGERY POSES RISKS TO BABY Circumcision can lead to excessive bleeding, infection, or injury to the penis. Some babies have died during this routine surgery.

THERE MAY BE LONG-TERM CONSEQUENCES Losing the foreskin could mean less pleasurable sex or even erectile dysfunction down the road.

does it hurt?

Yes, circumcision hurts. Some anti-circumcision groups say that there could be long-term effects, but ask any circumcised guy you know, and he doesn't remember his surgery. Babies are usually given a local anesthetic—an injection or topical cream—to prevent pain, and a pacifier dipped in sugar water can help, too. Keep in mind that you will have to pay extra attention and care to baby's penis as he heals, but it should be all better within ten days.

KICK TRACKER

In the third trimester, your doctor or midwife will start asking about the daily movement of baby, to be sure she is growing and developing properly. To keep track of baby's kicks, make copies of this page and keep recording. Alert your OB of any big changes to baby's movement patterns—the ideal is to feel at least ten movements in two hours.

level of movement: 1–10

(1 being very inactive or sleepy and 10 being a kick-crazy baby)

morning:

○ 1 ○ 2 ○ 3 ○ 4 ○ 5 ○ 6 ○ 7 ○ 8 ○ 9 ○ 10

midday/afternoon:

○ 1 ○ 2 ○ 3 ○ 4 ○ 5 ○ 6 ○ 7 ○ 8 ○ 9 ○ 10

evening/night:

○ 1 ○ 2 ○ 3 ○ 4 ○ 5 ○ 6 ○ 7 ○ 8 ○ 9 ○ 10

number of movements in two hours: ____________________

morning:

○ 1 ○ 2 ○ 3 ○ 4 ○ 5 ○ 6 ○ 7 ○ 8 ○ 9 ○ 10

midday/afternoon:

○ 1 ○ 2 ○ 3 ○ 4 ○ 5 ○ 6 ○ 7 ○ 8 ○ 9 ○ 10

evening/night:

○ 1 ○ 2 ○ 3 ○ 4 ○ 5 ○ 6 ○ 7 ○ 8 ○ 9 ○ 10

number of movements in two hours: ____________________

morning:

○ 1 ○ 2 ○ 3 ○ 4 ○ 5 ○ 6 ○ 7 ○ 8 ○ 9 ○ 10

midday/afternoon:

○ 1 ○ 2 ○ 3 ○ 4 ○ 5 ○ 6 ○ 7 ○ 8 ○ 9 ○ 10

evening/night:

○ 1 ○ 2 ○ 3 ○ 4 ○ 5 ○ 6 ○ 7 ○ 8 ○ 9 ○ 10

number of movements in two hours: ____________________

month 6

date: ______________ **weight:** ________

PRENATAL VISIT

tests i had:

symptoms/issues we discussed:

i saw/heard:

doctor's orders:

my next appointment is:

month SEVEN

(weeks 28–31)

baby's size

WEEK 28

acorn squash

WEEK 29

cucumber

WEEK 30

coconut

WEEK 31

buttercup squash

though you are ridiculously exhausted, you are also becoming the master of getting things done. From finding the cutest baby onesies to racing back and forth to doctor visits, it's a total whirlwind at this point! Try to relax when you can and sneak in your z's whenever possible. Oh, and (you will like this one) pamper yourself this month. Think prenatal massage, a good book, and lots of (lukewarm, of course) baths. Once you are relaxed, get cracking on those plans for labor (start filling in the birth plan on pages 112–114). Of course, no one knows how that day will actually go, but thinking through the possibilities will help you mentally prepare.

how baby is growing

You will probably feel baby kicking and jabbing much more now as he goes through an energy surge this month. Baby is putting on more and more fat and his wrinkly skin is smoothing out. His brain and nerves are developing at a rapid pace. Baby's five senses are fully functional. He can grasp with his fingers and his eyes can react to light!

how you are feeling

You are finding it hard to rest or get comfy. You have got some growing anxiety, too—totally normal!—about how labor will go and what it will be like with a baby to care for.

getting the lowdown on third trimester tests

And you thought you were done with tests! In the third trimester, there are a couple of tests to make sure you and baby are ready for the delivery you have planned.

GROUP B STREP TEST

Around week 36, all moms-to-be get a Group B strep test. The test screens for bacteria (called Group B strep) that are harmless to you but can be dangerous if transmitted to baby during delivery. Your doctor will swab your vagina and rectum to get samples, and will likely give you results within two days. If they do find Group B streptococcus, you will be given antibiotics to fight the strep so baby is not exposed to it at birth.

BIOPHYSICAL PROFILE

A biophysical profile is a combination of two tests: an ultrasound and a nonstress test, used to determine baby's (or babies') well-being. It is normally performed if you are carrying multiples, go past your due date, or have high-risk factors like high blood pressure or kidney or heart disease.

The profile will determine baby's heart rate, activity level, breathing movements, and muscle tone, and the amount of amniotic fluid in the uterus. The ultrasound will check baby's amniotic fluid level. For the nonstress test, you'll have sensors put on your belly to pick up baby's fetal heart rate and your uterus's contractions. Using the data from those two tests, your doctor can be sure baby is thriving. The tests will indicate the overall health of baby, and if he appears to be in any danger, your doctor may decide to deliver him early.

interviewing a doula

Think of a doula as a childbirth coach. A doula does not replace your health care practitioner (OB or midwife) but rather can add extra services, such as assisting you with pain management techniques during labor and even providing support and help during baby's early days. Many doulas have certification as lactation consultants as well. Find the right doula for you and your birth plan with our list of must-ask questions.

Can you provide two references?

What certifications do you hold? Are you a member of an association?

How many and what types of births have you attended?

What are your philosophies on childbirth? Pain medication?

How will you work with me, my doctor, and partner during and after birth?

What is your fee and what is covered?

touring the maternity ward

You won't even need to ask questions like "What does the room look like?" and "Where should we park?" to have them answered, but before you tour the hospital you should prep a list of anything else you want to know. Here is a start.

Am I able to preregister a couple of weeks before delivery? Can I do it online?

When we get here, do I need to check in at the front desk first, or can I make my way straight to the maternity ward?

What are your policies on camera and video camera usage?

Do you allow cell phones in all areas?

How many people can be with me in the delivery room?

Is there a place for my partner to stay the night?

How soon after my baby's delivery can I try to breastfeed?

What are my chances of having a private room? If it costs extra, does my insurance cover it?

Can baby stay in my room the whole time?

Will the nursery staff look after baby if I need to rest?

What sort of breastfeeding support is offered? How does it work?

writing a birth plan

While much of what happens during delivery is way beyond your (or anyone's!) control, creating a birth plan will at least make your wishes clear. Definitely talk over the plan with your doctor or midwife—it's important to be sure you are all on the same page. This checklist will help you get started.

MY INFORMATION

Due date or induction/c-section date: ______________

Doctor or midwife's name: ______________

Hospital or birthing center name: ______________

MY DELIVERY IS PLANNED AS

- ○ Vaginal
- ○ C-section
- ○ Induction
- ○ VBAC (vaginal birth after cesarean)
- ○ ______________

I WOULD LIKE . . .

- ○ Partner: ______________
- ○ Parents: ______________
- ○ Doula: ______________
- ○ ______________

. . . present before and/or during labor.

DURING LABOR, I WOULD LIKE

- ◯ Music (I will provide)
- ◯ The lights dimmed
- ◯ The room as quiet as possible
- ◯ As few interruptions as possible
- ◯ As few vaginal exams as possible
- ◯ Hospital staff limited to my own doctor and nurses (no students, residents, or interns present)
- ◯ To wear my own clothes
- ◯ My partner to film and/or take pictures
- ◯ My partner to be present the entire time
- ◯ To hydrate with clear liquids and ice chips
- ◯ To eat and drink as okayed by my doctor
- ◯ ______________________________

FOR PAIN RELIEF, I WOULD LIKE TO USE

- ◯ Epidural
- ◯ Systemic medication
- ◯ Breathing techniques
- ◯ Distraction
- ◯ Hypnosis
- ◯ Meditation
- ◯ Massage
- ◯ Accupressure
- ◯ Reflexology
- ◯ ______________________________

AS BABY IS DELIVERED, I WOULD LIKE TO

- ◯ Push spontaneously
- ◯ Push as directed
- ◯ Use a mirror to see baby crown
- ◯ Touch the head as it crowns
- ◯ Let the epidural wear off while pushing
- ◯ Have a full dose of epidural
- ◯ Avoid forceps and vacuum extraction, if possible
- ◯ Use whatever methods my doctor deems necessary
- ◯ Let my partner catch baby
- ◯ ______________________

I WOULD LIKE TO HOLD BABY

- ◯ Immediately after delivery
- ◯ After suctioning and weighing
- ◯ After being wiped clean and swaddled
- ◯ Before eye drops/ointment are given
- ◯ ______________________

AFTER DELIVERY, I WOULD LIKE

- ◯ To donate the cord blood
- ◯ To save the placenta
- ◯ Baby to receive Hepatitus B vaccination
- ◯ Baby to be circumcized
- ◯ ______________________

arranging for postbaby help

It might seem logical not to worry about who is going to lend a hand with care until baby arrives, but you really should be lining this up now. Here are a few of your options:

POSTPARTUM DOULA

This helper assists a new mom and family after baby arrives by helping with baby and mom care and, sometimes, household duties.

BABY NURSE

She is not actually a nurse—a baby nurse is more like a nanny who helps parents care for their newborn. Baby nurses usually stay in a family's home 24/7 or just at nighttime, and many new parents use them for a short period of time (two weeks to a month) so they can get some sleep at night.

LACTATION CONSULTANT

This feeding pro can help new moms figure out the ins and outs of breastfeeding. Trouble getting baby to latch (feed in the proper position), a cranky baby who is not feeding properly, or sore boobs are all reasons you might want one to visit. See if your ob-gyn or pediatrician has one on staff or can recommend one.

FRIENDS OR FAMILY MEMBERS

These are probably the most common new-baby helpers. Line up your mom, mother-in-law, or BFF now, so she can plan ahead to be there for you. But, before you make the call, think carefully about whom you will want around during what can be a stressful time.

deciding to breastfeed

The American Academy of Pediatrics says breastfeeding is the best way to feed baby. But why? These are some of the biggest reasons to give it a go.

IT'S THE PERFECT FOOD

Your body makes 100 percent personalized, nutritious food for your baby. The result? A healthy baby whose poop doesn't even smell bad—it's that perfect!

IT'S CONVENIENT

Your milk is accessible 24 hours a day, always at the right temperature, and is made to order. Your body produces exactly the amount of milk that your baby needs—no cooking or mixing required!

IT MAY HELP YOU SHED THE BABY WEIGHT

Breastfeeding burns an additional 300 to 500 calories a day and helps naturally contract the size of your uterus postlabor.

IT'S HAPPY

Breastfeeding is bonding time. It releases all sorts of positive, mood-lifting chemicals in you as you feed baby.

IT'S GOOD FOR YOU

In studies, breastfeeding has been shown to reduce a mom's risk for some breast and ovarian cancers.

IT'S GOOD FOR BABY

Baby gets mom's antibodies and immunities through breast milk and may be able to better fight off sickness. It also reduces the risk of sudden infant death syndrome (SIDS).

IT'S FREE

It's estimated that a formula-fed baby goes through $1,500 or more worth of formula during the first year of life. You will spend a fraction of that on a breast pump.

preparing for breastfeeding

Yes, there are a ton of reasons to do it, but you might need some of this advice to make it work.

CREATE A COMFY SPOT

Nursing babies tend to wake up more frequently at night than bottle-fed babies and have to eat roughly once every 2 to 3 hours (sometimes less). Have a cozy place to nurse, like a chair in the bedroom, and definitely invest in a nursing pillow to save your arms and upper back.

GET NAMES OF GOOD LACTATION CONSULTANTS IN ADVANCE

Ask your OB, pediatrician, and friends who breastfeed for recommendations. You and baby will have to learn to nurse together. Having someone you can call to instruct you, or at the first sign of a problem (such as a painful latch), will make the process much easier (and is worth every penny!).

GET TWO BREAST PUMPS

Breast pumps are expensive, but if you work, you will want two—one at the office and one at home. If you are not working, you will still want one, so you can go out for dinner after the baby is born. See if your health insurance plan pays for a double electric breast pump. Many do!

SHOWER GIFTS

Once the shower invitations go out, the presents start rolling in. You will want to keep track, not only so you know who to send a thank-you note to, but also to one day tell baby who showered him with gifts before his arrival. Go ahead and log them here.

name: __________
gift: __________
○ THANK-YOU SENT (YAY!)

name: __________
gift: __________
○ THANK-YOU SENT (YAY!)

name: __________
gift: __________
○ THANK-YOU SENT (YAY!)

name: __________
gift: __________
○ THANK-YOU SENT (YAY!)

name: __________
gift: __________
○ THANK-YOU SENT (YAY!)

name: __________
gift: __________
○ THANK-YOU SENT (YAY!)

name: __________
gift: __________
○ THANK-YOU SENT (YAY!)

name: __________
gift: __________
○ THANK-YOU SENT (YAY!)

name: __________
gift: __________
○ THANK-YOU SENT (YAY!)

name: __________
gift: __________
○ THANK-YOU SENT (YAY!)

name: __________
gift: __________
○ THANK-YOU SENT (YAY!)

name: __________
gift: __________
○ THANK-YOU SENT (YAY!)

name: __________
gift: __________
○ THANK-YOU SENT (YAY!)

name: __________
gift: __________
○ THANK-YOU SENT (YAY!)

name:

gift:

◯ THANK-YOU SENT (YAY!)

name:

gift:

◯ THANK-YOU SENT (YAY!)

name:

gift:

◯ THANK-YOU SENT (YAY!)

name:

gift:

◯ THANK-YOU SENT (YAY!)

name:

gift:

◯ THANK-YOU SENT (YAY!)

name:

gift:

◯ THANK-YOU SENT (YAY!)

name:

gift:

◯ THANK-YOU SENT (YAY!)

name:

gift:

◯ THANK-YOU SENT (YAY!)

name:

gift:

◯ THANK-YOU SENT (YAY!)

name:

gift:

◯ THANK-YOU SENT (YAY!)

name:

gift:

◯ THANK-YOU SENT (YAY!)

name:

gift:

◯ THANK-YOU SENT (YAY!)

name:

gift:

◯ THANK-YOU SENT (YAY!)

name:

gift:

◯ THANK-YOU SENT (YAY!)

name:

gift:

◯ THANK-YOU SENT (YAY!)

name:

gift:

◯ THANK-YOU SENT (YAY!)

name:

gift:

◯ THANK-YOU SENT (YAY!)

name:

gift:

◯ THANK-YOU SENT (YAY!)

date: ______________ weight: ________

PRENATAL VISIT 1

tests i had:

symptoms/issues we discussed:

i saw/heard:

doctor's orders:

my next appointment is:

date: ____________ weight: ________

PRENATAL VISIT 2

tests i had:

symptoms/issues we discussed:

i saw/heard:

doctor's orders:

my next appointment is:

baby's size

WEEK 32
celery stalk

WEEK 33
butternut squash

WEEK 34
pineapple

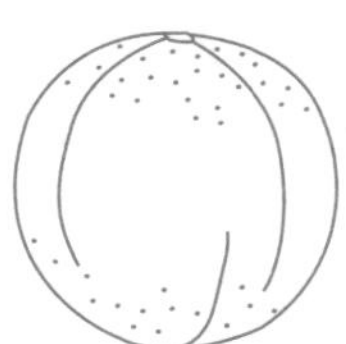

WEEK 35
honeydew melon

you are in the final stretch (sigh) of pregnancy. Mentally, you are consumed with so many things. Is baby in the right position? Is your home ready for a new person? It's true what they say: Your life will never be the same, but it's about to get ridiculously awesome. As soon as you see your newborn's face you will forget all about the aches and pains and lack of comfy sleeping positions you are dealing with.

how baby is growing

Baby is moving around as much as she can in her cramped quarters. At this stage, she is likely in position (head down)! Baby's breathing, swallowing, and sucking become more coordinated and her eyes open when she's awake. About now, she can recognize simple melodies and your voice—sometimes responding to a high-pitched noise with a kick. Her bones are hardening in anticipation of birth.

how you are feeling

The aches and pains are only getting worse now (sorry, mama). And don't be too shocked if you get some crazy lightning-bolt-like spasms in your groin and legs. When baby moves her head, it's a whole affair now! You are probably waking up two or three times a night, either to pee, switch positions, or because you just can't shut off your mind.

prepping baby announcements

Do the bulk of the work now, so that once baby comes, it's super-easy for you to announce the arrival in style.

DECIDE ON A MEDIUM

You can send an e-card, create a baby website, email a photo, and tons more! But if you prefer the traditional route, a printed, mailed announcement is the way to go.

MAKE A LIST

Who is getting the announcement? It doesn't have to be everyone you know! Only send a paper announcement to close family and friends, or those you know will want to post it somewhere at home. Grandmas and bosses tend to appreciate the gesture. Include anyone who came to your baby shower.

SET A BUDGET

A budget can easily determine if you go for high-end card stock, stick to only email, or have any money left over for a professional photo shoot. Remember to factor in extra postage if you go for an oversize card or are sending anything internationally.

CHOOSE YOUR WORDS

An announcement usually has an introduction—which can be as straightforward or sentimental as you choose; birth details—baby's birth date, weight, and length; and parents' names, followed by the names of the baby's siblings. Some parents add a personal note.

MAKE A PICTURE PLAN

If you are choosing a photo card, think ahead. Do you want your partner to take a snap or will you hire a professional photographer? Black-and-white or color?

GET SET

Buy your stamps and address your envelopes now, and choose a design, so you just have to add in a photo and baby's birth details once he or she arrives.

choosing an announcement style

Now, it's time to have fun! Here are some design questions to ask yourself:

Do you want your announcements to be gender specific (pink or blue with girl or boy motif) or neutral (yellows, greens)?

Do you want (pricey, yet pretty) lined envelopes?

Printed envelopes (or will you handwrite addresses)?

Rectangular card stock or square cards? Some stationers offer circle stock, too. (Just know that square, circle, and oversize cards might require extra postage.)

Special postage (like a "love" stamp)?

Matching return address labels?

Matching thank-you notes?

putting together the essentials

We know we gave you a huge registry list, and we don't want you to freak out if you don't have everything just yet. (You can shop after baby arrives and may receive more gifts postbirth.) But if you have reached this point in the book and do not have these items, make these your priority. You will need them in baby's first days.

- ◯ Crib or bassinet
- ◯ Fitted crib sheets
- ◯ Receiving blankets
- ◯ Diapers
- ◯ Wipes or washcloths
- ◯ Burp cloths
- ◯ Nursing pads
- ◯ Bottles (if you do not plan to breastfeed or plan to pump)
- ◯ Formula (if you will bottle-feed)
- ◯ Infant or convertible car seat

clothes to buy for baby

Only buy a few newborn-size outfits. In fact, some babies are born so big, they can skip right ahead to the 0- to 3-month size. This is what you should stock baby's dresser with:

- 4–8 bodysuits or onesies (wide head openings and loose legs)
- 4–8 undershirts or vests (kimono-style or with wide head openings)
- 4–8 one-piece pajamas
- 2 blanket sleepers for a winter baby
- 1–3 sweaters or jackets (front buttoned)
- 1–3 rompers or other dress-up outfits
- 4–7 pairs of socks or booties (shoes are 100 percent unnecessary until baby walks)
- 1–2 hats (broad-brimmed for a summer baby, soft cap that covers ears for a winter baby)
- No-scratch mittens
- Bunting bag or fleece suit for a winter baby
- Swimsuit for a summer baby

finishing the must-dos

You are heading toward the ultimate deadline, and you know what you need. But what else should you be doing?

- ◯ Wash the baby clothes.
- ◯ Wash crib sheets and baby blankets (while you are at it, wash your own bed sheets and leave a spare pair of clean ones out).
- ◯ Install the car seat. (If you don't own a car, make sure you know how to install it into a taxi. You will have to do this at the hospital.)
- ◯ Make your contact list. (Who will you call once you are in labor? When you head to the hospital? After baby arrives? Who will you email or text?)
- ◯ If you have another child, or a pet, have a plan in place for where they will stay once you go into labor.
- ◯ If you plan to breastfeed, sterilize all breast pump parts and a few bottles and parts. Have a good supply of breast milk storage bags on hand.
- ◯ If you plan to formula feed, sterilize all bottle parts.
- ◯ Make a week's worth of meals and freeze them. (Skip this if you simply don't have time. Grab some menus of restaurants that deliver instead.)
- ◯ Pack your hospital bag (see pages 132–133 for what to put in it).
- ◯ Preregister for your hospital admittance (forms can usually be found online via your hospital's website. Ask your doctor for more information).

making a first-aid kit for baby

It's scary to think about a newborn living in your home. But you will feel more prepared if your medicine cabinet has these health and safety must-haves:

- ◯ **THERMOMETER** Buy a digital rectal thermometer. It is more reliable to use a core (rectal) temperature for babies, which means you should not use an ear or forehead thermometer for now. Get petroleum jelly to lubricate the thermometer.
- ◯ **NAIL CLIPPERS OR FILE** You may be surprised how fast baby's nails grow. The kind of clippers made for babies are ideal for little fingers, so you do not snip skin by mistake. If even those freak you out, use a baby file instead.
- ◯ **BULB SYRINGE** Baby will not be able to blow her nose yet, so use this to suck out the congestion.
- ◯ **INFANT ACETAMINOPHEN (TYLENOL)** Fever in a newborn is worth a call to the doctor and an office visit. The pediatrician will probably prescribe acetaminophen.
- ◯ **SALINE** Put a drop or two in baby's nose to loosen mucus.
- ◯ **COTTON SWABS AND BALLS** Moisten them to clean out gucky eyes.
- ◯ **AQUAPHOR** This can be used for minor irritations, like chapped lips, dry skin, and diaper rash.
- ◯ **BABY COMB/SOFT BRISTLE BRUSH** You will need this if baby has hair or cradle cap.
- ◯ **GAS DROPS OR GRIPE WATER** Though there is no clinical evidence that these gas remedies work, many parents swear by them.

doing maternity leave paperwork

Keep a file of your employer's maternity leave policy, as well as of all emails and notes between you and your employer about your leave plans, your return to work, and your responsibilities while on leave, in case of confusion. Your last day on the job is approaching. Did you file all the forms you needed to?

- ◯ State family leave application
- ◯ FMLA (Family and Medical Leave Act) application
- ◯ Disability paperwork
- ◯ Vacation time request form, if applicable
- ◯ Any forms your doctor needs to fill out
- ◯ Any internal forms your employer requires

working in late pregnancy

It may get harder and harder to get into work, particularly if you have a long commute. If you are uncomfortable, see if working from home is an option. Otherwise, arrange to carpool or be dropped off—it isn't a good idea to drive a long distance this close to your due date.

top 10 fun things to do before you go into labor

Sure, there are lots of down-to-business to-dos, but make time for some fun, too.

1. **see a movie (or two, or three!).** Heck, see as many as you can before baby makes his appearance. After he is born, it could be months (or years!) before you go to the movies again.
2. **read a novel.** That thing we said about movies? Same goes for a long, detailed novel. Pick up something complex while you still can.
3. **go shopping (all day).** Granted, you will do zero shopping for yourself and more shopping for the nursery and baby, but it will still be fun and help you fulfill that nesting urge.
4. **sit at a café for as long as you like.** Lingering over a cup of decaf with a friend is sure to feel like a major treat in a month or so.
5. **spend the day in your pajamas.** There will be days in your future when this happens and it won't feel indulgent or fun, but when you do it by choice and can just watch movies, read a book, or watch the sunset, it's pretty nice.
6. **treat yourself to a prenatal massage.** This clearly does not need any explanation at all. These are so relaxing. If you have already had one (or plenty—lucky you!), get a facial or foot rub.

7. **nap.** Everyone will tell you that once baby is born, you should "nap when the baby naps," but that will be nearly impossible when you want to pump, eat a meal, take a shower, or even just brush your teeth during those first few weeks. So, nap while the getting is good!

8. **sleep in.** Go ahead. See how long you can stay in bed. Better yet, ask your partner for breakfast in bed.

9. **hang with your friends.** Yes, you will see your friends after baby arrives, but it might be harder to get in some fun one-on-one. Call your best girlfriends for a big dinner together. Choose the restaurant based on your biggest craving!

10. **go on a date.** Spend quality time with your partner. Pick a place you might not be able to take a small child. (We are talking about that trendy new spot you have been dying to try. Call for reservations early!)

packing a hospital bag

Get your bag ready! Place it by the door or in the trunk of your car, so it's easy to grab when it's go time.

FOR THE BIRTH

- ◯ Pairs of comfy, nonskid socks that can get ruined (you will wear these as you walk the hall in labor)
- ◯ Headband or ponytail holders
- ◯ Music for the delivery room (iPod and speaker)
- ◯ Insurance info, hospital forms, and birth plan (if you have one)
- ◯ Sugar-free hard candy or lozenges to keep your mouth moist during labor (candy with sugar will make you thirsty)
- ◯ Light reading (think celeb magazines)

FOR THE HOSPITAL STAY

- ◯ Pajamas (button front for easy boob access)
- ◯ A cozy robe or cardigan
- ◯ 2 maternity bras and nursing pads
- ◯ Lip balm (hospitals are very dry)
- ◯ Toiletries (like toothbrush, toothpaste, and deodorant)
- ◯ Sanitary napkins. The hospital will give you some, but you may prefer your own.
- ◯ Maternity underwear that can get ruined. While you will be given some disposable pairs, some women think they are gross.

- ◯ Pen and paper (to take notes from the pediatrician's visit, to fill out the birth certificate forms, to journal—you name it!)
- ◯ Camera (if you use one!) and an extra memory card, battery, or charger
- ◯ Change for any vending machines, and non-perishable snacks (you will most likely be hungry after labor, and the hospital cafeteria may be closed if it is late at night)
- ◯ Cell phone and charger and list of people to call after birth (if their numbers are not already programmed into your phone!)

FOR GOING HOME

- ◯ Going-home clothes in 6-month maternity size, and flat shoes
- ◯ Going-home outfit for baby (simple, cotton front-snap footed pajamas and a hat)
- ◯ Cozy blankets (for the ride home)
- ◯ Diaper bag with newborn diapers and a burp cloth, in case baby spits up in the car
- ◯ Car seat (okay, it won't be in your bag, but you need one to bring baby home)

top 10 ways to get better sleep

It's counterintuitive. You are so tired, but you can't seem to get a restful night of sleep. Try these tricks.

1. **skip the late-night snacks.** We know baby is hungry, but seriously, don't consume food or drink fewer than two hours before bedtime. You might get stuck with acid reflux or heartburn, which will only keep you wide awake and uncomfortable.

2. **move to the side.** You probably know you should sleep on your side if possible, since it will reduce the amount of pressure on your uterus and help you breathe better. Plus, the position can ease backaches. Sleeping on your left side can even increase the amount of blood and nutrients that flow to baby.

3. **prop your body.** Get a firm pillow, and use it to prop your head and upper body up a few inches. This position allows gravity to put less pressure on your diaphragm and helps you breathe easier. A full-body pillow can support your stomach and help you get comfy.

4. **quit tossing and turning.** If you can't sleep, don't just lie in bed miserable. Get up and do something. Better yet, do something unexciting, like walking around your house or folding laundry. It might feel weird, but we all know that mundane chores are sometimes a bore—so use that to your advantage. After your brain and body have calmed down a bit, go back to bed and see if you can fall asleep.

5. **make your bed comfy.** Check out a mattress pad, which can take pressure off your spine and in turn ease sore muscles.

6. **keep naps short and sweet.** If you have time to nap, go for it, but don't nap for more than 30 minutes. If you sleep for longer than that, your body will enter the stage of deep sleep and this will make it harder for you to wake up, leaving you groggy. And yes, it's okay to take a few 30-minute naps in a day.

7. **turn down the temp.** Your body heat increases during pregnancy. You might be feeling hot all the time, and a room that's too stuffy might cause you sleep trouble. Experiment with the thermostat to find a temperature that is most comfy for you—maybe a few degrees lower than you normally set it to. For most people, setting the thermostat to the low 60s creates an ideal sleeping temperature.

8. **unplug well before bedtime.** As long as possible before you go to sleep, stay away from any external stimulation—that means books, newspapers, television, or any potential source of noise or light. Also, you should avoid doing any strenuous activities like late-night workouts or deep-cleaning the house—you will stay wired.

9. **keep the bed for sleep and sex only.** Don't do work on your bed, like responding to emails on your laptop or paying your bills. Train your body to know that your bed is for resting.

10. **turn off the lights.** If you have an alarm clock with a bright light or any other electronics that have light sources, point the brightness away from you or put a piece of cloth over them. Artificial light can disturb natural sleep and inhibit the production of the hormone melatonin, which can mess with your sleep cycle. Invest in some blackout curtains if you need to, and keep them closed.

date: ______________ weight: ________

PRENATAL VISIT 1

tests i had:

symptoms/issues we discussed:

i saw/heard:

doctor's orders:

my next appointment is:

date: ______________ weight: _________

PRENATAL VISIT 2

tests i had:

symptoms/issues we discussed:

i saw/heard:

doctor's orders:

my next appointment is:

month NINE

(weeks 36–40)

baby's size

WEEK 36
romaine lettuce

WEEK 37
winter melon

WEEK 38
pumpkin

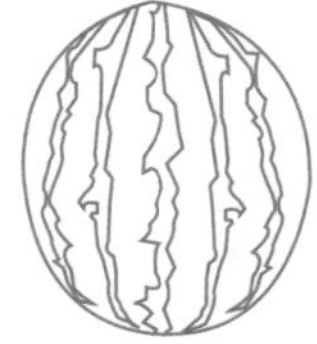

WEEK 39
watermelon

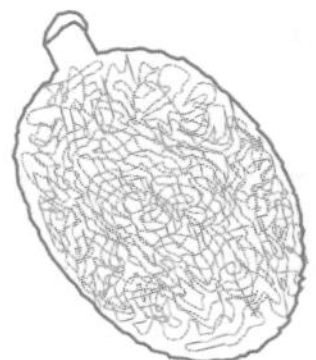

WEEK 40
jackfruit

ready or not . . . Right now you are either saying, "Get this baby out of me!" or "Wait, I'm not quite ready yet!" Busy your mind with your final preparations, like studying the signs of labor and cooking and freezing meals for after baby arrives.

how baby is growing

Once you reach week 39, baby will be considered full-term. Between now and your due date, baby continues to put on fat and practice all of his new skills (blinking, breathing, flexing, even pooping and peeing!). His lungs and brain are still rapidly developing as they prepare for life on the outside. He might have a full head of hair, too. His immune and circulatory systems are ready to go.

how you are feeling

You are probably getting more uncomfortable every day—swollen feet, stretching skin, difficulty breathing and even eating. Every cramp will suddenly make you think you are in labor and the emotional roller-coaster ride will begin. Don't worry, you won't suddenly pop out a baby. The doctor is constantly checking you for signs.

getting the labor day rundown

Now is the time to confirm all the details of exactly what you are supposed to do when you go into labor. Ask your OB these questions:

Should I call you when I first have contractions or wait until they are a specific amount of time apart?

What if my water breaks?

When should I go to the hospital? Do I meet you there?

Where do I check in?

Will you examine me or will a nurse?

Will I be able to walk around during labor? Eat? Drink? Shower? Bathe? Have visitors?

recognizing the signs of labor

We know you are freaked out about missing telltale signs that baby is coming. And in your final weeks of pregnancy you are likely to experience Braxton Hicks contractions (those "false labor" pains). How do you know the difference between "fake" contractions and the real deal? Below we have listed the signs that labor is imminent. Don't spend too much time analyzing, though—if you think you are in the early stages of labor, pick up the phone and call your doctor or midwife.

BLOOD-TINGED DISCHARGE

Sometimes called the "bloody show," this discharge occurs when labor is anywhere from minutes to hours away.

EXPULSION OF THE MUCUS PLUG

This thick, mucus-like membrane could come off all at once or when you are using the bathroom—or even little by little like a thick discharge in the days leading up to the birth.

RUPTURING OF THE AMNIOTIC SAC (AKA "WATER BREAKING")

If your water breaks, you may feel a gushing sensation and then notice the fluid. If you are feeling a trickle and don't know whether it is pee or leaking amniotic fluid, call your doctor. In very few cases, amniotic fluid leaks slowly before labor. You will need to be tested at your doctor's office or the hospital.

REGULAR CONTRACTIONS

True labor contractions are regular, have an obvious increase and decrease during fetal activity, and are centered in your pelvic area. Unlike Braxton Hicks contractions, true contractions will not go away when you change position or walk around.

top 10 crazy places women have gone into labor

Your birth plan is all set, but let's face it: Sometimes nature has her own plans. Here, TheBump.com moms share the crazy places where they started laboring. (Moral of these stories: Keep a change of clothes in your car or purse.)

1. at the salon

"I was getting my hair highlighted, and my hairdresser was about five foils away from being done. I felt a gentle 'pop,' and everything came gushing out over the floor! She washed my hair out and put a trash bag over the driver's seat in my car, and I drove to the hospital." —**JhawkCE**

2. on the train

"I started feeling contractions on my morning commute. I tried not to let on, but once I got closer to the office, my water broke! Two women saw me and helped me walk to the hospital. Luckily, it was right near the train station." —**Tara G.**

3. near the cold cuts

"My water broke when I was standing in front of the deli counter at the grocery store." —**Miranda S.**

4. during the last hurrah

"My girlfriends and I had a last girls' night out before baby arrived—my water broke at dinner!" —**Danielle K.**

5. at sunday service

"My water broke while I was on my way to church. I actually stayed for the whole service, while in labor, and then went straight to the hospital!" —**Carrie B.**

6. on the sidewalk

"I was walking out of my favorite Thai restaurant when my water broke. It was really cold out, and I had lots of layers on, so luckily, even though I was out in public, no one could tell!" **—ortenzia**

7. on an errand

"I was buying a washing machine when I went into labor." **—Ryan P.**

8. while eating spicy food

"We were at a Mexican restaurant when I went into labor. I was in denial that it was even happening, so I insisted that we wait for our food. I finally agreed to go to the hospital when I couldn't eat or walk and talk at the same time." **—Brittany N.**

9. in the middle of work

"I was showing a house to my client. As she was walking up the stairs, I started to go into labor at the bottom of the staircase! I had my baby boy 48 hours later—oh, and my client ended up buying the house, too!" **—Melissa H.**

10. during a celebration

"I was at a fireworks show on the Fourth of July. My water broke during the 'finale' when they shoot off massive amounts of fireworks at once. Guess my son wanted to know what was going on out there!" **—Jessica M.**

going past your due date

If you go past week 40, don't freak out. That's normal, especially for a first pregnancy. Some OBs recommend inducing labor if going too long past the due date could harm baby or you. Otherwise, hold tight. Baby will be here soon!

date: ______________ weight: ________

PRENATAL VISIT 1

tests i had:

symptoms/issues we discussed:

i saw/heard:

doctor's orders:

my next appointment is:

date: ______________ weight: ________

PRENATAL VISIT 2

tests i had:

symptoms/issues we discussed:

i saw/heard:

doctor's orders:

my next appointment is:

date: ____________ weight: ________

PRENATAL VISIT 3

tests i had:

symptoms/issues we discussed:

i saw/heard:

doctor's orders:

my next appointment is:

date: ______________ weight: ________

PRENATAL VISIT 4

tests i had:

symptoms/issues we discussed:

i saw/heard:

doctor's orders:

my next appointment is:

delivery

we have all seen way too many movies in which a pregnant woman's water breaks dramatically to alert her to the fact that she is indeed in labor. In reality, it's not the most typical way it happens for new moms. More often, labor is a slow build, beginning with contractions and in many cases, with mom's water breaking later at the hospital. Or you may be heading in for a scheduled c-section or induction. No matter how you deliver, it all ends the same way—with birth!

how baby is doing

At week 40, she is fully baked and ready to meet you.

how you are feeling

We are going to be straight with you: Contractions hurt like hell. But when you feel them, it will be welcome—the race is on! If you go past your due date, you will probably feel increasingly frustrated and anxious—remember, due dates are an approximation, not a promise.

preparing for delivery

It is almost delivery day. Make sure you are completely prepared for a mad dash to the hospital by doing this prep work.

FILL UP THE GAS TANK

You do not want to realize you need gas when you are in full-blown labor!

GET A BACKUP CHAUFFEUR

What if you cannot get a hold of your partner right away? On the off chance he is in a work meeting, or stuck on the subway without cell service, another family member or friend should be ready to take you to the hospital.

HAVE A BABYSITTER AND/OR PET SITTER

This should be someone who can take care of the kids and/or pet on short notice. He or she should know to expect a late-night phone call from you.

REVIEW YOUR BIRTH PLAN WITH YOUR PARTNER

Your partner will need to be your advocate while you are going through labor and delivery.

DO A PRACTICE RUN

Know exactly how long it takes to get to the hospital. Look it up online and then drive it at least once to be sure there is no construction. Make note of the appropriate entrance for labor and delivery, and the closest parking lot. If you need to pay to park, have cash on hand.

LEAVE A CHECKLIST BY THE DOOR

There will be a lot of panic and emotion in the moment, so you don't want to have to think too hard about what to do and bring. For example:

- ○ Bring your hospital bag (pages 132–133).
- ○ Bring your wallet with ID, money, and health insurance card.
- ○ Bring a plastic bag for the car (in case of puking—sorry!).
- ○ Turn off the lights, stove, curling iron, etc.
- ○ Bring this book. (We have important labor information in here, and you will want to write in it postlabor!)
- ○ Feed the pets.
- ○ Grab a birthing ball. (Yes, a typical exercise ball will do. Sitting on it during labor can help you progress.)
- ○ Double-check that the infant car seat is ready to go!

CONTRACTION TRACKER

Is it labor or not? Use this contraction tracker to note the start and stop time and length of each contraction. Keep your OB or midwife informed of your progress. Usually, when contractions are pretty consistently 5 minutes apart, your caregiver will instruct you to head to the hospital or birthing center.

START TIME	STOP TIME	LENGTH OF CONTRACTION	MINUTES SINCE LAST CONTRACTION

understanding those postpartum supplies

Baby is not the only one who will need TLC. Here is what you will need to take care of yourself. Thankfully, the hospital should provide most of these items, but it is a good idea to have a supply of them at home, so you do not need to worry about running to the drugstore after you and baby arrive.

- ◯ **ICE PACKS** In case of tearing or swelling
- ◯ **2–3 WEEK SUPPLY OF ULTRA-ABSORBENT SANITARY PADS** You will have a pretty heavy flow postdelivery.
- ◯ **HEMORRHOID WIPES AND CREAM** These can become necessary after labor, even if pregnancy was free of problems.
- ◯ **SITZ BATH** This bucket-like attachment sits over the toilet so you can give your delivery area a soothing steam bath, to encourage healing.
- ◯ **WITCH HAZEL PADS** Use these wipes to clean your entire tender area—chill them for extra relief.
- ◯ **DISPOSABLE MESH UNDERWEAR** Hey, they are not pretty, but these larger undies are great for keeping your heavy-duty maxi pads in place—it's pretty convenient to toss them in the trash when you are done, too.
- ◯ **PERI BOTTLE** Fill this bottle with warm water and spray yourself as you go to the bathroom.
- ◯ **DONUT PILLOW** It's not so easy to sit in the days after delivery, but this open cushion will help.
- ◯ **SKIN NUMBING SPRAY** Especially if you have had an episiotomy, this will relieve pain in tender areas.
- ◯ **MOTRIN OR IBUPROFEN** For pain management, and especially if you have had a c-section.

going through labor

The day you deliver your baby will be one of the craziest, most unpredictable days of your life.

STAGE 1: LABOR

Labor lasts from the first signs baby's coming (see "Recognizing the Signs of Labor," on page 141) until your cervix is fully dilated and you're ready to deliver. Contractions will be frequent, usually starting about 15 minutes apart and then speeding up to about 5 minutes apart.

EARLY LABOR Once you start having regular contractions, call your obstetrician's office and let them know what's happening. The doctor will tell you at what point you should head to the hospital, but be warned: It might not be right away. You may be told to wait a few hours before you can be admitted.

Finish packing your bag and relax. Staying calm and breathing deeply can help your body work its dilation magic, as can changing positions. Take a walk, nap, shower, listen to music, ask your partner for a massage—whatever you feel like doing.

Be in touch with your doctor regularly, so she can tell you when it's the right time to head to the hospital. The aim is usually to be there when your contractions have been about 5 minutes apart for about an hour (how far you are from the hospital will have a lot to do with her recommendation). You should be there by the time you go into active labor.

ACTIVE LABOR When your body shifts into active labor, the contractions will come on stronger. Now, you might not be able to walk or talk during a contraction. At this point, you'll likely be lying in bed, walking around, or sitting in a birthing tub or on a birthing ball. This is when things start to really hurt—and when most moms-to-be opt for pain relief. These strong contractions dilate your cervix from 4 cm to 7 cm.

THE TRANSITION The transition phase is when your cervix dilates from 7 cm to 10 cm, and it's pretty intense. The contractions come even faster and more furiously than before, lasting 60 to 90 seconds each. And because it's an overwhelming sensation, some women feel like giving up. Just know that the "I can't do it anymore" feeling is completely normal—it's a sign that this is almost over—and you most definitely can do it.

THE URGE TO PUSH You will start to feel the need to push (like having to go number two badly), but you shouldn't push until your doctor says your cervix is fully dilated (so you don't risk injury).

STAGE 2: DELIVERY

Once you are fully dilated and you are given the green light to push . . . go for it! You'll get coached as you bear down at each contraction. For some women, especially second- or third- (or more) time moms, the pushing stage may last only a few minutes. For others, it can take a few hours. Then there is the ultimate reward: baby!

STAGE 3: THE PLACENTA

After baby is born, you have to deliver the placenta. Your uterus continues to contract. (Don't worry—this normally doesn't hurt.) This causes the placenta to separate from the uterus and leave the body. Usually, this takes less than half an hour. Then you're (finally) done. Woo-hoo! Now enjoy that baby and try to rest.

important questions you may have in the delivery room

Some things can come up during labor that you'd never expect. This is what other moms say they wanted to know in the thick of labor. Speak up, and ask as many questions as you have, so you are informed about what is happening.

HOW LONG WILL THIS TAKE?

Women say the most probing question they had in the delivery room, by far, was "How long . . ." How long will I be in labor? How long will I push? How long do inductions take? Your body and your brain are programmed to get that baby out, and (obviously) because labor hurts, you'll be feeling pretty impatient. There's such a wide range of how long things can take, from a few hours to days, so there's no perfect answer.

WHAT HAPPENS WITH INDUCTION MEDICATIONS?

The doctor might offer to kick-start—or speed along—labor with induction medications. If your cervix is favorable, you may get oxytocin (Pitocin is the brand name), which is a natural hormone that can cause contractions or make them stronger. It will be administered through an IV. If your cervix isn't ready to go, you may get a prostaglandin like Cervidil (inserted vaginally), which can help ripen the cervix and cause mild contractions. After 12 hours of Cervidil, you'll probably be ready for some Pitocin.

HOW DOES THE EPIDURAL WORK?

Epidural medication is an anesthetic, aka numbing medication, that is delivered through a tiny, flexible tube that's inserted into your lower back, so it can reach the nerves in your spine. The epidural stays in your back so you can continue to receive the medicine, which will prevent the pain impulses from coming in, throughout labor. Many hospitals now have patient-controlled epidurals, which will allow you to push a button when your pain increases, to get a higher dose of the medication.

WHAT HAPPENS DURING A C-SECTION?

Even if you are not planning to have a c-section, know the basics—just in case: Your doctor will make an incision above your pubic hairline, going through your skin and abdomen. Then, another incision is made in your uterine wall. Your baby is then simply delivered through these incisions, the umbilical cord is cut, and the placenta is removed. Your uterus will be closed with dissolvable stitches, and more stitches or staples will close up your skin.

ARE THESE PAINS NORMAL?

Labor pains in your thighs? A "ring of fire" as you push? Some sensations might be total shockers—and we can't prepare you for all of them, since every woman experiences labor slightly differently. Most weird things are probably completely normal, but if anything feels especially odd, ask your doctor.

acing the newborn screenings

Know what the doctors are looking for when baby arrives—and what those tests are for.

ANTIBIOTIC EYE GEL

This is applied to baby to prevent infection.

APGAR SCORE

This is an evaluation of your baby's activity and muscle tone, pulse, grimace response (ability to get mad), appearance (skin color), and respiration. They'll give each of these a score from 0 to 2 (with 2 being the best score) and then add those numbers together. Generally, a score higher than 7 is considered healthy. A lower score means baby might need special attention—or she may just need a little time. Your doctor will let you know if there is any cause for concern.

VITAMIN K

It is administered to baby either orally or by injection (Vitamin K deficiency can cause hemorrhaging).

HEPATITIS B VACCINATION

Baby may receive this in the hospital, or later at your pediatrician's office.

BLOOD SAMPLE

This is taken from baby's heel (within the first two days). With just a few drops of blood, a lab can test for approximately forty genetic diseases and disorders.

HEARING TEST

Don't freak out if baby does not pass the hearing test on the first go. It's common, especially since the ears are still so full of amniotic fluid.

date: ______________

baby's weight: ______ **length:** ______ **head circumference:** ______

NEWBORN EXAM

vaccines/medicines at time of birth:

tests baby had:

symptoms/issues we discussed:

doctor's orders:

baby's next appointment is:

date: ______________

POSTPARTUM EXAM

tests i had:

symptoms/issues we discussed:

doctor's orders:

my follow-up appointment is:

newborn

congrats—and good luck! You are psyched to have made it to mommyhood and even though you are in love with that little alien in your arms, you are also wondering just what the heck you are supposed to do with her. Questions swirl through your head: When will the umbilical cord fall off? Will I ever sleep again? Why does breastfeeding hurt so freaking much? Answers: Around day 6, yes, and because your body is adjusting to something it's never done before. Hold tight. It all gets easier.

how baby is doing

Now that she is finally here, baby has a lot to figure out. Her learning curve will be super-high as she figures out how to eat, recognize the difference between night and day, and get used to life on the outside.

how you are feeling

A wave of hormones and emotions hit you when baby entered the world. You are recovering from the marathon of labor or your c-section surgery (or both!). Rest when you can. Accept help. Eat healthfully. And get in lots of cuddle time.

planning baby's checkups

Know when baby will need to see the pediatrician (a lot!), and what will happen when you get there. This is the schedule that the American Academy of Pediatrics (AAP) recommends for the first two years.

○ **AT EVERY APPOINTMENT, STARTING AT BIRTH**

Full physical exam: Baby will get a head-to-toe exam at each visit to check reflexes, skin tone, alertness, and hip stability. The doctor will check the shape of baby's head to make sure it's rounding out nicely.

Measurements: Baby's length (later referred to as his height), weight, and head circumference

Development: The doctor will gauge whether baby's development and behaviors are on track.

○ **3–5 DAYS AFTER BIRTH**

Full physical exam: If baby hasn't had a metabolic/hemoglobin screening yet, he will now, so mentally prepare for a blood draw.

○ **1 MONTH**

Full physical exam

Tuberculosis test

Immunizations (refer to pages 165–167)

○ **2 MONTHS**

Full physical exam

Immunizations (refer to pages 165–167)

○ **4 MONTHS**

Full physical exam

Hematocrit or hemoglobin screening: This blood screening helps indicate anemia.

Immunizations (refer to pages 165–167)

◯ 6 MONTHS

Full physical exam

Immunizations (refer to pages 165–167)

Influenza vaccine/flu shot (if this appointment falls during flu season)

OTHER TESTS YOUR DOCTOR MAY DO

Lead screening (to make sure baby hasn't been exposed to dangerous levels of lead, which can affect developmental and behavioral growth)

Oral health screening (baby may have her first tooth by now!)

◯ 9 MONTHS

Full physical exam

Development screening: The doctor will ask you a series of questions about baby's growth and behavior, and also may ask you to play with your baby to see how he behaves and moves. The intent is to see if your baby is learning basic skills at a normal rate.

Immunizations (refer to pages 165–167)

OTHER TESTS YOUR DOCTOR MAY DO

Oral health screening

◯ 12 MONTHS

Full physical exam

Immunizations (refer to pages 165–167)

OTHER TESTS YOUR DOCTOR MAY DO

Lead screening

Tuberculosis test

Oral health screening

- [ ] **15 MONTHS**

Full physical exam

Immunizations (refer to pages 165–167)

- [ ] **18 MONTHS**

Full physical exam

Autism screening: The doctor will check for a group of developmental disorders that can affect a child's behavior, social skills, and communication skills.

Immunizations (refer to pages 165–167)

OTHER TESTS YOUR DOCTOR MAY DO

Hematocrit or hemoglobin test to check for anemia (another blood draw)

Lead screening

Tuberculosis test

Oral health screening

- [ ] **24 MONTHS**

Full physical exam

Autism screening

Immunizations (refer to pages 165–167)

OTHER TESTS YOUR DOCTOR MAY DO

Hematocrit or hemoglobin screening

Lead screening

Tuberculosis test

Oral health screening

Dyslipidemia screening, which tests for signs of a lipid disorder

tracking baby's vaccines

Which shots happen when and what do they prevent? Use our guide to the CDC's recommended schedule.

HEPATITIS B VACCINE (HEPB)

IT PREVENTS Hepatitis B, a chronic or acute liver disease that can lead to liver failure and cancer

WHEN BABY GETS IT The first dose should be given before she's discharged from the hospital after birth. A second dose should happen between 1 and 2 months of age. If, for some reason, baby doesn't get the hepatitis B vaccine at the hospital, she'll need three doses—at 0, 1, and 6 months—and the final dosage no earlier than 24 weeks old.

ROTAVIRUS VACCINE (RV)

IT PREVENTS Rotavirus, the most common cause of diarrhea and vomiting in infants and young children, which can cause severe dehydration in babies. It's not a shot—this vaccine is taken orally.

WHEN BABY GETS IT Between 2 months and 4 months of age, in two to three doses, depending on the brand of vaccine she gets. She may also need another dose at 6 months, so double-check with your doctor.

DIPHTHERIA, TETANUS, AND PERTUSSIS VACCINE (DTAP)

IT PREVENTS This is a combination vaccine to protect against diphtheria, tetanus, and pertussis. Diphtheria used to be a major cause of childhood illness and death. Tetanus is a serious illness that causes painful tightening of the jaw muscles. Pertussis is also known as the whooping cough, a highly contagious respiratory infection.

WHEN BABY GETS IT At 2 months, 4 months, and 6 months, and between 15 and 18 months and 4 to 6 years

HAEMOPHILUS INFLUENZAE TYPE B CONJUGATE VACCINE (HIB)

IT PREVENTS "Hib" disease, which was the leading cause of bacterial meningitis in children before the vaccine was developed. Kids who contract Hib may suffer permanent brain damage or have serious complications, like pneumonia.

WHEN BABY GETS IT At 2 months, 4 months, and 6 months, and between 12 and 15 months

PNEUMOCOCCAL CONJUGATE VACCINE (PCV13)

IT PREVENTS Streptococcus pneumonia, an illness that can be serious and even lead to death. It can cause blood infections, ear infections, meningitis, and pneumonia in children.

WHEN BABY GETS IT At 2 months, 4 months, and 6 months, and a booster given between 12 and 15 months

INACTIVATED POLIOVIRUS VACCINE (IPV)

IT PREVENTS Polio, once a widespread epidemic that killed and paralyzed thousands of people

WHEN BABY GETS IT At 2 months, 4 months, 6 to 18 months, and 4 to 6 years

INACTIVATED INFLUENZA VACCINE

IT PREVENTS The flu, which is more dangerous to children than the common cold

WHEN BABY GETS IT Annually, from 6 months

MEASLES, MUMPS, AND RUBELLA VACCINE (MMR)

IT PREVENTS Measles, mumps, and rubella, dangerous diseases that can cause rashes and fevers and that can lead to serious conditions like pneumonia, meningitis, seizures, and deafness

WHEN BABY GETS IT One dose at 12 to 15 months and a second dose at 4 to 6 years

VARICELLA VACCINE

IT PREVENTS Chicken pox. Complications from chicken pox include a bacterial infection of the skin, swelling of the brain, and pneumonia.

WHEN BABY GETS IT One dose at 12 to 15 months and a second dose at 4 to 6 years

HEPATITIS A VACCINE (HEPA)

IT PREVENTS Hepatitis A, a disease that causes liver inflammation

WHEN BABY GETS IT One dose at 12 to 23 months and a second dose 6 to 18 months later

MENINGOCOCCAL CONJUGATE VACCINE, QUADRIVALENT (MCV4)

IT PREVENTS Meningococcal disease, which can cause meningitis, blood infections, and other infections

WHEN BABY GETS IT It is recommended that high-risk children between the ages of 9 and 23 months get four doses. Two doses of the vaccine are recommended for children and adolescents between the ages of 11 and 18 (the first at 11 or 12 and a booster at 16).

BABY FEEDING TRACKER

You are nursing so much in the first weeks that the feedings will start to blur together (thank you, baby brain!). So log them here. Make copies to use each day.

baby's name: *date:*

TIME	BREAST (left | right)	MINUTES/ OUNCES	WET DIAPER	DIRTY DIAPER

notes:

BABY SLEEP LOG

Logging baby's sleep is the easiest way to ensure he is getting enough, to identify any patterns (when you are trying to set a schedule), and to pick up on potential problems before they go too far.

	12 am	2 am	4 am	6 am	8 am	10 am	12 pm	2 pm	4 pm	6 pm	8 pm	10 pm
EXAMPLE	(12:15–4:30) ←→			(6:00–9:00) ←→								
SUN												
MON												
TUE												
WED												
THURS												
FRI												
SAT												

	12 am	2 am	4 am	6 am	8 am	10 am	12 pm	2 pm	4 pm	6 pm	8 pm	10 pm
SUN												
MON												
TUE												
WED												
THURS												
FRI												
SAT												

curing your postbaby blues

It's totally normal to have some form of the "baby blues." Your hormones are fluctuating tremendously, you're not sleeping, and you're doing around-the-clock feedings. For some people these feelings are more intense, but you can do certain things to help.

GET ENOUGH SLEEP

This is a challenge with a newborn in the house, but if it is possible to get support from a partner (or friends and family), block out time for sleep. Ask them to watch the baby for half an hour while you take a power nap, or sleep when baby sleeps, and let them do the laundry or make lunch or whatever else you would normally be doing.

MAKE HEALTHY CHOICES

Eat healthy foods, avoid alcohol, and get some physical activity, even if it's just a daily walk. (Talk to your doctor about when and how much you are allowed to start exercising after birth.)

AVOID ISOLATION

Let your partner, friends, and family know how you are feeling. Join a mom's group or local support group of women who have the baby blues.

MAKE TIME FOR YOURSELF

Sure, the first few days and even couple of weeks are going to be all about baby—and about recovering—but once the soreness subsides, and you start to fall into a daily routine, you will need to find ways to take care of yourself. Even doing little things like taking a shower, getting dressed, and seeing a friend can help you feel nurtured and elevate your mood.

TALK TO YOUR DOCTOR RIGHT AWAY IF YOU HAVE RISK FACTORS, SUCH AS:

A personal or family history of depression, anxiety, or postpartum depression

Premenstrual dysphoric disorder (PMDD)

Inadequate support in caring for the baby

Financial stress

Marital stress

Complications in pregnancy, birth, or breastfeeding

A major recent life event: loss of a loved one, house move, job loss

Multiples

An infant in the neonatal intensive care unit (NICU)

A history of infertility treatments

Thyroid imbalance

Diabetes (type 1, type 2, or gestational)

KNOW THE SYMPTOMS OF POSTPARTUM DEPRESSION (PPD)

Any of these symptoms means you should talk to a doctor:

Feelings of anger

Sadness

Irritability

Guilt

Lack of interest in the baby

Changes in eating and sleeping habits

Trouble concentrating

Thoughts of hopelessness

emergency contacts

You are exhausted, and you just want to make everything easy for yourself, so compile a list of contacts, to have at your fingertips—just in case. This also makes it simple to pass on all the important info to the sitter when you go out for your first dinner sans baby, or you go back to work.

Child's full name:

Child's date of birth:

Any allergies, medications, or special conditions:

Mom's full name:

Mom's work phone:

Mom's cell phone:

Dad's full name:

Dad's work phone:

Dad's cell phone:

Home address:

Closest major intersection:

Poison control: (800) 222-1222

Police department (nonemergency):

Fire department (nonemergency):

Child's doctor:

Child's dentist:

Hospital address and directions:

Insurance information:

Emergency contact 1:

Emergency contact 2:

Closest neighbor:

Other local/appropriate emergency numbers:

packing a newborn diaper bag

Okay, so you threw in the wipes. Here is everything else you will need in your diaper bag. Adjust according to season, the length of your trip (around the block or around the world?), and baby's age and special needs.

- ○ Diapers (1 for every 2 hours and a few extras)
- ○ Diaper wipes in a zip-top bag (these also work as hand wipes for mommy)
- ○ Changing pad
- ○ Diaper cream (put in the half-used one, so it lightens your load)
- ○ Plastic bags for dirty clothes and diapers
- ○ A change of clothes for every 2 hours you will be gone (you never know what can happen—yes, twice in a row)
- ○ Sweater for baby
- ○ Blanket
- ○ Hat for sun or cold
- ○ Water bottle (for mom)
- ○ Bottles
- ○ Formula (for a lighter load, measure powdered formula into clean bottles and mix with tap water at the destination, or pack bottled water)
- ○ Burp cloths and bibs
- ○ Pacifiers (pack with nipples in a clean bag)
- ○ Toys for comfort and distraction
- ○ Hand sanitizer
- ○ Antibiotic cream, fever and pain reducer, antihistamine
- ○ Emergency phone numbers and information

BABY GIFTS

Now that baby's here, you might experience a new wave of presents. Don't forget to keep track!

name:

gift:

THANK-YOU SENT (YAY!)

name:

gift:

THANK-YOU SENT (YAY!)

name:

gift:

THANK-YOU SENT (YAY!)

name:

gift:

THANK-YOU SENT (YAY!)

name:

gift:

THANK-YOU SENT (YAY!)

name:

gift:

THANK-YOU SENT (YAY!)

name:

gift:

THANK-YOU SENT (YAY!)

name:

gift:

THANK-YOU SENT (YAY!)

name:

gift:

THANK-YOU SENT (YAY!)

name:

gift:

THANK-YOU SENT (YAY!)

name:

gift:

THANK-YOU SENT (YAY!)

name:

gift:

THANK-YOU SENT (YAY!)

name:

gift:

THANK-YOU SENT (YAY!)

name:

gift:

THANK-YOU SENT (YAY!)

name:

gift:

THANK-YOU SENT (YAY!)

name:

gift:

THANK-YOU SENT (YAY!)

date: ______________

baby's weight: ______ **length:** _______ **head circumference:** _______

NEWBORN CHECKUP

vaccines/medicines:

____

____

____

____

tests baby had:

____

____

____

____

symptoms/issues we discussed:

____

____

____

____

doctor's orders:

____

____

____

____

baby's next appointment is:

____

____

date: ______________

baby's weight: ______ **length:** _______ **head circumference:** _______

NEWBORN CHECKUP

vaccines/medicines:

___

___

___

___

tests baby had:

___

___

___

___

symptoms/issues we discussed:

___

___

___

___

doctor's orders:

___

___

___

___

baby's next appointment is:

___

___

date: ______________

baby's weight: ______ **length:** ______ **head circumference:** ______

NEWBORN CHECKUP

vaccines/medicines:

tests baby had:

symptoms/issues we discussed:

doctor's orders:

baby's next appointment is:

6 weeks after delivery

date: ______________

FOLLOW-UP POSTPARTUM EXAM

tests i had:

symptoms/issues we discussed:

doctor's orders:

baby's
next steps

by now, the umbilical cord has fallen off, visitors have come and gone, and you are starting to get used to life with baby. If you are still feeling overwhelmed, that is totally normal. But you are quickly learning baby's likes and dislikes, and he is getting more used to his new home. Soon he will smile more and do more, and the fun will really begin. For now, remember your main jobs are to relax, respond, and bond.

baby milestones

Everyone worries about baby being "on track." But most moms expect progress way too quickly. Use this checklist of what most babies do at each age to see which milestones baby has reached—and which you can expect soon!

2 months

- ○ Begin to smile at people
- ○ Can briefly calm themselves (may suck on hand)
- ○ Coo, make gurgling sounds
- ○ Turn head toward sounds
- ○ Pay attention to faces
- ○ Begin to follow things with eyes and recognize people
- ○ Begin to act bored (cry, fuss) if activity does not change
- ○ Hold head up and begin to push up when lying on tummy
- ○ Make smoother movements with arms and legs

4 months

- ○ Smile spontaneously
- ○ Like to play with people and might cry when playing stops
- ○ Copy some movements and facial expressions
- ○ Begin to babble
- ○ Babble with expression and copy sounds they hear
- ○ Cry in different ways to show hunger, pain, or being tired
- ○ Let you know if they are happy or sad
- ○ Respond to affection
- ○ Use hands and eyes together (seeing a toy and reaching for it)
- ○ Reach for toy with one hand
- ○ Follow moving things with eyes from side to side
- ○ Watch faces closely
- ○ Recognize familiar people and things at a distance
- ○ Hold head steady, unsupported
- ○ Push down on legs when feet are on a hard surface
- ○ May be able to roll over from tummy to back
- ○ Hold a toy and shake it and swing at dangling toys
- ○ Bring hands to mouth
- ○ When lying on stomach, push up to elbows

6 months

- ○ Know familiar faces and begin to know if someone is a stranger
- ○ Like to play with others
- ○ Respond to others
- ○ Respond by making sounds
- ○ String vowels together when babbling ("ah," "eh," "oh") and like taking turns with parent

- ◯ Respond to own name
- ◯ Make sounds to show joy and displeasure
- ◯ Begin to say consonant sounds
- ◯ Look around at things nearby
- ◯ Bring things to mouth
- ◯ Show curiosity and try to get objects that are out of reach
- ◯ Begin to pass things from one hand to the other
- ◯ Roll over in both directions
- ◯ Begin to sit without support
- ◯ When standing, support weight on legs and might bounce
- ◯ Rock back and forth, sometimes crawling backward

9 months

- ◯ May be afraid of strangers
- ◯ Have favorite toys
- ◯ Understand "no"
- ◯ Make a lot of different sounds, like "mamamama" and "bababababa"
- ◯ Copy sounds and gestures
- ◯ Use fingers to point at things
- ◯ Watch something as it falls
- ◯ Look for things they see you hide
- ◯ Play peek-a-boo
- ◯ Put things in mouth
- ◯ Move objects smoothly from one hand to the other
- ◯ Pick up objects between fingers
- ◯ Stand, holding on
- ◯ Can get into sitting position
- ◯ Sit without support
- ◯ Pull to stand
- ◯ Crawl

1 year

- ◯ Are shy or nervous with strangers
- ◯ Cry when mom or dad leaves
- ◯ Hand you a book when they want to hear a story
- ◯ Do things to get attention
- ◯ Use simple gestures, like shaking head "no" or waving "bye-bye"
- ◯ Make sounds with changes in tone (sounds more like speech)
- ◯ Say "mama" and "dada" and exclamations like "uh-oh!"
- ◯ Try to say words you say
- ◯ Explore things in different ways, like shaking, banging, throwing
- ◯ Find hidden things easily
- ◯ Look at the right picture or thing when it's named
- ◯ Copy gestures
- ◯ Start to use objects correctly, like drink from a cup or brush hair
- ◯ Bang two things together
- ◯ Put objects in a container, take objects out of a container
- ◯ Let things go without help
- ◯ Poke with index (pointer) finger
- ◯ Follow simple directions
- ◯ Pull up to stand, walk holding on to furniture ("cruising")
- ◯ May take a few steps
- ◯ May stand alone

babyproofing for a crawler

Start getting your home ready for having a crawler as soon as baby can sit up and pivot on her tummy (around six months). Here is your guide. (If you missed the babyproofing basics, go back to page 94.)

THROUGHOUT THE HOUSE

- ◯ Move all dangerous items (cleaners, heavy objects, medications) to cupboards out of baby's reach.
- ◯ Use babyproofing safety latches to secure doors, cupboards, and drawers within baby's reach; install baby-safe doorstops to prevent accidental closings.
- ◯ Put lockable covers on garbage cans, or place them inside latched cupboards.
- ◯ Move electric cords behind furniture.
- ◯ Put safety covers over electrical outlets.
- ◯ Secure bookcases to walls to prevent tipping.
- ◯ Put TVs and other heavy items on sturdy furniture, and move them close to the wall or corner.
- ◯ Move all tall, wobbly lamps behind furniture.
- ◯ Put baby gates at the top and bottom of stairs.
- ◯ Block access to all floor heaters and radiators.
- ◯ Use garden fences or Plexiglas to block spaces of more than four inches between stair rails.
- ◯ Install window guards and stops, and put safety bars or gates on all windows, landings, and decks.
- ◯ Place food and water for pets out of baby's reach.
- ◯ Install fireplace screens around all hearths.

BATHROOMS

- ◯ Make sure all medications have childproof tops and are stored high out of baby's reach.
- ◯ Place soft covers on the bath spout and knobs.
- ◯ Put nonslip mats in and beside the bathtub.
- ◯ Purchase a bathtub ring for baby to sit in (and never leave baby alone in the tub, even for a moment!).
- ◯ Install safety locks on toilets.

GARAGE

- ◯ Put all tools and toxic substances in locked storage.
- ◯ Check that the garage door safety sensor works.

NURSERY

- ◯ Remove hanging mobiles from above the crib.
- ◯ Move the crib away from anything that could be used for climbing.
- ◯ Lower baby's crib mattress.

KITCHEN

- ◯ Install covers for stove and oven knobs, a latch for the oven door, and a stove guard to block burners.
- ◯ Put safety latches on refrigerator and freezer doors.
- ◯ Get in the habit of cooking on the back burners, turning pot handles toward the wall.

BACKYARD

- ◯ Make sure backyard gates latch securely.
- ◯ If you have a pool, surround it with a locked fence at least 4 feet tall.

CHORE CHART

It was tough enough maintaining a home before you gave birth, and it takes a while to get organized afterward. If you are having the chore wars with your partner, use this guide to divvy things up. It seems a little ridiculous, we know, but it helps to see exactly what needs to be done, and to actually make decisions rather than trying to read each other's minds.

CHORES	ME	YOU	TAKE TURNS
DAILY			
change diapers			
make the bed			
prep meals			
cook meals			
do dishes			
dress baby			
play with baby			
take baby to day care/babysitter			
pick up baby from day care/babysitter			
feed baby			
clean up today's mess			
bathe baby			
put baby in pajamas			
put baby to bed			
empty diaper pail			
run errands			

CHORES	ME	YOU	TAKE TURNS
WEEKLY			
do laundry			
shop for groceries			
make weekend plans			
find a babysitter			
clean the bathroom			
dust			
vacuum			
do yard work/mow lawn			
take out trash			
pick up dry cleaning			
change sheets			
clean refrigerator			
have "me time" (okay, it's not a chore, but both of you need some!)			
MONTHLY			
do bulk shopping (diapers, wipes, paper towels, and more)			
take baby to doctor appointments			
pay bills/deal with mail			
YEARLY			
plan vacation			
plan birthdays/celebrations/parties			

date: ______________

baby's weight: ______ **length:** _______ **head circumference:** _______

BABY CHECKUP

vaccines/medicines:

tests baby had:

symptoms/issues we discussed:

doctor's orders:

baby's next appointment is:

6 months

date: ______________

baby's weight: ______ **length:** _______ **head circumference:** _______

BABY CHECKUP

vaccines/medicines:

tests baby had:

symptoms/issues we discussed:

doctor's orders:

baby's next appointment is:

date: ____________

baby's weight: ______ **length:** ______ **head circumference:** ______

BABY CHECKUP

vaccines/medicines:

tests baby had:

symptoms/issues we discussed:

doctor's orders:

baby's next appointment is:

12 months

date: ______________

baby's weight: _____ **length:** ______ **head circumference:** ______

BABY CHECKUP

vaccines/medicines:

tests baby had:

symptoms/issues we discussed:

doctor's orders:

baby's next appointment is:

one last box to check

○ *we did it. we're parents.*

and a final list

. . . of people we would like to thank.

Bumpies—for your constant questions, unique ideas, thought-starters, and undying love of lists!

Elena Donovan Mauer, Rebecca Dolgin, Kellee Kratzer, Meredith Franco Meyers, Maria Bouselli, Lauren Daniels, Meghan Corrigan, and Renata De Oliveira for helping to turn our infinite pregnancy and baby knowledge into bite-size pieces for busy moms-to-be.

Aliza Fogelson, Cathy Hennessy, Ana Leal, Jane Treuhaft, Alison Hagge, Doris Cooper, Pam Krauss, Aaron Wehner, and the whole Potter Style team for making sure every checkbox was actually important to check.

Chris Tomasino for your inspiration and enduring support for The Bump books.

Laura E. Riley, MD, Medical Director, Labor and Delivery at Massachusetts General Hospital; Michele M. Hakakha, MD, FACOG; and Stephanie Clarke, MS, RD; and Willow Jarosh, MS, RD, co-founders of C&J Nutrition; for helping us present the most accurate information possible in this book.

The obstetricians, midwives, pediatricians, and other experts on TheBump.com for giving us the real deal on everything the pregnant woman needs to know. (Oh, and by the way, those fruit sizes are not an exact science, but we have a new appreciation for the many variations of squash now.)